NMR IN CHEMISTR'

Winners of the Nobel Prize in Physics 1952.

The late Felix Bloch (above) and Edward M. Purcell (left, taken in 1953). On Purcell's right is the home-made magnet with which he observed nuclear magnetic resonance. In Bloch's first account of his simultaneous work, he said 'We have thought of various investigations in which this effect can be used fruitfully'.

Photographs courtesy Stanford University (Bloch) and Harvard University (Purcell).

NMR in Chemistry

A Multinuclear Introduction

WILLIAM KEMP

MACMILLAN

First published 1986 by
THE MACMILLAN PRESS LTD
Houndmills, Basingstoke, Hampshire RG21 2XS
and London
Companies and representatives
throughout the world

ISBN 0–333–37291–3 (hardcover)
ISBN 0–333–37292–1 (paperback)

A catalogue record for this book is available
from the British Library.

12	11	10	9	8	7	6	5	4
03	02	01	00	99	98	97	96	95

Printed in China

To Louie, Again

CONTENTS

Preface

In the last few years the horizons of nuclear magnetic resonance spectroscopy have all but been pushed out of sight as new and ever more sophisticated instruments are built and reports of new applications flood the literature.

For chemists who are active developers of the science, in whatever aspect, it is difficult merely to read all of the new publications. For chemists who use the method, among other methods, to solve their chemical problems it is well-nigh impossible to keep up to date.

This book is an attempt to introduce NMR to a wide audience of users, in such a cohesive way that all of its potential can be tapped and exploited: it is not a book about the physics and mathematics of NMR, but concerns the interpretation of NMR spectra by those who do not consider themselves particularly mathematical by inclination: the minimum prerequisites are some knowledge of general spectroscopic principles and a familiarity with the chemical properties of common functional classes.

Clear non-mathematical pictures of magnetic resonance must inevitably be distortions of more fundamental laws, but a worthwhile sacrifice is made in forming a bridge between physics and chemical application. The book is obviously not monographic in style or depth, but it will serve its intent if, having read it, the reader is thereby equipped and encouraged to tackle the necessarily more rigorous specialist works.

The emphasis is multinuclear, with a deliberate attempt being made to demystify the NMR studies of the less common NMR elements. Likewise, Fourier transforms and superconducting magnets are introduced very early, and are not given any special status as 'recent developments': continuous wave spectrometers are not referred to as 'conventional', and the use of the terms upfield and downfield is minimised for the same pedagogic reasons (being replaced by lower frequency and higher frequency respectively).

The problem of order of presentation, of finding a beginning, a middle and an end, is not unique to the study of NMR: the chapter sequence adopted should not therefore be taken as a recommended learning programme, but merely as an approximate indicator of the way in which most teachers introduce the subject, building upon the familiar to construct a framework of advanced understanding.

Chapter 1 is set at the most elementary conceptual level, and is an obligatory launching point for the multinuclear approach.

Chapter 4 (on proton NMR) and chapter 5 (on carbon-13 NMR) form the mainstay of the subject; some teachers begin with proton while others begin with carbon-13. Surprisingly little theory is needed to interpret such spectra: for this reason, while chapter 2 is fairly full in explanation, most students will tend to attack this chapter in several short sorties, as the need to know becomes more expansive. The same is true of the instrument details given in chapter 3 which, while fairly detailed and self-contained, can profitably be absorbed in separate parts at different times.

The set of chapters 2, 3, 4 and 5 completes a study of NMR to intermediate level.

Chapters 6 and 7 interrelate with each other at the next most advanced conceptual level: here are introduced the theories and practice made accessible only by microprocessor controlled instrumentation. An argument can be made for introducing some of the chapter 6 theory at an earlier stage, and of course this is not precluded: but there is a strong case to be adduced for consolidating the basic applications in the early chapters before tackling the three-dimensional complexities of the rotating frames of reference, with all the perceptual traps involved.

The study of dynamic molecular processes by NMR is treated separately in chapter 8. Some of the simpler ideas of dynamic NMR are, however, interspersed in the earlier chapters, since to gather them all in a late chapter would be artificial and distorting.

Chapters 9–13 are all self-sufficient to a degree, and are the barest indications, by example, of the kind of information contained in the NMR spectra of a selection of other nuclei. Given the multinuclear treatment of the earlier chapters, there is no need here for extensive detail.

Chapter 14 very much embodies two personal views.

Many details of physics are easily forgotten (or may not have been learnt) and having them gathered together serves as a useful aide-memoire for non-physicists. We also often learn nothing about the people who helped to assemble the enormous construct of science, and the sparse biographical notes given here on a few of the famous names in NMR may whet an appetite or two.

Although informative data are supplied as necessary throughout the book, chapter 15 contains a large amount of reference data, which can be accessed for systematic or detailed needs. Extensive tables of chemical shifts, coupling constants and relaxation times are gathered here, with details of common NMR solvents.

There are many problem examples throughout the book. It has been established that one major reason for lack of success in problem solving is an inability to collect and identify only that information which is necessary for solution. In an endeavour to side-step this difficulty, most of the problem examples are preceded by worked examples, so that confidence will rise through knowing which method to apply. Most problems are also seen within the context of the learning objectives under discussion (although other problem examples test more comprehensive understanding).

While it is demonstrably possible to interpret many NMR spectra without intimate study of theory or of spectrometer operation, hopefully the presentation of the subject matter in this book will stimulate an intellectual curiosity, such that a spectrum can be interpreted in the morning, and explained in the afternoon. If the book fulfils its purpose, the user will go back the following morning for more. There is always another experiment to be done.

Heriot-Watt University, Edinburgh   W. K.

Acknowledgements

Thanks are due to innumerable people for help and information: for the supply of spectra, or for the permission to reproduce copyright material used in the figures in this book, several companies (and their personnel) have contributed, and this is recognised with gratitude.

The photograph of Felix Bloch shown in the Frontispiece was kindly supplied by Stanford University, California: that of E. M. Purcell was furnished by E. M. Purcell himself.

Bruker Spectrospin published the material in figures 5.3, 5.13, 5.14, 6.12, 7.4, 7.14, 7.16 and 13.2.

Japan Electronic Optical Laboratories, JEOL, supplied the photographs of the spectrometers shown at the head of chapter 3, and the spectra in figures 1.13, 5.1(b), 5.2 (lower), 5.4, 6.14, head of chapter 7 (also used on the book cover), 8.4 and 11.1.

Oxford Instruments supplied the photograph of the superconducting magnet core and are copyright holders of the diagram showing the cryostat system in figure 3.1.

Oxford Research Systems supplied the photographs of the brain images in figure 7.21 and of the whole-body NMR magnet shown at the head of chapter 10.

Perkin-Elmer published the spectra used in figures 4.18, 4.24, 8.2, 9.2 and at the head of chapter 6.

The figures at the head of chapters 8 and 12 were used with the permission, respectively, of the Royal Society of Chemistry and the American Chemical Society.

Varian Associates granted permission to use the spectra from their NMR Spectra Catalog, namely figures 4.6, 4.7, 4.8, 4.9, 4.10, 4.14, 4.15, 4.20, 4.25, 4.26, 4.27 and 4.28. Other figures which used spectra published by Varian are figures 5.2, 5.11, 5.12, 7.2, 7.5, 7.9, 7.17, 10.2, 10.4, 11.3, 11.4, 12.2, 14.5(c), 13.1, 13.3, 13.4 and 13.5; also those at the heads of chapters 9, 11 and 13.

The following were reproduced, with permission, from Kemp, *Organic Spectroscopy*, 3rd edn, London, Macmillan (1991): 3.2, 4.1, 4.2, 4.3, 4.4, 4.5, 4.12, 4.13, 4.17, 4.23, 6.7, 8.6, 14.5(a).

Johnson and Jankowsky, *Carbon-13 NMR Spectra*, New York, Wiley (1972) was the source (with permission) of figures 5.1(a), 5.5, 5.6, 5.7, 5.8, 5.9, 5.10 and 9.4.

Dalton's table of atomic symbols, which appears at the head of chapter 15, is reproduced by permission of the Trustees of the Science Museum (London).

Many colleagues helped by argument, or by reading part or all of the manuscript (Bill Steedman, Kevin McCullough and Alan Boyd — who also recorded several of the spectra): all are thanked for their encouragement.

Introduction to Nuclear Magnetic Resonance — NMR

1

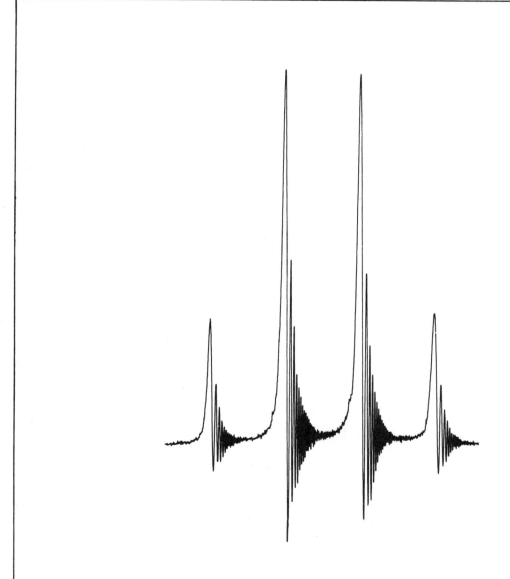

NMR signal from the aldehyde proton in acetaldehyde (CH$_3$CHO)

This chapter presents an overview of the NMR experiment and the chemical information which it can provide; it will not be essential reading for those who have previously met the basics of the technique, but for others it will supply a perspective which would be lacking if the beginnings were treated too rigorously.

1.1 THE PRINCIPLES OF NMR SPECTROSCOPY

The atomic nuclei of many elements are magnetic because they are charged and because they behave as if they were spinning. We can investigate this magnetic property by studying the way in which these nuclei interact with an externally applied magnetic field, B_0. Typical magnetic nuclei are those of hydrogen (^1H), carbon (the ^{13}C isotope only), nitrogen (^{14}N and ^{15}N), oxygen (^{17}O only), fluorine (^{19}F), and phosphorus (^{31}P).

The simplest case is exemplified by the nucleus of

tions which result in two different orientations being allowed — either *aligned with* the field or *opposed to* the field. These two orientations clearly have different energies, the aligned position being of lower energy than the opposed.

> Whenever an external magnetic field is present, some of the nuclei in the sample become aligned (adopt the lower energy configuration) while others become opposed (adopt the higher energy configuration).

The situation is summarised in figure 1.1.

The energy difference (ΔE) between the two nuclear configurations corresponds to a particular, precise electromagnetic frequency since, by the Bohr relationship, $\Delta E = h\nu$. These energy relationships are illustrated in figure 1.2. To take a specific example, if the external magnetic field strength is 2.35 tesla (T), then the energy gap (ΔE) for the hydrogen nucleus is approximately

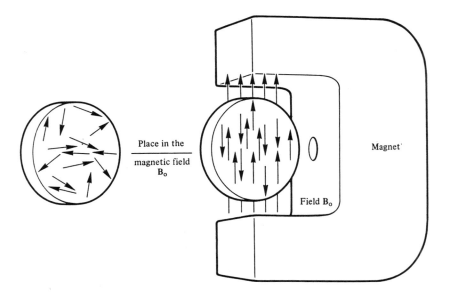

Figure 1.1 In the absence of the field B_0, the magnetic nuclei in the sample are oriented randomly. In the magnetic field, they must adopt either the aligned orientation (of lower energy) or the opposed orientation (of higher energy)

hydrogen (the proton) and also by the nucleus of carbon-13 (^{13}C). These nuclei behave like bar magnets in an applied field, and in the manner of compass needles tend to align themselves along the same direction as the field. Unlike bar magnets and compass needles however, which always come to rest *aligned with* the field, magnetic nuclei such as ^1H and ^{13}C have quantum restric-

6.6×10^{-26} J, and the corresponding frequency (ν) is 100 MHz (lying in the radiofrequency (RF) band of the electromagnetic spectrum). For ^{13}C nuclei in the same magnetic field, the energy gap (ΔE) is 1.7×10^{-26} J, and the frequency $\nu = 25$ MHz.

If a sample containing ^1H nuclei is placed in such a magnetic field, and the sample then irradiated with the

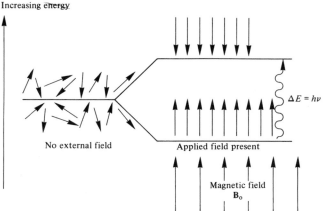

Figure 1.2 In the absence of B_0 the magnetic nuclei all have the same energy. When B_0 is applied, the aligned and opposed orientations correspond to different energies, the energy difference, ΔE, having the dimension $h\nu$

correct radiofrequency, we find that the nuclei interact with the radiofrequency.

Some of the lower-energy nuclei *absorb* radiation and move up to the higher-energy state: that is, they undergo a transition from being aligned with the field to become opposed to the field. At the same time, some of the higher-energy nuclei are stimulated to *emit* energy, and they therefore change their opposed orientation and become aligned with the field.

These transitions will only arise when the magnetic energy gap between the nuclear energy levels is matched exactly with the incoming radiofrequency, that is, when they are 'in resonance', and $\Delta E = h\nu$. The process can be pictured as in figure 1.3.

In Table 1.1 are listed a few important nuclei, with the corresponding RF energy necessary to bring about the nuclear magnetic resonance condition and to stimulate transitions among the available magnetic energy levels. (For more comprehensive details see the Appendix at the back of the book.)

The study of nuclear magnetic resonance (NMR) is concerned with these energy levels, and with the frequency of radiation absorbed during resonance.

1.2 THE NMR SPECTROMETER

A primitive lay-out for an NMR instrument is shown in figure 1.4, with a magnetic field strength of 2.35 T. Assuming that the sample contains carbon and hydrogen, then the ^{13}C nuclei will be partitioned between their two allowed energy levels (1.7×10^{-26} J apart); likewise the protons will be partitioned between their two allowed energy levels (6.6×10^{-26} J apart).

With the RF transmitter/receiver tuned to 25 MHz, the ^{13}C nuclei will undergo upward and downward transitions between the levels and this resonance condition will be detected by observing the absorption of radiofrequency power.

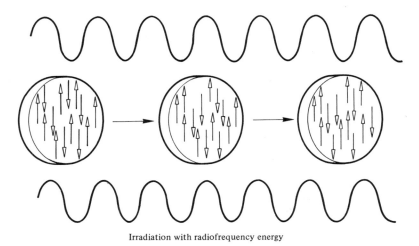

Irradiation with radiofrequency energy

Figure 1.3 When the nuclei (in the magnetic field) are irradiated with radiofrequency energy of the appropriate frequency, some of them undergo transitions from the aligned to the opposed orientations and vice versa

Table 1.1 Common magnetic nuclei. The values shown for ΔE (in joules) and for ν (in MHz, 10^6 s^{-1}) are for nuclei in a magnetic field of 2.35 T

Nucleus	Natural abundance (%)	For $\mathbf{B_O}$ = 2.35 T	
		$\Delta E/J$	ν/MHz
^{1}H	99.98	6.6×10^{-26}	100
^{13}C	1.1	1.7×10^{-26}	25
^{19}F	100	6.2×10^{-26}	94
^{31}P	100	2.7×10^{-26}	40.5
^{14}N	99.63	0.5×10^{-26}	7
^{15}N	0.37	0.6×10^{-26}	10
^{17}O	0.037	0.9×10^{-26}	13.5

ample are surrounded by different electron densities compared with those attached to oxygen or nitrogen atoms; this affects their magnetic susceptibilities.

> Depending on their chemical environment the precise resonance frequency will be shifted from 100 MHz by a few parts per million; we name this phenomenon *chemical shift*, and it is the most important reason for the development of NMR as a routine and powerful analytical technique in chemistry.

Tuned to 100 MHz, the instrument will again record the absorption of RF power, this time because the protons are in resonance and undergoing transitions. The spectrometer will detect ^{19}F at 94 MHz and ^{31}P at 40.5 MHz, and so on.

By convention, the static magnetic field of the instrument is labelled $\mathbf{B_0}$, and the RF electromagnetic field is labelled $\mathbf{B_1}$.

For a simple organic molecule like *tert*-butyl alcohol (see figure 1.5) there are protons in two different chemical environments — nine of them are in methyl groups and one is attached to oxygen. The nine methyl protons come to resonance about 130 Hz higher in frequency than 100 MHz (that is, about 1.3 parts per million to higher frequency) and the OH proton absorbs at about 400 Hz (about 4 ppm) higher frequency than 100 MHz.

> Figure 1.5 is the proton magnetic resonance spectrum (^{1}H NMR spectrum) for *tert*-butyl alcohol; it is essentially a plot of RF absorption against frequency.

1.3 CHEMICAL SHIFTS

Not all protons resonate at exactly 100 MHz in this instrument. Protons attached to carbon atoms for ex-

Note that the integrated area of the larger peak (for the methyl protons) is nine times that of the smaller (OH) signal; in other words

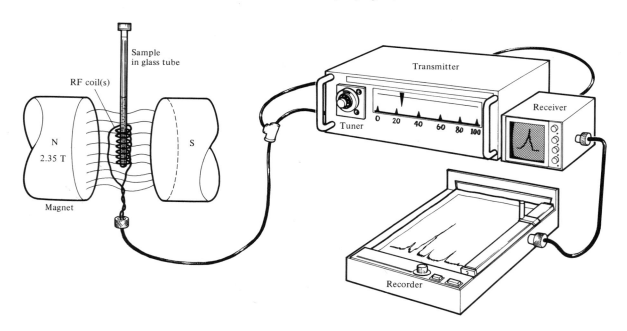

Figure 1.4 Nuclear magnetic resonance spectrometer. The sample is placed in the magnetic field; when the radio-frequency transmitter is tuned to the resonance frequency, a signal arises in the receiver

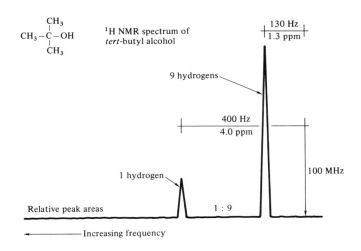

Figure 1.5 Chemical shift. In the proton magnetic resonance spectrum (^{1}H NMR spectrum) of *tert*-butyl alcohol, the nine methyl protons give a signal 1.3 ppm higher in frequency than 100 MHz. The hydroxyl proton signal is about 4.0 ppm higher than 100 MHz. The field strength for this 100 MHz proton NMR spectrum is 2.35 T

> Signal intensity is proportional to the number of protons present in each of the chemical environments within the molecule.

Figure 1.6 is the carbon-13 NMR spectrum for *tert*-butyl alcohol. Again, since there are only two different kinds of carbon atom in the molecule (the three CH$_3$ carbons and the C–OH carbon) each comes to resonance, not at 25 MHz, but chemically shifted so that the CH$_3$ carbons give a signal about 750 Hz higher in frequency,

and the C–OH carbon signal appears around 1750 Hz higher in frequency. Note again that the signals are of different intensity; for reasons that we shall meet later, it is not as easy in ^{13}C NMR to treat these intensities quantitatively.

The carbon-12 isotopes in the sample of *tert*-butyl alcohol make no contribution to this spectrum since they are non-magnetic; the fact that only 1.1 per cent of the carbon atoms are ^{13}C (see table 1.1) makes the carbon-13 NMR spectrum more difficult to record than the proton spectrum. A glance at table 1.1 shows that

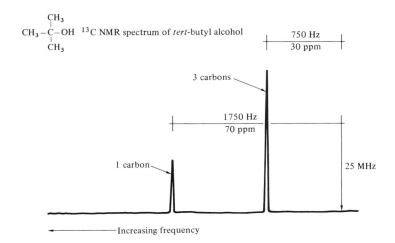

Figure 1.6 Chemical shift. In the routine carbon-13 NMR spectrum of *tert*-butyl alcohol, the three methyl carbons give a signal 30 ppm higher in frequency than 25 MHz. The C–O signal is 70 ppm higher than 25 MHz. The field strength for this 25 MHz ^{13}C NMR spectrum is 2.35 T

^{15}N spectra are even more difficult to obtain, with a natural abundance of only 0.37 per cent, and that ^{17}O is exceedingly rare; ^{19}F and ^{31}P NMR spectra in contrast are relatively easily recorded.

Worked Example 1.1
For the molecule of methyl acetate (methyl ethanoate) CH_3COOCH_3, (a) state how many different chemical shift environments exist for the hydrogen, carbon and oxygen nuclei, (b) note from table 1.1 the natural abundance of each principal magnetic isotope and (c) state the frequency at which each NMR spectrum would be recorded in a spectrometer with a 2.35 T magnet.

Answer 1.1
There are two chemically distinctive hydrogen environments: the natural abundance of the most important hydrogen isotope (^{1}H) is 99.98 per cent, and the spectrum would be recorded at 100 MHz and 2.35 T. There are three carbon environments: carbon-13 abundance is only 1.1 per cent, and the required frequency (for 2.35 T) is 25 MHz. (Carbon-12 is non-magnetic and does not exhibit NMR.) There are also two oxygen environments; oxygen-17 NMR at natural abundance is handicapped by the very low natural abundance (0.037 per cent) but oxygen-17 NMR spectra are acquired at 13.5 MHz in a 2.35 T instrument. (Oxygen-16 is non-magnetic and does not exhibit NMR.)

Problem Example 1.1
Formula 1.1 is an imaginary 'isotope isomer' or *isotopomer* of acetamide. In a 2.35 T magnet, state the frequencies at which the NMR spectrum of each element would be recorded. For each spectrum, state how many signals (that is, chemical shift positions) would be seen. (Detail: because of restricted rotation around the C—N bond, consider the protons on nitrogen to be in different environments, one being nearer to oxygen than the other.)

$$
\begin{array}{ccc}
 & ^1H & ^{17}O \\
 & | & \\!\\!\\!/\\!/ \\
^1H - & ^{13}C - ^{13}C & \\
 & | & \\backslash \\
 & ^1H & ^{15}N - ^1H \\
 & & | \\
 & & ^1H
\end{array}
\qquad (1.1)
$$

1.4 FIELD STRENGTH AND FREQUENCY

Figure 1.2 and table 1.1 show that magnetic nuclei can occupy various magnetic sublevels, and that the frequency necessary to cause nuclear transitions is different for each element or isotope. This resonance frequency is found to vary in direct proportion to the applied field (for *all* magnetic nuclei); thus the larger the magnetic field the higher the frequency necessary to achieve resonance. That is

$$\nu \propto \mathbf{B}_0$$

For the proton we can represent this fact as in figure 1.7.

Although the arithmetic of these field–frequency relationships is simple, a few examples will help to emphasise their crucial importance.

Worked Example 1.2
What is the frequency needed to induce transitions between the ^{13}C nuclear energy levels, when the field strength is (a) 4.7 T and (b) 1.88 T?

Answer 1.2
Since from table 1.1 the ^{13}C NMR frequency is 25 MHz at 2.35 T, then by simple proportion it is 50 MHz at 4.7 T and 20 MHz at 1.88 T.

Problem Example 1.2
What field strength is necessary in an instrument designed for studying proton NMR at (a) 60 MHz, (b) 200 MHz, (c) 600 MHz?

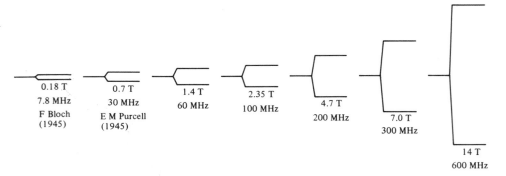

Figure 1.7 Field–frequency relationship. The energy gaps ($\Delta E = h\nu$) are shown for protons in different field strengths. For other elements the same simple proportion holds; table 1.1 lists frequencies for a field strength of 2.35 T

1.5 THE UNITS OF CHEMICAL SHIFT

In the ^1H NMR spectrum for *tert*-butyl alcohol (figure 1.5) the methyl protons show a signal at a higher frequency than the reference frequency of 100 MHz, and this 'chemical shift' can be quoted as either 130 Hz or 1.3 ppm (that is, 1.3 parts per million in 100 million hertz). If the NMR spectrum of this compound were recorded at 4.7 T (when the operating frequency for protons would be 200 MHz) the chemical shift for the methyl protons would be 260 Hz but still 1.3 ppm (that is, 1.3 ppm of 200 MHz). Since chemical shift values expressed in hertz vary with the field strength, it is more convenient and uniform to express them in parts per million from the reference frequency, which is a *field-independent* unit.

This difference in frequency leads to the symbol δ for all chemical shifts; thus a chemical shift of 1.3 ppm is given as δ = 1.3 or simply δ 1.3.

1.6 FREQUENCY STANDARDS

Remembering that field and frequency are mutually linked, the preferred procedure for measuring chemical shifts is to reference them to an internal frequency standard. For both proton and carbon-13 NMR the most convenient standard is tetramethylsilane, TMS (I) (formulae 1.2).

TMS is chosen for several reasons. It can be used to reference both ^1H and ^{13}C in the same sample; it contains 12 equivalent protons and 4 equivalent carbons, and the resultant strong signals mean that only a small amount (about 1–5 per cent by volume) need be added; it gives rise to sharp NMR signals, well clear of most other proton or carbon resonances; it is chemically inert, soluble in most organic compounds, and sufficiently volatile to be easily removed from the sample after the spectrum has been recorded. TMS is now so universally adopted that magnetic field strengths in commercial NMR instruments are designed to bring the TMS protons

to resonance at the exact nominal working frequency of the machine, that is, 60 MHz, 100 MHz, 200 MHz, etc.

We can now refine the definition of chemical shifts (for both proton and carbon).

> The chemical shift position is expressed in δ units, being the difference in frequency, in ppm, from the TMS signal: when δ is positive, the shift is to a higher frequency.

TMS is not water-soluble; for aqueous work commonly used internal standards are sodium 4,4-dimethyl-4-silapentanesulphonate, DSS (II), or the deuterium-substituted carboxylic acid salt (III).

For nuclei other than ^1H and ^{13}C the choice of a satisfactory standard is not so easily resolved, but figure 1.8 shows approximate chemical shifts for ^{14}N and ^{15}N (with respect to an external sample of liquid ammonia) and ^{17}O (with respect to water). ^{31}P chemical shifts can be measured with respect to an external sample of 85 per cent H_3PO_4, and ^{19}F shifts with respect to $CFCl_3$.

Worked Example 1.3
The chemical shift position for the proton resonance in benzene (all six protons being equivalent) is δ 7.27. How many hertz is this from the TMS resonance when the instrument is working at (a) 100 MHz, (b) 60 MHz?

Answer 1.3
Since δ is positive, the benzene resonance is at a higher frequency than that of TMS. At 100 MHz, 1 ppm corresponds to 100 MHz, therefore 7.27 ppm corresponds to 727 Hz. At 60 MHz, 1 ppm corresponds to 60 Hz, thus 7.27 ppm corresponds to 436.2 Hz.

Problem Example 1.3
In figure 1.5, the methyl signal and the OH signal are 270 Hz apart (δ 1.3 and δ 4.0 respectively); what will be the respective chemical shifts, from TMS, if the spectrum is recorded on a 200 MHz instrument, and how many hertz apart will the signals be?

$$CH_3-Si-CH_3 \quad (with\ CH_3\ above\ and\ below)$$

tetramethylsilane

TMS

(I)

$$CH_3-Si-CH_2CH_2CH_2SO_3^-Na^+ \quad (with\ CH_3\ above\ and\ below)$$

4,4-dimethyl-4-silapentanesulphonic acid (Na salt)

DSS

(II)

$$CH_3-Si-CD_2CD_2|COO^-Na^+ \quad (with\ CH_3\ above\ and\ below)$$

2,2,3,3-tetradeuterio-4,4-dimethyl-4-silapentanoic acid (Na salt)

TSP-d_4

(III)

(1.2)

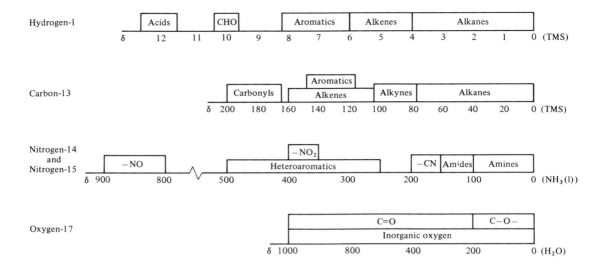

Figure 1.8 Chemical shift. Nuclei in different chemical environments have slightly different resonance frequencies. We measure these differences in parts per million from an appropriate reference standard

Problem Example 1.4

Perform a like calculation for the two carbon-13 resonances in figure 1.6, remembering that on a 200 MHz instrument, the operating frequency for carbon-13 is 50 MHz.

1.7 CHEMICAL SHIFT ASSIGNMENTS

Figure 1.8 sets out the approximate chemical shift positions for a few representative chemical environments. Using this, we can make a preliminary assessment of the likely NMR spectrum for a wide range of compounds. A more exact approach will be introduced later in the book.

Worked Example 1.4

Use figure 1.8 to state how many different chemical shift ranges there will be in the (a) ^1H and (b) ^{13}C NMR spectra of toluene ($C_6H_5CH_3$).

Answer 1.4

(a) There are two groups of protons in toluene; the aromatic protons will give a signal around δ 7 and the alkyl protons will come to resonance between δ 0 and 4.
(b) Likewise there are two main carbon environments; the aromatic carbons will give a signal around δ 140 and the methyl carbon signal will appear between δ 0 and 80.

Problem Example 1.5

Predict the approximate chemical shift ranges in the (a) ^1H and (b) ^{13}C spectra of acetophenone ($C_6H_5COCH_3$) and in acetamide (CH_3CONH_2). Predict also the chemical shift range expected for the ^{15}N NMR signal in acetamide.

(In chapters 4 and 5, more detailed assignments permit the differentiation of *ortho-*, *meta-* and *para-* environments in aromatic rings.)

1.8 TWO MODELS OF NUCLEAR MAGNETIC RESONANCE

There are two quite distinct approaches to an understanding of NMR, each with separate merits and limitations. Some observed effects are more easily interpreted using one model, whereas others are best rationalised with the alternative model. In the end, we must develop both theories, allowing them where appropriate to intertwine, but using each according to its greatest strengths.

1.8.1 Quantum Mechanics

Quantum theory is concerned with nuclear energy levels and this is the theory which we have used thus far in developing figures 1.2 and 1.7. The restrictions imposed by quantisation are familiar in all spectroscopic methods, including NMR. We will return to details in chapter 2.

1.8.2 The Precessing Nucleus

In this picture of NMR we compare the properties of the nucleus with the classical mechanical model of a gyroscope. The motion of a spinning gyroscope is illustrated in figure 1.9(a). (Details of the angular momentum of gyroscopes are given in chapter 14.) Because it is *spinning* and because gravity exerts a *downwards pull* upon it, the axis of the gyroscope moves around a conical path. This waltz-like motion is named *precession*; the necessary and sufficient conditions for precession are (1) spin and (2) a force which tends to pull the gyroscope over.

Just as precession arises in a massive spinning body subject to the action of gravity, so a charged spinning body subject to an applied magnetic field behaves analogously.

The nuclei of magnetic elements, notably those of hydrogen-1 and carbon-13, behave as spinning charged bodies; if we subject them to the influence of a torque in the form of a magnetic field ($\mathbf{B_0}$) they will precess as in figure 1.9(b). This precession, first described by Sir Joseph Larmor for the case of an electron, is usually referred to as *Larmor precession* (see section 14.5.1).

Precession is a familiar phenomenon in mechanical engineering and in astronomy, and it is known that the rate of precession (the *precessional frequency*) depends on several factors including the mass of the spinning body, the spinning frequency, and the strength of the applied torque. For toy gyroscopes, the time needed to complete one cycle of precession is a few seconds; for planets such as earth it takes 30 000 years.

As for gyroscopes and planets, the frequency of precession for atomic nuclei depends on several factors within the nucleus of each unique element, and on the strength and direction of the applied magnetic field $\mathbf{B_0}$. We can say in particular

$$\nu \propto \mathbf{B_0}$$

which is the same relationship introduced in section 1.4 and exemplified in figure 1.7: both theories arrive at the same conclusion.

In figure 1.9(b) if we set the value of $\mathbf{B_0}$ at 2.35 T, we find that a proton will precess around the direction of $\mathbf{B_0}$ at 100 MHz. Looking also at the layout for a simple NMR instrument shown in figure 1.4 then the NMR experiment described according to the precession model shows that

> A precessing proton can absorb electromagnetic energy from the radiofrequency transmitter provided the frequency of this precession is exactly equal to the radiofrequency, that is, when the two are in resonance.

The precessional frequencies (at 2.35 T) for a few magnetic nuclei are just those shown in table 1.1. These

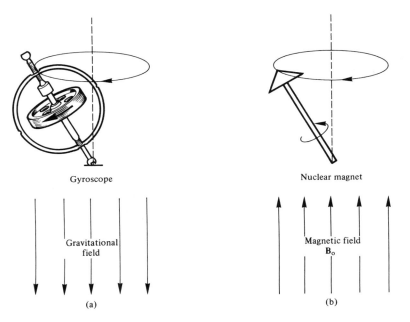

Figure 1.9 (a) The precession of a gyroscope in the earth's gravitational field is comparable to (b) the precession of a magnetic nucleus in a magnetic field

frequencies relate therefore to the two alternative pictures of the resonance condition: (1) they correspond to the precessional frequency when we envisage nuclei as analogous to gyroscopes; and (2) they correspond to the quantised energy gap ($\Delta E = h\nu$) between the two possible orientations of a nuclear dipole in an applied magnetic field.

In figure 1.10 we can now show the amalgamation of the two theories of NMR, as it applies to simple dipolar nuclei such as the proton. We shall specify that the direction of the applied field $\mathbf{B_0}$ is drawn acting towards the top of the page, and maintain this convention throughout the book. In this applied field, the proton can adopt one of the two possible situations.

> The low-energy situation has the proton precessing with the magnetic dipole moment pointing *with* the applied field $\mathbf{B_0}$. The high-energy situation has the proton magnetic moment precessing *against* the applied field.

For convenience in identifying these states, the lower energy (aligned with the field) is usually labelled α (or +) while the upper energy state is labelled β (or −). The sign + implies that parallel to (with) the field is of lower energy: this is untrue for electrons and for the nuclei of

a small number of elements, when the opposite is the case, and we will have to return to this problem in chapter 6.

Worked Example 1.5
From the Bohr relationship, $\Delta E = h\nu$, calculate ΔE for (a) protons in a 1.4 T magnet, (b) ^{13}C in a 1.4 T magnet.

Answer 1.5
(h = Planck's constant, 6.6×10^{-34} J s.) For protons at 1.4 T, ν = 60 MHz = 6.0×10^7 s^{-1}, $\Delta E = h\nu = (6.6 \times 10^{-34}$ J s) $(6 \times 10^7$ s^{-1}) = 4×10^{-26} J.

This is the value for *one* proton; for a mole of protons we must multiply by the Avogadro constant $N_A = 6 \times 10^{23}$. Thus $\Delta E = 24 \times 10^{-3}$ J mol^{-1} or 0.024 J mol^{-1}.

For carbon-13 at 1.4 T, ν = 15 MHz, which is one quarter of the frequency of precession of the proton. ΔE likewise is one quarter that for the proton, so ΔE = 0.006 J mol^{-1}.

Problem Example 1.6
What are the corresponding ΔE values for protons and carbon-13 in a field of 7.0 T, when ν for protons is 300 MHz?

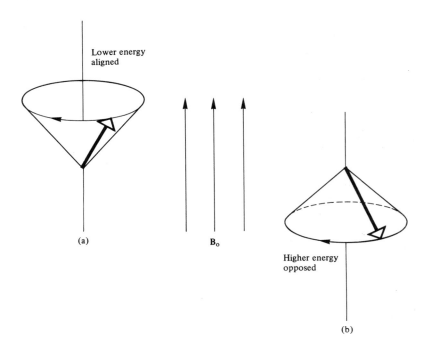

Figure 1.10 Precessional model of the proton precessing in an applied magnetic field $\mathbf{B_0}$. (a) The lower energy state is aligned with the direction of $\mathbf{B_0}$; this is designated the + (or α) state. (b) The higher energy state is opposed to $\mathbf{B_0}$; this is named the − (or β) state

1.9 COUPLING AND DECOUPLING OF MAGNETIC NUCLEI

Not all spectra consist of single-line absorption bands as in figures 1.5 and 1.6, as splitting of the lines frequently appears as a complicating feature. The splitting arises because the spins of neighbouring nuclei interact (or *couple*) with one another and only the briefest introduction will be justified at this stage. When the signal from any given nucleus is split, then the degree of splitting (the observed *multiplicity*) depends on the number of nuclei to which it is coupled, and the simplest cases are shown in figure 1.11.

Note that the splitting can arise whether the coupling nuclei are of the same element or not, and that the spacings of the lines in related multiplets are equal.

As the coupling process complicates the NMR spectra, it is often advantageous to be able to *decouple* nucleus A from nucleus B. This is achieved by recording at the resonant frequency of A (with the normal RF source, B_1) and a second radiofrequency source, B_2, is then used to irradiate the nucleus B, with the B_2 RF frequency tuned to the resonant frequency of B. By this technique of *double irradiation* of B, the signal for nucleus A is simplified, and examples are shown in figures 1.12 and 1.13.

Neither of the figures 1.5 or 1.6 shows the effects of coupling, although the reasons for this are different; in particular, carbon-13 NMR spectra are normally recorded with the coupling to protons removed for simplicity by double irradiation, and such spectra are called *proton-decoupled* carbon-13 NMR spectra.

Spin coupling, and a plethora of decoupling methods, constitute a major part of the study of NMR spectra; the topic is discussed in greater detail in several later parts of the book.

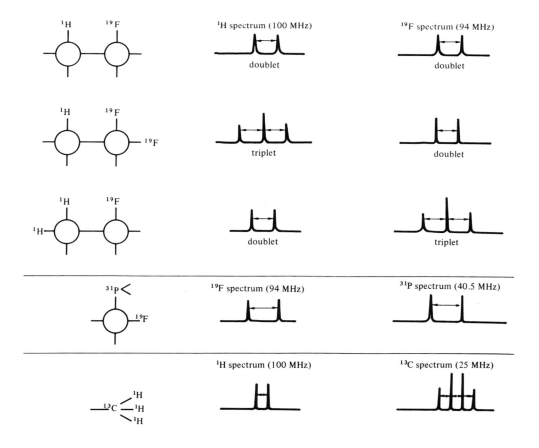

Figure 1.11 Splitting of NMR signals by neighbouring magnetic nuclei. For these simplest cases, the number of lines observed in the signal for nucleus A equals the number of B nuclei, n, plus one, that is $(n + 1)$. The frequencies shown relate to $B_0 = 2.35$ T

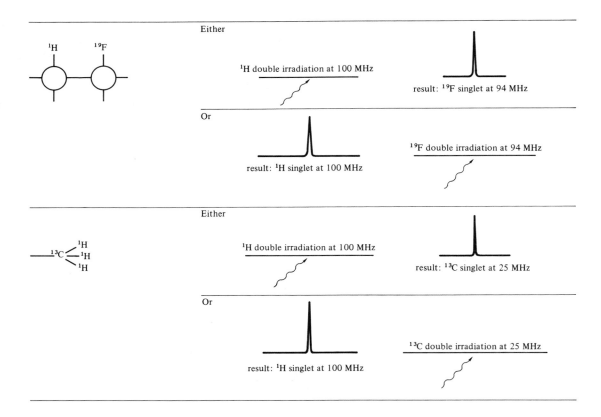

Figure 1.12 Double irradiation at the resonant frequency of nucleus A simplifies the spectrum of B. The converse experiment (decoupling B from A) leads to a corresponding simplification of the spectrum of A

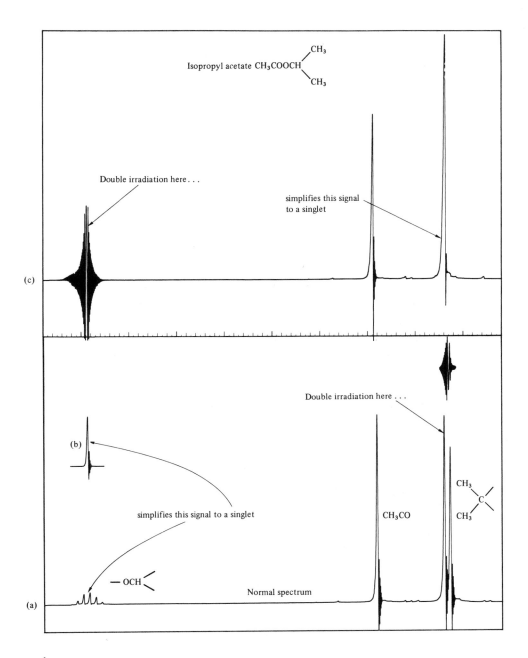

Figure 1.13 ^{1}H NMR spectrum of isopropyl acetate. Double irradiation (spin decoupling) experiments: the protons in the isopropyl group can be decoupled from each other by double irradiation at either the CH$_3$ frequency or the CH frequency. (Spectra recorded at 100 MHz.) (a) Normal spectrum; (b) with double irradiation at the (CH$_3$)$_2$ frequency; and (c) with double irradiation at the CH frequency

2 The Fundamental Basis of Magnetic Resonance

¹H nucleus
1 proton
magnetic

²H nucleus
1 proton
1 neutron
magnetic

⁴He nucleus
2 protons
2 neutrons
non-magnetic

¹²C nucleus

6 protons
6 neutrons

non-magnetic

¹³C nucleus

6 protons
7 neutrons

magnetic

Much of the vocabulary of NMR comes from physics, and we need to be familiar with the fundamental properties of electrons, protons and neutrons before we can fully understand and utilise all of the information which can be extracted from NMR spectra.

This chapter presents these fundamentals in a way most useful to the later application of NMR in chemistry.

Whilst we are here primarily concerned with magnetic resonance in atomic nuclei, two sister phenomena exist which affect the mainstream arguments. Corresponding to the magnetic properties of nuclei are the magnetic properties of electrons, and *electron spin resonance spectroscopy* (ESR) relates to these. Nuclei are also governed in behaviour by their electric charges, and the distribution of these can be studied by *nuclear quadrupole resonance spectroscopy* (NQR). The neutron has no charge but nevertheless possesses magnetic properties which influence the total magnetic properties of all nuclei except the nucleus of hydrogen (containing just one proton).

2.1 THE SPIN OF ELECTRONS AND NUCLEI

In order to rationalise the fine structure in atomic spectra, and especially the effect of an applied magnetic field, it was necessary to assume that electrons possessed magnetic dipole moments, and that half of the electrons had their magnetic moments aligned in one sense (let us say, parallel) with respect to the external magnetic field, and the other half were aligned antiparallel. To explain the origin of this dipole, it was postulated in the 1920s that the electrons possessed the property of spin; in the macro world, moving charged bodies generate electric and magnetic fields (see 14.3.2) and the analogy was adopted that a spinning electron would do so too. Convenient though this has proved to be, strictly speaking it is an example of modelling; using this idea, we can rationalise descriptively many of the experimental conclusions of physics, but however successful and satisfying may be these pictures, we must always accept that they are considerably oversimplified.

The proton has magnetic properties which can likewise be accounted for by applying the mathematics of spin. The neutron is uncharged, but it has a magnetic moment and its properties can be rationalised if we describe it as having spin.

2.2 ANGULAR MOMENTUM AND MAGNETIC MOMENTS OF THE ELECTRON AND THE PROTON

If we ignore for the purposes of this book the *orbital* angular momentum of the electron, then we can contrast the electron and the proton in respect of the *spin* angular momentum of each. Figure 2.1(a) pictures the electron as a spinning, negatively-charged body, and we can represent the spin angular momentum by the vector **I** (see section 14.1), obeying the right-hand screw rule for vectors. (Note that the spin angular momentum is sometimes represented by the letters **p**, or **P**, or **J**: we can regard these differences as merely conventional, and of no consequence to the arguments.)

Now the *magnetic dipole* generated by this spinning charged body can be represented by the vector μ; note that electron flow is in the opposite sense to the flow of conventional current (as noted in section 14.3.2). This leads to a most important conclusion.

> The vector representing spin angular momentum for the electron is in the *opposite sense* from (*opposite in sign* to) the vector representing its magnetic moment.

Figure 2.1(b) offers the comparable picture for the spin of the proton: note now the important contrary deduction.

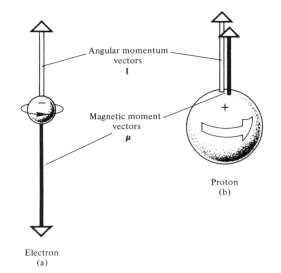

Figure 2.1 (a) The spinning electron and (b) the spinning proton. Both are shown with the same direction of spin thus their angular momentum vectors point in the same direction. The vectors representing their magnetic moments point in opposite directions however

> The vector representing spin angular momentum for the proton is in the *same sense* (that is, of the *same sign*) as the vector representing its magnetic moment.

2.3 ANGULAR MOMENTUM AND MAGNETIC MOMENTS OF OTHER NUCLEI

The nucleus of the hydrogen-1 atom is unique in having only one proton, whilst all other nuclei contain neutrons as well as protons. Current theories are unable to calculate how proton spins and neutron spins combine vectorially, and we must rely on experiment to examine the net spin of each different nucleus; some simple empirical rules will be enunciated shortly, but an important generality must be stated here.

Some atomic nuclei have zero net spin (for example those of carbon-12, oxygen-16 and helium-4); this implies an overall cancellation (or pairing) of the proton and neutron spins within the nucleus concerned. Although these nuclei are all positively charged, they are observed to have no magnetic moment (which apparently corresponds to their having zero spin angular momentum); such nuclei do not exhibit nuclear magnetic resonance.

Many atomic nuclei do have a magnetic moment and, by implication, a net spin angular momentum: it is with these 'magnetic' nuclei that this book is concerned.

By far the largest proportion of these magnetic nuclei generate a magnetic moment vector with the *same sign* as the spin angular momentum vector (as does the proton), but a few have a magnetic moment vector *opposite in sign* to their angular momentum vector (examples being the nuclei of nitrogen-15 and oxygen-17). How can we picture this? At this point we can see that we have pushed the modelling too far, because we have no simple means of counting up the number of protons and the number of neutrons present and deducing from that the relative signs of $\mathbf{I}$ and μ. We can only invoke the complexity of nuclei and accept our inability to offer a persuasive macro-model (see 14.6). Certainly the experimental evidence is there to prove that $\mathbf{I}$ and μ must have opposite sign in certain nuclei, and we shall deal with the inherent consequences as the need arises.

2.4 THE SPIN QUANTUM NUMBER

The dimension of spin angular momentum for all nuclei is quantised and can be characterised by a *spin quantum number*, designated by I. The allowed values of I may be zero, integer, or half-integer and examples are shown in table 2.1.

While purely empirical, the rules which summarise the relationship between the composition of a nucleus (the number of protons and neutrons, p and n respectively) and its spin quantum number are

(a) if p and n are both *even numbers* I is zero (^{12}C, ^{16}O for example);
(b) if (p + n) is an *odd number* I is half-integer (^{1}H, ^{13}C, ^{15}N, ^{17}O for example);
(c) if *both* p and n are *odd numbers* I is integer (^{2}H, ^{14}N for example).

Whatever value of I a nucleus is observed to take, it specifies two other important facts about that nucleus.

Table 2.1 Spin quantum numbers and derived quantities

Spin quantum number I	Examples	Angular momentum, $\mathbf{I}$ $\sqrt{I(I+1)}$ in units of $h/2\pi$	Number of spin states (allowed orientations) $2I+1$	Magnetic quantum number – the z-axis components of $\mathbf{I}$ (allowed values of spin) m_I					
0	^{4}He ^{12}C ^{16}O	0	0			0			
1/2	^{1}H ^{13}C ^{15}N ^{19}F ^{29}Si ^{31}P	$\sqrt{\frac{3}{4}} = 0.87$	2			$\frac{1}{2}$	$-\frac{1}{2}$		
1	^{2}H ^{14}N	$\sqrt{2} = 1.41$	3		1	0	-1		
3/2	^{11}B ^{23}Na ^{35}Cl ^{37}Cl	$\sqrt{\frac{15}{4}} = 1.94$	4		$\frac{3}{2}$	$\frac{1}{2}$	$-\frac{1}{2}$	$-\frac{3}{2}$	
2	^{8}Li* ^{20}F*	$\sqrt{6} = 2.45$	5	2	1	0	-1	-2	
5/2	^{17}O ^{27}Al	$\sqrt{\frac{35}{4}} = 2.96$	6	$\frac{5}{2}$	$\frac{3}{2}$	$\frac{1}{2}$	$-\frac{1}{2}$	$-\frac{3}{2}$	$-\frac{5}{2}$

*Radioactive.

2.4.1 The Dimension of Spin Angular Momentum

Spin angular momentum is given by

$$\text{angular momentum, } \mathbf{I} = \frac{h}{2\pi} \sqrt{I(I+1)}$$

We must not confuse the spin quantum *number*, I, which is a pure number, with the spin *angular momentum*, $\mathbf{I}$, which is a vector, measured in units of $h/2\pi$ (often shown as $\hbar$); Planck's constant, h, has the value 6.6×10^{-34} J s. These quantised values of spin angular momentum are shown in table 2.1.

2.4.2 The Direction of Spin Angular Momentum

Unlike spinning macroscopic bodies, which can be made to spin in any direction, there are quantised limits to the direction of the nuclear angular momentum, subject to a few simple rules.

First, the number of allowed orientations for the angular momentum is restricted, and defined by the formula $(2I + 1)$; thus for nuclei $I = \frac{1}{2}$, only two directions are allowed, and if $I = 1$, then three directions are allowed and so on. Having defined the number of orientations, the allowed values for the dimension of the momentum can also be deduced; these are the magnetic quantum numbers, m_I. Here are the rules (which differ slightly for nuclei with integer values of I and for nuclei with half-integer values). The allowed values of spin, m_I, are

$I, I-1, I-2, \ldots, 0, \ldots, 2-I, 1-I, -I$ (for integer I)
$I, I-1, I-2, \ldots, \frac{1}{2}, -\frac{1}{2}, \ldots, 2-I, 1-I, -I$ (for half-integer I)

Note that, in each series, each quantum number m_I differs from its neighbour by 1 — the most fundamental of all quantum rules.

Table 2.1 shows the number of orientations (usually simply named *spin states*) for common cases and the allowed values $(1, \frac{1}{2}, -\frac{1}{2}$ and so on) usually referred to, somewhat loosely, as the values of 'spin'.

We must now address the question of how we can measure $\mathbf{I}$ by experiment, since this imposes further restrictions on our knowledge.

If we measure $\mathbf{I}$ by supplying a magnetic field $\mathbf{B_0}$ with which $\mathbf{I}$ can interact (and this is the basis of the NMR experiment) then we can only measure components of $\mathbf{I}$ along the magnetic field. No experiment can be performed that will measure the whole spin angular momentum of a nucleus; this is so fundamental that we must formalise it precisely, but to do so we will define now (and throughout the rest of the book) that the direction of the applied field will be designated as lying along the

z-axis of a set of rectangular cartesian coordinates. (The z-axis will always be shown pointing to the top of the page.) Having made this clear, then

> The spin angular momentum vector ($\mathbf{I}$) can only adopt those orientations which have components along the z-axis ($\mathbf{I_z}$) equal to the allowed values of spin.

2.5 NUCLEI WITH SPIN QUANTUM NUMBER = $\frac{1}{2}$

It will be helpful to take the simplest case and work through the various consequences. Nuclei with spin quantum number equal to $\frac{1}{2}$ have only two allowed values of spin, that is $+\frac{1}{2}$ and $-\frac{1}{2}$. The angular momentum arising from spin is (from table 2.1) 0.87 units. What does this mean? It means that the magnitude of the angular momentum vector is 0.87; but there are only two allowed orientations for the angular momentum vector with respect to the z-axis, and these must have components along the z-axis of 0.5 ($+\frac{1}{2}$, in the lower-energy case) and -0.5 ($-\frac{1}{2}$, in the higher-energy case).

Figure 2.2(a) shows the orientation of the angular momentum vector which will allow a component of +0.5 on the z-axis; here, as in all cases, the applied field $\mathbf{B_0}$ points toward the top of the page. Figure 2.2(b) shows the second allowed orientation of the angular momentum vector, such that the component on the z-axis is -0.5. The angle θ can be calculated since

$$\cos \theta = \frac{0.5}{0.87} = 0.57, \text{ so } \theta = 55°$$

If we recall that, experimentally, only the angular momentum component along the z-axis can be specified, the corollary is that *this vector is orientated randomly* with respect to the x- and y-axes.

If then we construct two cones, each of half angle 55° (as in figure 2.3), the angular momentum vectors can lie anywhere on the surface of these cones: if a nucleus is of lower energy, it will lie on the surface of the cone as in figure 2.3(a), and if it is of higher energy, it will lie as in figure 2.3(b).

2.6 THE NUCLEAR MAGNETIC MOMENT VECTOR, μ

Since we have seen earlier that for the proton and for the nucleus of carbon-13 (two of the most important nuclei with spin $\frac{1}{2}$) the angular momentum vector and the magnetic moment vector lie in the same direction and with the same sign, we can therefore picture these magnetic moment vectors as also being oriented on the

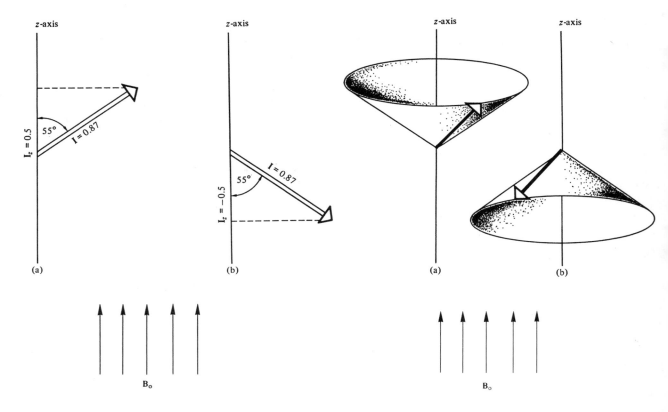

Figure 2.2 For spin $\frac{1}{2}$ nuclei, the total spin angular momentum is 0.87 units ($h/2\pi$). The component along the z-axis (I_z) can only take two values: (a) 0.5 ($+\frac{1}{2}$) or (b) -0.5 ($-\frac{1}{2}$). The angle (55°) can be calculated from its cosine: 0.5/0.87

Figure 2.3 The 'cones of precession' for nuclei with spin quantum number $\frac{1}{2}$. The angular momentum vectors (and the magnetic moment vectors) lie on the surfaces of cones of half-angle 55°. With B_0 acting along the z-axis, (a) is of lower energy than (b)

surface of cones as illustrated in figure 2.3. We saw earlier however that we cannot in general calculate the magnitude of nuclear magnetic moments: we must rely on experiment for these values.

We can now complete a useful picture for the NMR phenomenon from figure 2.3, taking the case of the proton as an example.

In the absence of an applied field, protons may be regarded as spinning randomly. When an external field is supplied (say 2.35 T) the protons must adopt one of two orientations; a lower-energy state (more or less *aligned* with the field) and a higher-energy state (more or less *opposed* to the field). In these states we can depict the magnetic moment vectors as precessing around the surfaces of the two cones of figure 2.3, and the frequency of this precession will be 100 MHz.

When radiofrequency power at 100 MHz is supplied to the system, the resonance condition can be envisaged

as causing the precessing protons to flip from one orientation to the other, so that each proton will spend part of its time precessing around the cone in figure 2.3(a) and part of its time precessing around the cone in figure 2.3(b).

This picture is a more quantitative extension of those shown in figures 1.1 and 1.10.

We should remember at this point that the Heisenberg Uncertainty Principle applies. If both the magnitude of the spin angular momentum I and its position with respect to the z-axis I_z are known, then I_x and I_y must be 'uncertain' — otherwise we would have a precise knowledge of both the dimension *and* position of I, which is in contradiction to the Heisenberg Uncertainty Principle. When we draw the cones of figure 2.3, we can only say that the magnetic moment vectors lie *somewhere* on the surfaces: it is a simplification (legitimate and convenient) to call them precession cones.

2.7 THE STRENGTHS OF NUCLEAR MAGNETS – THE NUCLEAR MAGNETON UNIT, μ_N

The dimensions of nuclear magnetic dipoles (the strengths of the magnets) can be expressed as multiples of a term derived from that of the simplest nucleus – the proton; the unit used is the *nuclear magneton*, μ_N.

Just as a spinning point charge in classical physics (see 14.3.2) generates a magnetic dipole given by

$$\mu = \frac{\text{charge} \times \text{angular momentum}}{2 \times \text{mass}}$$

we can use the same definition for protons (even though they are not strictly point charges). Thus since protonic charge = e, protonic mass = m and its angular momentum is in units of $h/2\pi$

Nuclear magneton μ_N = Proton magnetic moment

$$= \frac{\text{proton charge} \times \text{angular momentum units}}{2 \times \text{mass}}$$

$$= \frac{e \cdot h/2\pi}{2m}$$

The dimension of the nuclear magneton, μ_N, is 5.05×10^{-27} J T^{-1} (joules per tesla).

For nuclei other than the proton we must take account of increased mass, and increased charge (the number of protons present) and also the value of the spin angular momentum, in particular its z-component I_z ($+\frac{1}{2}$, $-\frac{1}{2}$, for example).

The (z-component of) magnetic moment for a nucleus of mass M, with p protons present, and with angular momentum I_z is proportional to the following

$$\mu_z \propto \left\{ \frac{e}{2m} \cdot \frac{h}{2\pi} \right\} \cdot \frac{p}{M} \cdot I_z$$

This can be further simplified by substituting μ_N, the nuclear magneton. Thus

$$\mu_z \propto \frac{p}{M} \cdot \mu_N \cdot I_z$$

For any particular nucleus of mass M and charge p we can then define a constant of proportionality g, incorporating M and p, such that

$$\mu_z = g \cdot \mu_N \cdot I_z$$

This *nuclear g-factor*, g, cannot be calculated: it must be determined experimentally for each nucleus and it then completes the relationship between the nuclear magnetic dipole moment, μ_z, and the spin angular moment from which it derives.

2.8 THE MAGNETOGYRIC RATIO – γ

An alternative constant, γ, for each nucleus can usefully be defined, combining the proportionality constant, g, with the unit of nuclear magnetic moments, the nuclear magneton, μ_N, so that $\gamma = g\mu_N$. This leads to

$$\mu_z = \gamma I_z \quad \text{or} \quad \gamma = \frac{\mu_z}{I_z}$$

Thus γ is the ratio between the magnetic dipole and the angular momentum; it is usually called the *magnetogyric ratio*, but is also called the *gyromagnetic ratio* (Italian: *girare*, to turn). The value of γ for any nucleus is simply g for that nucleus multiplied by μ_N, 5.05×10^{-27} J T^{-1}. Like g therefore, γ is an experimental parameter, and values are listed in the Appendix for the most useful NMR elements. (The magnetogyric ratio appears in another crucial context, as we shall see in section 2.9.)

Recall from section 2.3 that for most nuclei μ and I have the same sign, but that a few nuclei (for example ^{15}N) have magnetic moment vectors opposite in sign to their angular momentum vectors.

> The value of γ (and g) may be positive or negative.

There are relatively few consequences of negative γ values that need concern us, but we must return to the fact when we study ^{15}N NMR spectra.

2.9 PRECESSIONAL FREQUENCY AND γ – THE LARMOR EQUATION

If we return now to figure 2.3, we have a nucleus (in this case the proton) being acted upon by a magnetic field of strength $B_0 = 2.35$ T which supplies a torque (vector) to the spinning nucleus, causing its magnetic moment (vector) to precess.

The angular frequency, ω, in radians per second, of this Larmor precession is found to relate to B_0 as in the Larmor equation originally applied to the electron (see 14.5.1). Thus

$$\omega = \gamma B_0 \quad \text{or} \quad \gamma = \frac{\omega}{B_0} \quad \text{(in units of rad T}^{-1} \text{ s}^{-1})$$

If we choose to express this in frequency units (s^{-1}, Hz) then since $\nu = \dfrac{\omega}{2\pi}$

$$\nu = \frac{\gamma B_0}{2\pi}$$

This is undoubtedly the most important of the fundamental equations in NMR spectroscopy.

2.10 SUMMARY OF NMR THEORY

The entire theory of NMR thus far discussed can now be summarised

(a) Many nuclei have spin angular momentum, $\mathbf{I}$.
(b) Because of this they have a magnetic moment μ, and $\mu = \gamma \mathbf{I}$.
(c) The magnetogyric ratio, γ, is a unique constant for each nucleus.
(d) In an applied field of strength $\mathbf{B_0}$, the frequency of precession, ν, is equal to $\dfrac{\gamma}{2\pi}\,\mathbf{B_0}$. From this $\nu \propto \mathbf{B_0}$.

Worked Example 2.1
Calculate the magnetogyric ratio for the proton.

Answer 2.1
γ is simply the constant of proportionality between field strength, $\mathbf{B_0}$, and frequency (in rad s^{-1}). From table 1.1 we know that the precessional frequency for the proton in a 2.35 T field is 100 MHz, which is 100×10^6 s^{-1}, or $2\pi \times 100 \times 10^6$ rad s^{-1}. Thus

$$\gamma = \frac{2\pi\nu}{\mathbf{B_0}} = \frac{2 \times 3.143 \times 100 \times 10^6 \text{ rad s}^{-1}}{2.35 \text{ T}}$$

$$= 2.675 \times 10^8 \text{ rad T}^{-1} \text{ s}^{-1}$$

Problem Example 2.1
Given that the carbon-13 NMR frequency is 25 MHz in a 2.35 T magnet, calculate γ for carbon-13. What will γ for carbon-13 be at 4.7 T?

Worked Example 2.2
Calculate the nuclear g-factor, g, for the proton.

Answer 2.2
We saw in section 2.8 that $\gamma = g \times \mu_N$, and from section 2.7 the value of μ_N is 5.05×10^{-27} J T^{-1}. The calculation in worked example 2.1 gave us γ for the proton = 2.675×10^8 rad T^{-1} s^{-1}, but we must now convert this into the same units as μ_N (J T^{-1}, which is energy × field strength^{-1}). Angular velocity in radians per second is converted to frequency by dividing by 2π (there being 2π radians in one cycle). In turn, frequency (in s^{-1}) is converted to energy (in J) by multiplying by Planck's constant, h, since $\Delta E = h\nu$; $h = 6.63 \times 10^{-34}$ J s, and so $\gamma = 2.675 \times 10^8$ rad T^{-1} s^{-1} which we can multiply by 2π and h to give $\gamma = 2.675 \times 10^8 \times 2 \times 3.143 \times 6.63 \times 10^{-34}$ (T^{-1} s^{-1}) (J s). To find g, we divide this by μ_N and, since all the units cancel out,

$$g = \frac{2.675 \times 10^8 \times 6.63 \times 10^{-34}}{2 \times 3.143 \times 5.05 \times 10^{-27}} = 5.586$$

(a pure number)

Problem Example 2.2
Calculate the nuclear g-factor for carbon-13.

Problem Example 2.3
Given that the mass of the proton is 1837 times the mass of the electron, use the arguments in section 2.7 to calculate, for the electron, a constant corresponding to μ_N for the proton.

2.11 ELECTRON SPIN RESONANCE SPECTROSCOPY

Most of the theory developed above for the case of the proton can be adapted to apply to the electron (although historically the chronology was the other way round). Apart from the vital difference of sign, electrons have spin = $\frac{1}{2}$ and we can envisage them in an applied magnetic field precessing with the magnetic dipole oriented on the surface of cones, either aligned with or opposed to the external field. (The lower energy case for the electron is the β, or $-$ state.)

If energy of the correct amount ($\Delta E = h\nu$) is supplied then the electrons will undergo transitions at the resonance frequency, moving from aligned to opposed orientations, etc.

For electrons, as for all magnetic nuclei, ν depends on $\mathbf{B_0}$, a typical value being 8000 MHz in a field of 0.3 T. These much higher frequencies lie in the microwave region of the electromagnetic spectrum, and experimental techniques vary accordingly.

The study of microwave absorption by electrons in an applied magnetic field is the basis of electron spin resonance spectroscopy.

ESR spectroscopy can examine only those species which contain an unpaired electron and are therefore paramagnetic, such as organic free radicals or transition metal ions; the alternative name, electron paramagnetic resonance (EPR), emphasises this aspect.

2.12 NUCLEI WITH SPIN QUANTUM NUMBER = 1

Having looked in detail at the case of spin = $\frac{1}{2}$ nuclei, we can now readily extend the principles embodied in figures 2.2 and 2.3 to other nuclei. We know that quantum rules specify both the number of orientations for the angular momentum vector and also the component of this along the z-axis.

From table 2.1 the angular momentum vector for spin = 1 nuclei is $1.41 \times h/2\pi$; there are three possible orientations for the vector ($2I + 1$) and the z-components must be $+ 1$, 0, and $- 1$. This is shown in figure 2.4. As for the spin $\frac{1}{2}$ nuclei, only the z-components can be

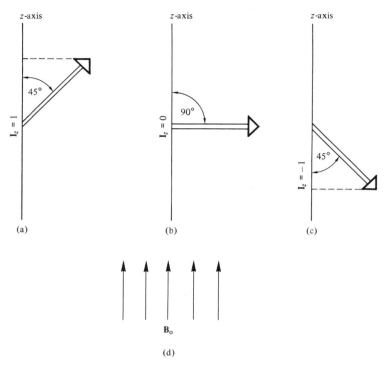

Figure 2.4 Allowed orientations for the angular momentum vector of a nucleus with spin quantum number = 1. Only the components on the z-axis can be measured; the only allowed values are +1, 0 and −1

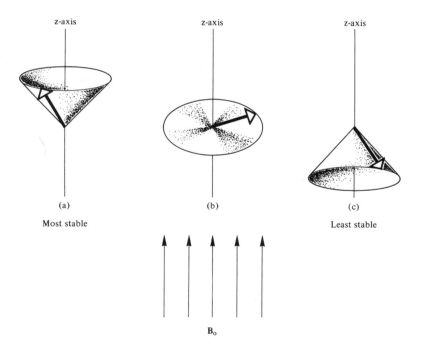

Figure 2.5 Precession modes for the magnetic moment vector of a nucleus with spin quantum number = 1. It can precess freely on the surfaces of cones (a) or (c), each with half-angle 45°, or it can precess on the xy plane as in (b)

measured, and the nucleus is free to precess around the
z-axis on the surface of cones (with half-angle $\theta = 45°$)
when I_z is $+ 1$ or $- 1$. The precession takes place on the
xy plane when $I_z = 0$.

In figure 2.4(a) and (c), where I_z is +1 and −1 respectively, the vector makes an angle with the z-axis such
that its cosine is $1/1.41$, and thus the angle is $45°$. In
figure 2.4(b), when the z-axis component of I is zero,
the angle is $90°$.

Figure 2.5 shows the corresponding degrees of free-
dom for the magnetic moment vector. There are three
allowed orientations; in (a) and (c) it can precess on the
surfaces of two cones of half-angle $45°$, or in (b) it can
precess on the xy plane. Taking ^{14}N as the best known
example, the precessional frequency for a field of 2.35 T
will be 7 MHz (see table 1.1). Irradiation with 7 MHz
will induce the ^{14}N nucleus to undergo transitions
among the three possible spin states − the resonance
condition.

2.13 NUCLEI WITH SPIN QUANTUM NUMBER GREATER THAN 1

Table 2.1 shows the number of orientations (that is, the
number of spin states) for nuclei with higher values of I.
From a consideration of these, and a knowledge of the
frequency required to bring each to resonance (this is
shown in the Appendix) we can proceed later to look at
the application of NMR to the study of the most important elements involved.

All nuclei with spin equal to or greater than one
$(I \geqslant 1)$ possess an electric quadrupole moment as well as
a magnetic moment; this fact too we can incorporate
into the study.

For such nuclei, we can again construct a picture of
their precession modes from a knowledge of (1) the
number of allowed orientations and (2) the components
of the spin angular momentum on the z-axis. As an
example figure 2.6 shows the construct for nuclei with
$I = 2\frac{1}{2}$, or $\frac{5}{2}$. From table 2.1 the total angular momen-

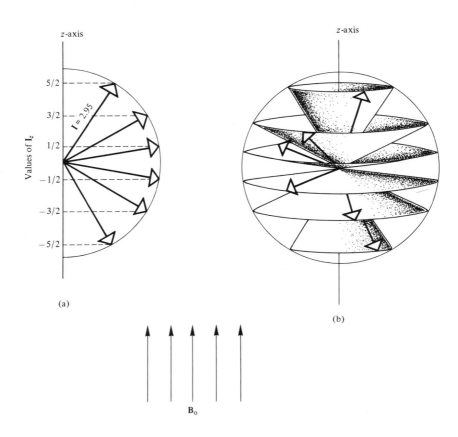

Figure 2.6 For a nucleus of spin quantum number = 5/2 the total angular momentum is 2.96 $h/2\pi$, and the z-axis
components are as in (a). The corresponding allowed precession modes are shown in (b). The nuclei of
^{17}O and ^{27}Al have $I = 5/2$

tum is 2.95 units $(h/2\pi)$, and there are six allowed orientations with z-axis components of $2\frac{1}{2}, 1\frac{1}{2}, \frac{1}{2}, -\frac{1}{2}$ and $-2\frac{1}{2}$. Figure 2.6(a) shows the six orientations of **I** with the allowed z-axis components, and figure 2.6(b) shows the set of precession modes for these six orientations. The half angles of the cones can as usual be calculated from the respective cosines.

Problem Example 2.4
Calculate the half angles for the cones in figure 2.6(b).

2.14 QUADRUPOLE MOMENTS

With respect to an applied field, nuclei with spin = 1 have three orientations associated with the magnetic moment of the nucleus. Another feature of spin = 1 nuclei, which distinguishes them from spin = $\frac{1}{2}$ nuclei, is their charge distribution.

Spin = $\frac{1}{2}$ nuclei have their positive charge distributed within the nucleus symmetrically, so they may be regarded as uniformly charged spheres; when this uniform electric charge is spinning it creates a magnetic field, and because the charge is symmetrical only a simple magnetic dipole can arise, positioned along the spin axis.

Spin = 1 nuclei however have the nuclear charge distributed non-uniformly; we must picture them, not as symmetrical spheres of charge but as distorted spheres, which may be either flattened or elongated (bringing to mind pumpkins and rugby footballs). Figure 2.7 illustrates uneven charge distribution in these nuclei.

Since the charge density is uneven, there exists a *charge gradient* within the nucleus (that is an *electric field gradient*). In the study of electrostatics, the simple dipole (see figure 2.7(c)) is familiar: the arrangement of monopoles in figure 2.7(d) is referred to as an *axial quadrupole*, from which name is derived *quadrupolar nuclei* (see also section 14.4).

Nuclei with an electric quadrupole interact with any nearby electric field gradient, the strength of interaction being measured as a *quadrupole moment*. This moment is quantised as usual, with only certain orientations being allowed; we can measure the transitions between these nuclear orientations (which constitute different energy levels) by applying the appropriate amount of energy.

This is the basis of nuclear quadrupole resonance spectroscopy, NQR. Although this is a quite separate spectroscopic technique, it will be instructive to take one example to illustrate quadrupole spectroscopy, since without some idea of its principles it would be difficult to appreciate the significance to NMR of this nuclear property.

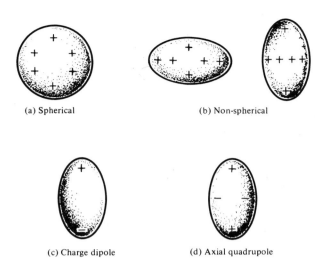

(a) Spherical	(b) Non-spherical
(c) Charge dipole	(d) Axial quadrupole

Figure 2.7 Charge distribution in nuclei may be spherically symmetrical as in (a) or distorted as in (b). In electrostatics, (c) is a dipole and (d) is an axial quadrupole

2.15 NUCLEAR QUADRUPOLE RESONANCE SPECTROSCOPY – NQR

Consider the electron distribution within the molecule of piperidine (perhydropyridine); we can see that there is high electron density at the nitrogen end, and that the

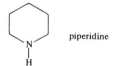

piperidine

molecule is highly symmetrical. One single crystal of frozen piperidine consists of a completely regular array with all of the molecules oriented in the same direction; there is therefore a static electric field gradient within each molecule along the crystal. The electric field gradient within the nitrogen nucleus tends to align with the electric field gradient in the molecules (the lowest energy state) but other orientations, quantum restricted, are possible; the energy gap (ΔE) between orientations in this case corresponds to a frequency $\nu = 3$ MHz; irradiation with radiofrequency at 3 MHz produces a resonance condition, with nitrogen nuclei undergoing transitions between the allowed alignments. The absorption of radiofrequency gives rise to the NQR spectrum for piperidine.

Observe that no external magnet is needed for NQR spectroscopy: the nuclei are interacting with electric field gradients which are already within the molecule of piperidine.

If now the sample of piperidine is melted, molecular tumbling will disorient one molecule with respect to another, but will not disorient the direction of the field gradient within each individual molecule. Consequently, the nitrogen nucleus within each molecule will try to stay precisely oriented with respect to the molecule of which it is a part.

What happens if now we apply an external magnetic field to the molten sample of piperidine?

(1) The magnetic moment of the nitrogen nucleus will tend to make all of the nuclei take up the same orientations with respect to the magnetic field.
(2) The electric quadrupole moment will tend to make each nucleus retain its orientation with respect to its parent molecule − which is tumbling randomly with respect to the magnetic field.

The decisive factors in this competition are (1) the strength of the nuclear *magnetic* moment (and its interaction with the applied *magnetic* field) and (2) the strength of the nuclear *electric* quadrupole moment (and its interaction with the *electric* field gradient within the molecule).

Later, we will see that the nucleus of nitrogen-14 has a fairly weak electric quadrupole moment, and that it is possible to study the magnetic moment without too many complications arising from the electric quadrupole. For other nuclei with electric quadrupoles (notably chlorine-35) the reverse is the case and the electric quadrupole influence is dominant.

Problem Example 2.5
Consider qualitatively the electron distribution in (a) ammonia, (b) methylamine and (c) the ammonium ion. In each case, how strongly might the electric field gradient in the molecule (or ion) determine the orientation of the nitrogen nucleus?

2.16 BOLTZMANN DISTRIBUTIONS IN NMR − EFFECTS OF FIELD STRENGTH AND TEMPERATURE

We have largely been concerned with the theory of NMR applied to single nuclei; we must now consider recording the NMR spectrum of a real sample containing an ensemble of millions of nuclei.

The introduction of NMR given in chapter 1 allowed us to picture, for spin $\frac{1}{2}$ nuclei such as the proton, the two energy levels between which the nuclei divide themselves. If we consider a sample of a compound containing protons at room temperature (say $17°C$ or 290 K) and in the absence of an applied magnetic field, then the protons will have no order to their orientations. This is illustrated in figures 1.1 and 1.2.

Supply a magnetic field, and the protons will distribute themselves between the two energy levels, and once thermal equilibrium has been achieved, we can calculate from the Boltzmann Distribution Law the relative numbers occupying each level.

The Boltzmann Law can be written

$$\frac{N_\alpha}{N_\beta} = e^{\Delta E/kT} \quad \text{or} \quad \exp\left(\frac{\Delta E}{kT}\right)$$

where N_α and N_β are the numbers of nuclei in the α (lower energy) and β (higher energy) states respectively. T is the absolute temperature and k is the Boltzmann constant ($k = 1.38 \times 10^{-23}$ J K^{-1}).

We need to know ΔE (which equals $h\nu$). If the field strength is 2.35 T, then ν for protons is 100 MHz, and we can calculate (see section 1.8) that ΔE is 6.7×10^{-26} J.

An exponential function e^x (often written $\exp x$) can be evaluated directly: alternatively e^x can be approximated to $(1 + x)$ with sufficient accuracy for the present purpose. We need to find the value for $\Delta E/kT$: then

$$\frac{N_\alpha}{N_\beta} = \exp\left(\frac{\Delta E}{kT}\right) = \exp\frac{(6.7 \times 10^{-26} \text{ J})}{(1.38 \times 10^{-23} \text{ J K}^{-1})(290 \text{ K})}$$
$$= 1.000017$$

Alternatively, since $\Delta E/kT$ is a very small number, higher powers (square, cube) are vanishingly small and $\exp(\Delta E/kT)$ approximates to $1 + \Delta E/kT$. Thus

$$\frac{N_\alpha}{N_\beta} = 1 + \frac{\Delta E}{kT} = 1 + \frac{(6.7 \times 10^{-26} \text{ J})}{(1.38 \times 10^{-23} \text{ J K}^{-1})(290 \text{ K})}$$
$$= 1 + 0.000017$$

Let us write this for emphasis in the form

$$\frac{N_\alpha}{N_\beta} = \frac{1\,000\,017}{1\,000\,000}$$

then we can see with clarity that, for every million nuclei in the higher energy state (for protons at $17°C$ in a 2.35 T magnet) there is an excess of only 17 in the lower energy state (an excess of 17 ppm).

Worked Example 2.3
Calculate the Boltzmann distribution as above, but for carbon-13 nuclei at $17°C$ and 2.35 T.

Answer 2.3

At 2.35 T, ν for carbon-13 is 25 MHz and (from section 1.1) $\Delta E = 1.7 \times 10^{-26}$ J so

$$\frac{N_\alpha}{N_\beta} = \exp \frac{1.7 \times 10^{-26}\text{ J}}{(1.38 \times 10^{-23}\text{ J K}^{-1})(290\text{ K})} = 1.000004$$

The excess in this case is merely 4 ppm.

Problem Example 2.6

Calculate the Boltzmann distribution as above for an ensemble of protons at 17°C in (a) a 4.7 T magnet, (b) a 7 T magnet.

Problem Example 2.7

Calculate the Boltzmann distribution as above for protons in a 2.35 T magnet at (a) −100°C, (b) 100°C.

The nuclei in a sample do not achieve equilibrium among the energy levels instantaneously when a magnetic field is applied, and the time constant for the rate at which they approach thermal equilibrium is an important NMR parameter to which we shall return.

Likewise the importance of temperature in determining the populations of spin states will be a valuable concept when we have to consider the distribution among several possible spin states as in nuclei with spin $\geqslant 1$; the general rule will hold that, at thermal equilibrium, the population follows an exponential distribution.

2.17 RELAXATION PHENOMENA

If we restate the fundamental NMR experiment, it involves orienting nuclei with respect to an applied magnetic field, and irradiating them with a radiofrequency excitation which induces them to undergo transitions among allowed nuclear energy levels; in this process, radiofrequency energy is absorbed, and the resonance condition allows us to record an NMR absorption signal. Figure 2.8 will allow us to contemplate this whole process in detail.

Let us suppose that figure 2.8(a) represents an ensemble of protons distributed between the α and β states at thermal equilibrium. (We need to ignore for the moment that at 2.35 T there is only a 17 ppm excess in the α state!) The α protons are represented by cones of precession (see figure 2.3) *with* the field, and the β protons by cones lying *against* the field.

Irradiation with a 100 MHz source stimulates transitions; upward *and* downward transitions are equally stimulated, but upward transitions are more probable (by 17 ppm) than downward.

> Net absorption of radiofrequency by the sample only arises because there exists at thermal equilibrium an excess of nuclei in the lower energy state.

Absorption of energy arises when one of the α protons flips into the β state, passing to the upper energy level (at the right of figure 2.8(a)). At the left of the figure, one α moves up and a β moves down: there is no change in the total energy of the system as a result of this exchange. Over all, figure 2.8(b) represents a system of higher thermal energy than figure 2.8(a); there has been absorption of radiofrequency, and the spin populations are no longer that of thermal equilibrium.

If the input of radiofrequency energy is sufficient to create the situation at figure 2.8(c) then

> Because the populations of the two states are equal, there will be no further net absorption of radiofrequency energy and the system is said to be saturated.

The practical consequence of this saturation is that the NMR absorption signal will no longer be observable. Net absorption can only be restored if nuclei *relax* from β to α states, and thus restore the condition symbolised in figure 2.8(b) or 2.8(a).

2.17.1 Spin–Lattice Relaxation and T_1

The relaxation process leading from (c) to (b) to (a) in figure 2.8 implies a loss of energy from the system of nuclear spins. Where does the energy go? Some will be re-emitted as radiofrequency, but much is lost by radiationless transfer to the surroundings of the nuclei within the sample.

Around the nuclei, complex vibrational changes are taking place which are both intramolecular and intermolecular (including the involvement of solvent molecules); the random tumbling of molecules and the vibrations of bonds and electrons set up many fluctuating electric dipoles and a proportion of these will be of appropriate magnitude to interact with the higher energy nucleus and absorb from it its excess of energy. We describe this process as transferring spin energy to the surrounding lattice (be it a crystal lattice or simply an array of solvent molecules), and it is named *spin–lattice relaxation*.

Spin-lattice relaxation is a first-order rate process and the time constant for it is defined as T_1 the *spin–lattice relaxation time*. A more mathematical definition will be delayed until chapter 6.

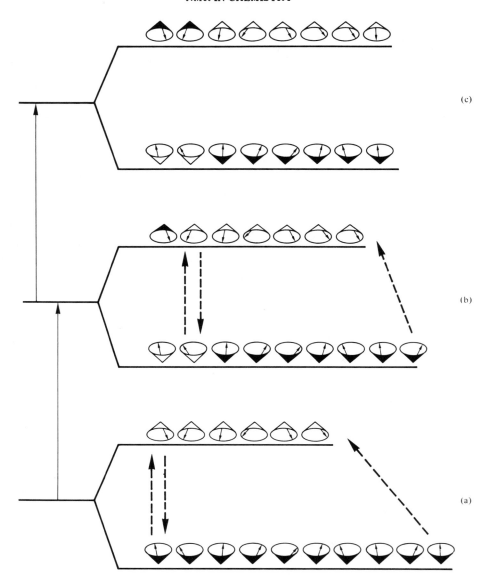

Figure 2.8 Irradiation of a sample of nuclei promotes lower energy nuclei to the upper energy state. At (c) the populations are equal and no further net absorption can occur until relaxation takes place. When nuclei 'change places' (see left) the overall energy of the system does not change

2.17.2 Spin–Spin Relaxation and T_2

From figure 2.8 we can see that each nucleus can spend time both in the lower and in the upper energy level, so that we can consider that in each of these states it has a particular life-time. Whereas the process of spin–lattice relaxation shortens the life-time of spin states, and in so doing leads to a net loss of energy in the system, the interchanges taking place at the left of the figures (a) and (b) also shorten spin state life-times but with no net loss in energy from the system.

This process of spin–spin exchange leads to randomising of the spin states: it is part of the process of spin–spin relaxation.

As for spin–lattice relaxation and its time constant T_1, we will later define precisely a corresponding time constant for spin–spin relaxation, T_2.

2.18 THE HEISENBERG UNCERTAINTY PRINCIPLE AND THE WIDTH OF ABSORPTION LINES

It is a fundamental property throughout spectroscopy that there is a built-in uncertainty in the accuracy with which we can measure the energy of a sub-atomic particle and this uncertainty is inversely proportional to the life-time of the particular energy state. This *Heisenberg Uncertainty Principle* is most usefully expressed in the form

$$\Delta E \times \Delta t \approx \hbar \approx 10^{-34} \text{ J s or simply } \Delta E \times \Delta t = \text{constant}$$

In NMR, if the life-time of any spin state is very short, that is if Δt is small, then ΔE must be large — which means a large uncertainty in the measurement of the energy of that spin state. If it were possible to be infinitely exact in measuring ΔE (and for this the life-time would have to be infinitely long) then an NMR absorption signal would be a sharp *line* at precisely the precessional frequency of the nucleus concerned. The Uncertainty Principle leads instead to absorption bands, whose widths allow us to say something about the life-times of nuclear spin states. By convention, the spread of frequencies around the mean can be specified by defining the *line width at half height*, as shown in figure 2.9.

Of course the accuracy with which we can measure an NMR absorption frequency depends on several instrumental factors, not least of which is the homogeneity of the magnetic field; the Heisenberg Uncertainty Principle has nothing to do with instrumental limitations, but is an integral part of the basic extraordinary behaviour of sub-atomic particles.

2.18.1 Effect of T_1 and T_2 on NMR Line Widths

Figure 2.8 showed two main influences on the life-times of nuclear spin states — spin–lattice relaxation and spin–spin relaxation, each with characteristic rates whose time constants are defined as T_1 and T_2 respectively. From the Uncertainty Principle, if T_1 and T_2 are both long (spin state life-times are long) then we can measure ΔE for the NMR absorption with high accuracy, and the line width will be narrow. Any factor which shortens the spin state life-times and leads to more rapid relaxation processes will lead to broader NMR signals.

There are many ways in which the spin state life-times can be shortened, and we will discuss them in detail as appropriate later in the book.

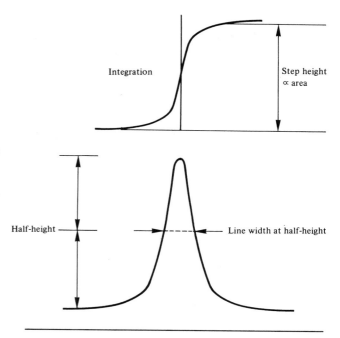

Figure 2.9 Theoretical line shape in NMR absorption. Integration is carried out electronically by the instrument, and peak area is proportional to the integration step-height

2.18.2 Line Shape and Peak Areas

Theoretical calculations relating to the NMR experiment show that the absorption curve — or line shape (figure 2.9) — follows ideally the equation for Lorentzian functions (named after H. A. Lorentz, see section 14.5.1) and incorporates the value of T_2. The so-called 'natural line width' is $(\pi T_2)^{-1}$, but in practice the observed line widths are much wider than would be predicted from this relationship, mainly due to irregularities (inhomogeneities) in the magnetic flux experienced by different nuclei in different parts of the experimental sample. When we come to measure the areas under NMR signals, the characteristics of Lorentzian line shapes become important, since we must decide how much on each side of the mean frequency to include in our area measurement. Theory shows that if we set the limits at ±5 linewidths around the centre, then we will only be measuring about 85 per cent of the total area; ± 10 linewidths includes about 94 per cent, and ± 30 linewidths includes about 98 per cent. While these factors are not troublesome for sharp lines (as in most proton spectra) it does affect quantitation where broad signals are obtained, since ± 30 linewidths can represent an exceedingly wide compass.

The area under the curve is proportional to the number of nuclei concerned, so that it is a valuable aid to spectrum analysis. It is measured by integration, and either printed out by computer or plotted on the spectrum as in figure 2.9, so that the step heights of several peaks give the relative numbers of magnetic nuclei in each environment.

The NMR Spectrometer

NMR spectrometers – 60 MHz and 500 MHz

The modern NMR instrument embodies much more high technology than that outlined in figure 1.4, although the fundamental features are still (a) a magnet, (b) a radio-frequency source and detector and (c) data handling/display facilities. These instrument parts are all inter-dependent, and it is impossible to discuss them in strictly ordered isolation. Detailed instrumental capabilities are also scrutinised in later chapters where appropriate.

3.1 NMR MAGNETS

The property of a magnet which determines the preces-sional frequency of nuclei in an NMR spectrometer is defined in SI units as the *magnetic induction field* or the *magnetic flux density*, with the symbol **B**, measured in tesla (T). While it may be inexact to call this property *magnetic field strength* (see, for example, Purcell's text book on *Electricity and Magnetism* listed in Further Reading) there is no possibility of misinterpretation, and we shall adopt this universally used label throughout.

All manufacturers of NMR spectrometers describe their instruments in relation to the *proton frequency* obtained in the machine; thus a '100 MHz NMR spectro-meter' has a 2.35 T magnet, and, if able to observe carbon-13 signals, it would then operate at the appro-priate frequency for that nucleus (25 MHz).

There are three different types of magnet in use in NMR spectrometers.

3.1.1 Permanent Magnets

Permanent magnets have been used successfully at field strengths up to 2.1 T (and less successfully up to 2.35 T). They have considerable advantages in running costs, which are essentially zero, and installation is simple. The small NMR machine photographed at the head of this chapter operates on protons only at 60 MHz, and has a 1.4 T permanent magnet weighing 350 kg.

3.1.2 Electromagnets

Electromagnets are used for all field strengths up to 2.35 T (100 MHz with respect to proton NMR). The power consumption for a 1.4 T electromagnet (60 MHz instrument) is around 3.5 kW; water cooling equipment must be provided to maintain the temperature of electro-magnets constant, since the field fluctuates with tem-perature change. The total power needs of a complete 100 MHz instrument package, with the electromagnet

solenoid (weighing nearly 1000 kg), water cooler, air compressor and operating control console, will be well in excess of 10 kW. The upper limit for electromagnets with the necessary stability and uniformity for NMR work is 2.35 T.

3.1.3 Superconducting Magnets

Superconducting magnets are used in NMR instruments to generate field strengths up to 14 T (600 MHz). These are solenoid magnets immersed in liquid helium at a temperature of 4 K ($-269°C$), at which temperature the niobium alloy windings lose all electrical resistance and become 'superconducting'. Once current has been set flowing around the solenoid, the power source is removed and the ends of the solenoid windings shorted together; the magnetic field is then permanently established. It will be maintained with minimal losses so long as it is kept unperturbed and fed with liquid helium. Any dis-turbance may cause the windings to become 'resistive' again, whereupon the stored electrical energy is transfer-red thermally to the surrounding bath of liquid helium, which then evaporates (rapidly!) in what is called a 'magnet quench'. The solenoid must then be recooled and re-energised.

The construction of a typical superconducting NMR magnet system is shown in figure 3.1 and a complete 500 MHz spectrometer is photographed at the head of the chapter. The weight of the magnet in such an instal-lation is only about 250 kg, and the power consumption is zero (although ancillary equipment such as compres-sors, amplifiers, fans and the computer may need a few kilowatts). The principal running costs for the magnet are in liquid gases, particularly liquid helium.

The magnet itself consists of thousands of metres of fine metal filament. Niobium-titanium alloy is normally used up to 9.4 T, but beyond that it does not behave as a superconductor, and the core part of the solenoid must then be made of Nb_3Sn. This is not simply an alloy, but an intermetallic compound between Nb and Sn. It is not sufficiently ductile to be formed directly into solenoid windings; instead, niobium filament is wound within a bronze matrix, and the entire solenoid baked for some days at $700°C$, when the tin diffuses out of the bronze and reacts with the niobium to form Nb_3Sn *in situ*.

To minimise helium evaporation losses to around 0.5 litres per day, an elaborate cryogenic insulation system, including silver plated Dewar vessels and a liquid nitrogen jacket, is incorporated around the magnet.

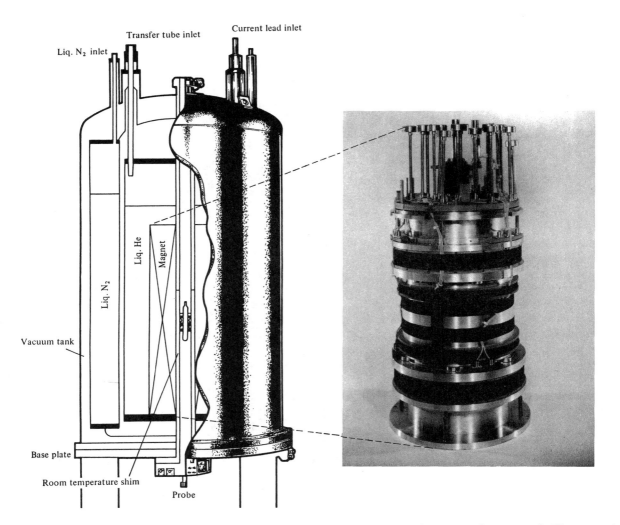

Figure 3.1 High field (11T) superconducting magnet for NMR spectroscopy (470 MHz for protons). The magnet solenoid assembly (shown separately on the right) is totally immersed in liquid helium at $-269°C$ (4 K). Insulation by vacuum tanks and liquid nitrogen helps to minimise helium evaporation

3.1.4 The Search for Bigger Magnets — Resolution and Sensitivity

Two advantages accrue from the building of NMR spectrometers with ever more powerful magnets.

In section 2.16 we were able to calculate the populations of nuclear energy levels from Boltzmann distribution theory, and problem example 2.6 showed that the population differences for protons at 100 MHz is 17 in a million, at 200 MHz it is 33 ppm and at 300 MHz it is 50 ppm. Net absorption of RF by a sample is related to the probability of upward transitions among the energy levels, and this is in turn related to the differences in populations between the levels. Increasing field increases these population differences, and this leads to a stronger

RF absorption (corresponding to greater sensitivity). Other factors which affect sensitivity are discussed in section 3.6.

Chemical shift values expressed in δ units are field-independent, but if we measure shifts in hertz then there is a direct proportionality between shift and field strength: the calculation to illustrate this is in worked example 1.2. The net effect of increasing the magnetic field strength is to spread out the difference in chemical shift, and hence improve the resolving power of the instrument. Further consequences of the effect are given in section 4.10.

Of these two parameters, sensitivity and resolution, the former is important particularly in experiments involving rare nuclei such as carbon-13 and nitrogen-15; increased resolution enables the spectra from extremely complex molecules to be interpreted in fine detail, and many biologically important problems have benefited from these advantages.

3.1.5 The Direction of B_0 — the z-axis Convention

At the resonance condition, nuclei experience the combined effects of two magnetic fields: (1) that of the magnet and (2) that of the electromagnetic radiation in the form of the RF current. These are given the symbols B_0 and B_1 respectively, as discussed in section 1.9.

Apart from exceptional spectrometers used in medicine, biology or physics, for a variety of design reasons permanent magnets and electromagnets are so disposed that their magnetic fields (represented by lines of force) act horizontally, while in instruments with superconducting solenoid magnets the field acts vertically. It is now a convention in all NMR theory, explicitly adopted by Bloch in his calculations, that the direction of B_0 shall be designated as lying along the z-axis; similarly, in all diagrammatic descriptions relating to the influence of B_0 on nuclei, the z-axis is always depicted vertically (with its positive direction pointing to the top of the page).

To minimise the confusion of this contrary geometry of magnet layout, throughout this book B_0, and thus also the z-axis, will be shown vertically, which is the real situation in the majority of superconductor instruments only. It has to be remembered that in virtually all other instruments (such as figure 1.4) the z-axis is horizontal and the y-axis is taken to be vertical.

3.2 MAGNETIC FIELD HOMOGENEITY AND SPECTROMETER RESOLUTION

Resolution, in any spectroscopic technique, is a measure of the ability to distinguish signals lying close together in the spectrum, and it can be defined in several ways. In NMR spectroscopy it is done by specifying the linewidth of a specified band, typically one of the bands in the proton NMR spectrum of o-dichlorobenzene or acetaldehyde (see section 2.18.2 and page 1). A critical factor in determining linewidth (spectrometer resolution) is the uniformity of the magnetic field experienced by molecules in different parts of a sample being examined. The homogeneity of modern magnets is truly astonishing, being better than one part in 10^8; even low cost instruments achieve this uniformity, which leads to quoted resolution in carbon spectra of less than 0.5 Hz, while

research instruments can record proton linewidths of less than 0.1 Hz.

3.2.1 Shim Coils

However carefully a magnet is manufactured, the production process will not directly lead to high homogeneity and some means of adjustment must be incorporated into the design. We can recognise that the inhomogeneity will consist of gradients in the field strength between the pole faces of the magnet; these gradients may be linear or they may be curved (described as being of 'higher order'). To annul these gradients (both in permanent magnets and electromagnets) small electromagnets are fixed to the pole faces, and these are of precisely arranged geometry to create small spatially different magnetic fields. By adjusting the currents in these 'shim coils', the total magnetic flux across the pole faces can be corrected to a high degree of uniformity. This is a tedious process, since the shim coils overlap one another, and the alteration of current in one shim may upset the field generated by another, so that the process of tuning is iterative. With stable magnets, only a few of the shim coils should need frequent attention.

In superconducting solenoid magnets there are no pole faces, but adjustment of the homogeneity is still necessary by shim coils; some of these are closely attached to the solenoid and are thus also at 4 K (low temperature shims), while others are close to the sample near ambient temperature (room temperature shims).

3.2.2 Sample Spinning and Spinning Side-bands

With the magnet carefully adjusted, part of any remaining inhomogeneity can be averaged out within the sample by spinning the tube (at up to 25 Hz) by means of an air turbine. Each part of the sample thus experiences the same time-averaged field.

The sample tube in all instruments is held vertically, and thus spins around a vertical axis; magnetic inhomogeneity is therefore averaged out only on the horizontal plane. Spinning does not improve any errors in the vertical component of the field.

In superconducting solenoid magnets, sample spinning averages out the field along the x- and y-axes (the horizontal plane), leaving the z-axis unimproved; in operation, it is the shim coils which control the z-axis field which thus require most frequent adjustment to maintain homogeneity.

In permanent magnets and electromagnets the y-axis shim coils are most in need of adjustment, for the reasons discussed in section 3.1.5.

If the tube walls are uneven in thickness then the sample will not be contained in a perfectly regular cylinder, and the spinning of such a sample causes modulation of the spectrum lines; this in turn produces sidebands astride the principal signals, and separated from them by plus/minus the spinning frequency. These 'spinning side-bands' can be minimised by using specially selected sample tubes, and by ensuring that the tube spins without wobbling: they can be recognised easily in the spectrum, since their position changes with spinning frequency (that is, with modulation frequency).

3.3 MAGNET STABILITY AND FIELD–FREQUENCY LOCK

If we wish to measure signal positions with great accuracy, we must ensure that the field strength and the RF signals remain constant throughout the recording of the spectrum. Since field and frequency are linked (see sections 1.4 and 2.9) the ideal way to achieve this is to incorporate a feedback circuit which measures the field strength with respect to a reference RF signal; any drift in this signal due to changing magnetic field can be corrected by continuously adjusting the field. The reference RF signal which thus 'locks' field and frequency together can for example be the TMS signal in a proton spectrum; this is called *internal homonuclear lock*, since the TMS is *internal* and we are locking *proton to proton*. Another arrangement for locking proton signals has a sealed water sample with its own separate transmitter circuit permanently affixed near that of the sample. The proton signal from the water is used as the lock signal: this is *external homonuclear lock*.

Most carbon-13 NMR spectrometers have an arrangement to lock internally to the deuterated solvent in the sample; thus the instrument is observing the *carbon-13* signals of the sample and simultaneously observing the *deuterium* resonance of the solvent, and using the latter to control the accuracy with which the former is recorded. This is *internal heteronuclear lock*. Careful instrument design around these principles can limit spectrometer drift to around one part in 10^9 per hour. Because superconducting magnets have inherently greater stability than external lock could provide, only internal lock is used.

(The lock signal is invariably detected in the dispersion mode since this allows the feedback circuit to detect whether the drift is positive or negative — see section 3.7.4.)

Since external lock systems have circuitry separate from that of the sample, they continue to operate even while the sample is removed from the instrument and replaced. Internal lock however monitors field stability *within* the sample being examined, and thus leads to finer control of the field–frequency relationship. For long-running experiments, internal lock is obligatory to sustain the necessary stability.

3.4 FIELD SWEEP AND FREQUENCY SWEEP — CONTINUOUS WAVE NMR SPECTROSCOPY

In the simplified NMR spectrometer shown in figure 1.4, the resonance condition ($\Delta E = h\nu$) was reached by holding the magnetic field at 2.35 T and scanning the RF transmitter through the frequencies (for example a proton spectrum would require the transmitter to search around 100 MHz). We could equally well have kept the transmitter fixed at 100 MHz and reached resonance by adjusting the field strength around the value 2.35 T until a signal was generated in the RF receiver, since we saw in sections 1.4 and 2.9 that field strength and frequency are mutually proportional.

These two approaches to resonance are called *frequency sweep* and *field sweep* respectively.

Field sweep is achieved, both in permanent magnets and in electromagnets, by attaching to the pole faces additional low-power electromagnet windings. A controlled DC current passing through these *sweep coils* increases or decreases the total magnetic field strength by the necessary few ppm to scan through the resonance. Frequency sweep is most easily understood by considering a tunable frequency synthesiser, but this is difficult to design with the stipulated accuracy of one part in 10^9, and various electronic tricks have been used to simulate the effects of true frequency sweep, these often being labelled pseudofrequency sweep. Section 3.7 deals in more detail with RF matters.

Since in NMR we record chemical shift positions in field-independent units (δ values) as ppm differences from a reference standard such as TMS, then whatever method is used produces the same spectrum of signals. The δ values specify both ppm differences in field and ppm differences in frequency.

Following the practices in ultraviolet and infrared spectroscopy, it is conventional to plot NMR spectra with frequency increasing from right to left; the discussion of figures 1.5 and 1.6 implies that they were recorded at fixed field with frequency sweep.

For the proton spectrum in figure 1.5, consider how it would be recorded in the field sweep mode, with the RF transmitter fixed at 100 MHz. The signals from nuclei with *highest* precessional frequency will come to resonance (100 MHz) at the *lowest* values of applied field; conversely, only at high field will the slowly-precessing nuclei (especially those in TMS) finally precess fast enough to reach resonance with the 100 MHz transmitter. This leads us to state an important feature of all NMR spectra.

> NMR spectra are recorded with frequency increasing from right to left, which corresponds to field strength increasing from left to right. Chemical shift positions (in δ units) are the same, whichever scan mode is used.

In practice it has been easier to construct field sweep NMR instruments, and these are more common than frequency sweep machines. (Both Bloch and Purcell used the field scan mode in their original work.) In both techniques note that the sample is under continuous irradiation from the radiofrequency transmitter and both methods can be classified as *continuous wave* (CW) processes; the time taken to record a full NMR spectrum may vary from a few minutes to half an hour, depending on the desired amount of detail sought.

It is a long-established norm in field sweep CW NMR to describe signal positions as being *downfield* or *upfield* of one another. Since this has no meaning in pulsed experiments (see section 3.5) and since frequency is a common property of all spectroscopic methods, these terms are now discouraged: it is preferable to state that the relative signal positions are at *higher* or *lower frequency* respectively.

3.5 PULSED RADIOFREQUENCY – FOURIER TRANSFORM NMR SPECTROSCOPY

An attractive alternative to continuous wave methods such as frequency sweep (in which individual nuclear frequencies are excited in succession) is to irradiate all of the frequencies simultaneously by supplying a powerful pulse of RF current, lasting only a few microseconds. At the end of this excitation pulse the RF recorder then picks up a signal coming back from the irradiated sample. This signal dies away exponentially as indicated in figure 3.2 and it contains information on all of the frequencies that are included in a frequency sweep spectrum; the only problem is that, since they all come to the recorder at once, they are recorded as a composite interference pattern which has to be analysed and separated into the individual contributing frequencies as in figure 3.2.

3.5.1 Fourier Transforms

The basic mathematics necessary to express the interference pattern in figure 3.2 (top) in terms of the individual frequencies shown at the bottom are those enunciated firstly by Jean Baptiste Fourier (see section 14.5.1) and the interconversion process is called a Fourier Transform. The continuous nature of the interferogram must first be digitised in an analogue-to-digital convertor (ADC), and a computer program then rapidly performs the Fourier Transform (FT) operation to reveal the individual frequencies which contributed to the

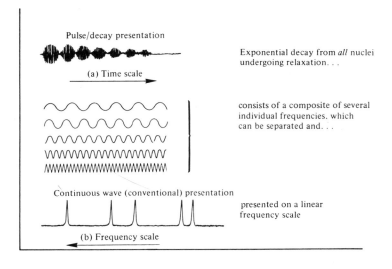

Pulse/decay presentation

Exponential decay from *all* nuclei undergoing relaxation...

(a) Time scale

consists of a composite of several individual frequencies, which can be separated and...

Continuous wave (conventional) presentation

presented on a linear frequency scale

(b) Frequency scale

Figure 3.2   After excitation by a radiofrequency pulse, the NMR signal is detected as an interferogram (above) which can be analysed as the interaction among a number of individual frequencies (below). The interferogram plot is in units of time (s), while the frequency plot is in units of reciprocal time (s^{-1} or Hz)

shaping of the interferogram. Both the interferogram, and the conventional NMR plot of frequencies, contain the same information; Fourier Transforms permit us to plot this information either in the *time domain* (the interferogram) or in the more usable *frequency domain* (the NMR spectrum). Note that the units in the time domain are *seconds*, and in the frequency domain they are *hertz* (seconds^{-1}), so that, as in all transforms, a reciprocal relationship is involved.

An excellent analogy to the pulsed FT NMR method is a comparison with the audiofrequencies generated by a stringed instrument such as a six stringed guitar. If the open strings are strummed together, or if the guitar is dropped, then all of the frequencies interfere to produce cacophony: an analysis of the total sound reveals that its contributory components are the same six individual frequencies which produce the normal melodious music of the guitar.

3.5.2 Advantages of the Pulsed FT NMR Method

Whereas the recording of a CW NMR spectrum is a slow affair, the pulse method, followed by computer calculation of the Fourier Transform, is exceedingly fast; the actual pulse duration is measured in microseconds and the FT calculations take only a few seconds. An early barrier to the widespread development of FT NMR spectroscopy was the obligation to interface an expensive dedicated computer to the spectrometer. Reductions in computer costs (and simultaneous increase in power and memory capacity) have pushed the art of NMR to the position where the pulse FT method is ubiquitous in all but low-cost instruments.

The computer, now being integral with the spectrometer, can diversify its functions and act as controller and timer of the radiofrequency pulse program and it can similarly operate the display features of the instrument, including the pen recorder. These aspects of control are so versatile that a whole branch of NMR spectroscopy has been spawned from the development of complex pulse sequences: see chapters 6 and 7.

PULSE DURATION AND PULSE REPETITION RATE

These can be timed within limits approaching a few tens of nanoseconds (10^{-9} s). The theory associated with pulse duration is discussed later (in section 6.7.2) but typical pulse lengths are a few microseconds. After each burst of RF energy, the populations of the nuclear energy levels are disturbed and a delay must intervene to allow the nuclei to undergo relaxation before the next pulse is applied: too frequent a repetition rate (too short

a delay) progressively leads to saturation and to diminution in the signal intensities, and an example (figure 5.4) is discussed in section 5.2. In practice, the delay which is required depends on the longest relaxation time of the group of nuclei being irradiated, but it may vary from a few seconds to several minutes.

SIGNAL STRENGTH

This depends on many variables including the amount of magnetic nuclei present in the sample. In proton NMR spectroscopy there is a large magnetic moment; therefore the signal is inherently strong, and the magnetic nuclide in this case has a natural abundance of nearly 100%; proton spectra can easily be obtained unless it happens that the compound under examination is available only in small amounts (as are many biologically-derived compounds) or if its solubility in the NMR solvent is low. For less abundant nuclei such as carbon-13 the sensitivity problem is so acute that, for all practical purposes, satisfactory spectra can only be achieved if several recordings are made of the spectrum and these subsequently added together. In this way, spectrum noise averages to zero in the algebraic summation (since noise transients appear randomly) while the true spectrum signals add coherently.

SIGNAL AVERAGING

This is carried out by digitising the spectrum, followed by computer summation, so the total process is a convenient instrumental adjunct to the FT method. The computer averaging of transients (CAT) has been applied in CW NMR, but is now virtually obsolete.

The proton NMR spectrum of a typical organic compound can be acquired in less than a minute by averaging, say, 10–20 scans; the carbon-13 spectrum of a similar molecule may take three or four minutes, depending on the number of scans collected.

IMPROVEMENT IN SIGNAL STRENGTH

This can be measured from the signal-to-noise ratio (see 14.3.4), and the increase is proportional to the square root of the number of scans collected and averaged. Thus the summation of 100 pulses will lead to signal enhancement by a factor of ten. Some of the NMR spectra reproduced in this book result from the summation of many thousands of scans, perhaps involving overnight accumulation of signals.

This is an outstanding advantage of pulsed FT NMR spectroscopy; rare magnetic nuclides can now be studied in a reasonable time scale by recording a large number of spectra in a matter of minutes, where CW methods might provide but one scan in the same time.

> Multinuclear NMR spectroscopy depends for its
> success on the simultaneous advantages brought by
> computer techniques to pulse excitation, Fourier
> transforms, and signal averaging.

$$\text{sensitivity of nucleus X} = \left[\frac{\text{magnetic moment of X}}{\text{magnetic moment of }^1\text{H}}\right]^3 \times$$

$$\frac{(I+1)/I^2 \text{ for X}}{(I+1)/I^2 \text{ for }^1\text{H}}$$

We can equally well use the cubed ratio of the mag-
netogyric ratios, γ, since μ and γ are themselves proportional (see sections 2.7 and 2.8).

Worked Example 3.1
Calculate the sensitivity, with respect to proton, of the
carbon-13 nucleus.

Answer 3.1
From the Appendix, the magnetogyric ratios for carbon-
13 and the proton are respectively 26.75 and 6.73. The
carbon–proton ratio of γ is 0.2516 and its cube (the relative sensitivity of carbon to hydrogen) is 1.59×10^{-2}.
(Since both nuclei have $I = \frac{1}{2}$, the right hand part of the
expression above cancels out to 1.)

Problem Example 3.1
Calculate the sensitivity, with respect to proton, of (a)
fluorine-19, (b) tritium (hydrogen-3), (c) nitrogen-15
and (d) nitrogen-14. Answers in the Appendix.

3.6 SENSITIVITY IN MULTINUCLEAR NMR

Higher field magnets have contributed significantly to
improvements in signal-to-noise ratios (see section 3.1.4)
and developments in instrument design have also played
a major role; between these two, commercial spectrometers over a period of twenty years have been able to
multiply this specification by a factor approaching two
hundred. The amount of sample presented to the instrument is important; sample tubes of outside diameter
5 mm are commonly used, but increased sensitivity is
reached with 10 mm tubes or larger. Of course more
sample must be available, and the magnet gap and homogeneity must be designed for this feature; the receiver
coil must be as close as possible to the sample, thus using
a 5 mm tube in a 10 mm probe will involve a sensitivity
penalty, since the detector cavity is not filled (the so-
called 'filling factor').

Besides these instrumental limitations, there are
fundamental properties at work in determining sensitivity.

3.6.1 Relative Abundance

Not all of the isotopes of elements possess magnetic
moments, and the partial list in table 1.1 (supplemented
in the Appendix) shows that relatively few elements
have abundant magnetic isotopes. Without isotope enrichment, carbon-13 NMR spectra are nearly 100 times
more difficult to record than proton NMR spectra for
this reason; oxygen-17 is nearly 3000 times less abundant
than hydrogen-1.

3.6.2 Sensitivity and Nuclear Magnetic Moments

The strength of signal induced in a receiver coil is a
function of the strength of the nuclear magnet which
engenders it.

Relative sensitivity at this nuclear level is frequently
quoted with respect to the proton, and it is a function
which falls off with spherical distribution and so varies
with the third power of the magnetic moments. The spin
quantum number is also an important factor; the sensitivity of nucleus X with respect to the proton is given by

When we say that the sensitivity of carbon-13 is
1.59×10^{-2} that of the proton, the comparison is valid
only if (a) the field strength is the same when we make
the measurements, (b) the temperature is the same,
(c) the number of nuclei in each sample is the same. The
comparison is therefore only meaningful if we compare
one proton with one carbon-13 nucleus (or N protons
with N carbon-13 nuclei); the discrepancy in their natural
abundances must be taken into account in addition to
this inherent difference in relative sensitivity. It is common to quote an *absolute sensitivity* which is given by
multiplying *relative sensitivity* by *natural abundance*.
Values for the important NMR nuclei are listed in the
Appendix.

3.7 RADIOFREQUENCY CIRCUITS

The study of the behaviour of RF currents lies properly
in highly specialised domains of physics and electronic
engineering, but a minimum knowledge is necessary to
understand the language of the subject which has filtered
through to the chemical applications of NMR. At the
root of this discussion lies the familiar experience that a
radio receiver will only receive a broadcast signal from a
radio station when their frequencies are 'tuned'; tuning
involves altering the capacitance of the tuning circuit,
and we do this when we turn the tuning knob on the
radio.

3.7.1 Radiofrequency Sources in Multinuclear NMR

Crystal oscillators produce accurate and constant frequencies as a consequence of the precise capacitance of the particular crystal used. (The principle is familiar in the electronics of a quartz wrist watch.) This fundamental frequency can be electronically multiplied to give higher overtones; these can then be modulated by another oscillator operating at audiofrequencies, so that the end product is a pair of side-bands shifted away from the original radiofrequency or its overtone by plus and minus the audiofrequency. Since the audiofrequency oscillator is capable of being controlled with high linearity, then the side-bands likewise can be shifted from the centre band with equally great accuracy. A combination of multiplication and side-band mixing can generate the wide range of frequencies needed in multinuclear NMR (from 7 to 100 MHz at 2.35 T). Frequencies can also be generated from digital synthesisers, starting with a basic frequency of 10 MHz, and using digital techniques to perform the necessary multiplication and mixing.

3.7.2 Single Coil and Crossed Coil Detection

There are two ways of detecting the NMR phenomenon, and each stems from the separate original experiments of Purcell and Bloch.

Radiofrequency Bridge

This circuitry operates with only one RF coil, closely wound around the sample as shown in figure 1.4. At resonance, there is an imbalance generated in this coil by virtue of the developing magnetisation of the sample, and this out-of-balance is detected in the RF circuit, the principle being roughly analogous to the out-of-balance in a Wheatstone Bridge circuit in DC resistance measurement. This single coil geometry was used by Purcell in his pioneering work in 1945.

Nuclear Induction

This was demonstrated for the first time by Bloch's experiments. Electromagnetic induction is a familiar idea which takes many forms, and its history goes back to Faraday in the 1830s; the example we focus on here involves the transfer of electromagnetic energy from an alternating current passing along a coil of wire to an adjacent coil at right angles to the first coil. Bloch showed that this energy transfer (induction) was effected by magnetic nuclei in a sample placed between the two coils, so long as the RF current in the first coil was in resonance with the nuclear transitions.

He used the *crossed coil* configuration, and excited the nuclei with an RF current in the first coil wound round the x-axis, and detected the nuclear induction in the second coil wound around the y-axis. The direction of the static magnetic field (B_0) was taken as acting along the z-axis, as discussed in section 3.1.5. The crossed coil arrangement is shown diagrammatically in figure 3.3: note that the magnetic field of the RF excitation is labelled B_1.

The single coil geometry is widely used in modern spectrometers, and it is possible to design the circuitry to tune the probe to transmit and receive different frequencies. For the later purpose of presenting complex theories in a uniform and understandable way, it is however convenient to assume that we are dealing always with the crossed coil geometry shown in figure 3.3. If we accept this arbitrarily, then all references to the conventional x-, y- and z-axes (excitation, detection, B_0) remain constant throughout the arguments: where an instrument is in fact using the single coil geometry, then the theory remains the same even though the practice differs.

The development of probe design has reached a high order, and spectrometer manufacturers have approached the difficulties in different ways, each choosing different compromises in the search for maximum sensitivity. Specialist details are not the present concern, but it is interesting to realise the limits within which the RF engineer must work.

Each coil must be designed to match the particular frequency involved, and must be wound to lie as closely as possible to the sample: the number of turns in the coil varies to accommodate the first of these criteria, and the chosen shape meets the second criterion. Coil shape depends on the magnet geometry: solenoid windings are used if the coil is coaxial with the sample tube (as in figure 1.4) while saddle coils must be used if the sample tube is orthogonal to the coil axis. Thus, in figure 3.3, the diagram is helpful in emphasising the principle of crossed coils, but the shape of the windings would in practice have to be in the saddle format shown in the figure insert.

Decoupler coils must also be provided around the sample, and their characteristics matched to optimise performance in respect of number of turns and geometry. Clearly, there is limited space around a 5 mm sample tube, and great ingenuity in circuitry and care in manufacture are demanded to minimise interference and to maximise signal-to-noise ratios.

Because of the wide range in frequencies needed in multinuclear spectrometers, it is difficult to design one

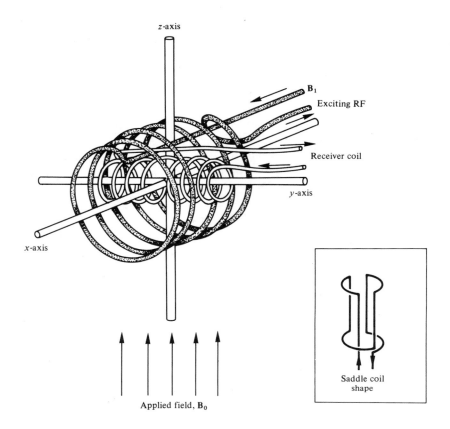

Figure 3.3 Crossed coil geometry in an NMR probe. B_0 acts along the z-axis, the excitation (B_1) is delivered along the x-axis, and the NMR signal is detected in the receiver coil along the y-axis. The coils must be shaped to lie close to the sample, and the insert shows the saddle geometry that is often adopted

probe which will efficiently operate over the entire range, and it is common practice to supply more than one probe, each covering a sensibly limited frequency range.

3.7.3 Forced Induction and Free Induction

If RF current is passed continuously along the x-axis coil (the basis of CW NMR) then nuclear induction leads to a continuous signal along the y-axis coil; Bloch named this *forced induction*.

Although contemporary technology denied him the opportunity to supply a pulsed RF excitation, Bloch nevertheless predicted that, after the end of such a pulse, the nuclei would continue for a short time to exhibit the effects of the nuclear induction and, even in the absence of the excitation, would produce a continuing signal along the y-axis. He named this *free induction*. The exponentially decaying interferogram recorded in pulsed NMR (see figure 3.2) is named the *free induction decay* (FID).

A detailed difference arises in the appearance of CW and pulsed FT NMR spectra which relates to these ideas. Note that the majority of the proton spectra shown in chapter 4 were recorded in the CW mode, while for the carbon-13 spectra in chapter 5 the pulsed FT mode was mostly used. In all CW spectra, each signal has a distorted appearance caused by the recorder pen oscillating rapidly after the peak maximum has been passed. In the chapter 4 spectra, which were scanned from high to low frequency, the oscillations are on the low frequency side of the signal. The oscillations are called *ringing*, and further discussion is given in section 6.8.4; briefly, it is a beat phenomenon. The CW scan passes through the resonance and leaves behind some net magnetisation at the resonance frequency: as the scan continues, the new frequencies generated interact with the residual frequency to produce the interference beats. There is no counterpart in the pulsed FT experiment. Magnet homogeneity can be assessed by the persistence of the ringing pattern and by its symmetry: the example shown at the head of chapter 1 was recorded on a well adjusted spectrometer.

3.7.4 The Components of RF Signals

POLARISATION OF ELECTROMAGNETIC RADIATION

Just as visible light can be polarised (passing it through Polaroid sun glasses is one method) RF currents with their much lower frequencies can also be polarised. By an extension of figure 14.5, an alternating electric current passing along a coil of wire produces a fluctuating magnetic field which is *polarised along the axis of the coil*. In figure 3.3 then, the RF current in the x-axis coil produces a magnetic field linearly polarised on the x-axis as shown in figure 3.4(a). It will be convenient to resolve this into two counter-rotating (circularly polarised) magnetic components as shown in figure 3.4(b) and (c).

The component (b) is rotating in the same direction as the precessing nuclei in figure 1.10; when component (b) and the nuclei have the same angular velocity, then they are in resonance, and this is the component which satisfies the resonance requirement that frequency of precession equals RF frequency.

The counter-rotating component (c) will 'meet' the precessing nuclei twice in each revolution. It is thus out of phase by a factor of two and does not contribute to resonance.

PHASE AND PHASING

The fluctuating fields created by the RF currents in the x-axis coil will only be transferred to the RF detector if their frequency characteristics are matched with each other. In chapter 6 we look in more detail at the resolution of the signal along the x-, y- and z-axes, but if we ignore for the moment the z-axis, then there exist two components at 90° to each other (that is, with a phase difference of 90°) and the detector can be adjusted

(tuned) to record either one of these components. The resulting signal is different in either case, the two forms being shown in figure 3.5 (see also section 2.18.2). The

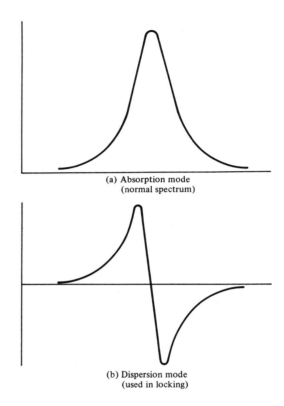

(a) Absorption mode
(normal spectrum)

(b) Dispersion mode
(used in locking)

Figure 3.5 The radiofrequency detector can be tuned to detect either a signal in the absorption mode (a) or, 90° out of phase with this, in the dispersion mode (b)

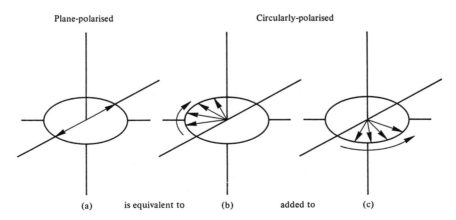

Plane-polarised   Circularly-polarised

(a)   is equivalent to   (b)   added to   (c)

Figure 3.4 Plane-polarisation can be resolved into two components of circularly-polarised radiation rotating in opposite directions

absorption mode (a) is normally detected and displayed as the NMR spectrum, but the dispersion mode (b) has the valuable feature of being zero at exactly the midpoint of the signal, and of being either positive or negative depending on whether we travel to left or right respectively. The circuitry associated with field-frequency lock (see section 3.3) is tuned to detect the lock signal in the dispersion mode.

The dispersion mode signal arises in phase with the excitation RF while the absorption mode signal is 90° out of phase with the excitation.

3.7.5 Phase Sensitive Detectors and Quadrature Detection

In order to measure frequencies accurately, it is common to have the exciting RF (from the oscillator) and the detector amplifier coupled together, so that the signal which the detector receives is referenced to and in phase with the oscillator frequency. If the signal coming to the detector from the sample is of exactly the same frequency as the oscillator, then the signals cancel and the detector sees this as direct current; if the two frequencies (oscillator and detected signal) are different, then the detector passes this as alternating current.

In this arrangement (called *phase sensitive detection*) the detector is unable to distinguish whether this difference arises because of the oscillator or detector having the higher value or the lower value of frequency (since only the difference between them is detected). If the detector incorporates two circuits, the second one being tuned 90° out of phase with the oscillator, then the ambiguity in the sign of the difference in frequency can be overcome. This arrangement is called *quadrature*

detection; it allows the detector to distinguish signals from spurious noise, and in so doing improve the signal-to-noise performance of the instrument. There is a second, more esoteric advantage of quadrature detection: sampling errors may arise in the digitising of the free induction decay, FID (see section 3.8.1), to obviate which the RF pulse is placed at one end of the NMR spectrum frequency; in a spectrometer with quadrature detection these errors are eliminated and the RF pulse frequency can be chosen in the centre of the spectrum, giving more effective irradiation over the range of frequencies involved.

3.7.6 RF Pulses and their Fourier Transforms

Figure 3.6(a) shows the wave form of a radiofrequency pulse, as a plot of intensity against time: it is a *time domain* presentation. The calculated Fourier Transform of such a square wave form leads to the *frequency domain* presentation of figure 3.6(b). This seemingly puzzling 'juxtrarelation' is of great practical import.

It means that an intense pulse of radiofrequency current corresponds to the delivery of not just one unique frequency, but a spread of frequencies of differing amplitudes and phase relationships; we can as well define the nature of a pulse by its power and duration as by its spectrum of frequencies (its bandwidth), since each is the Fourier transform of the other.

The shorter the pulse duration (t_p) the wider the frequency spread, in agreement with the Heisenberg Uncertainty Principle. In practical terms the spread of frequencies around the centre is $\pm 1/t_p$, so that the total spectral width is $2/t_p$.

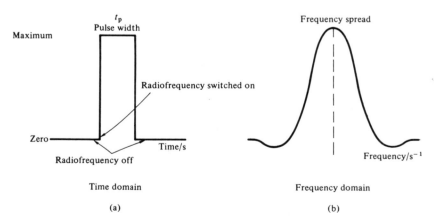

Time domain
(a)

Frequency domain
(b)

Figure 3.6 A radiofrequency pulse lasting for t_p seconds is equivalent to the supply of a range of radiofrequencies; the spread of frequencies, also called the spectral width or bandwidth, is equal to $1/2t_p$, but all of these frequencies are present at differing intensities as shown in (b)

Worked Example 3.2
Calculate the spread of frequencies (spectral width) generated by an RF pulse of duration 1.0 μs.

Answer 3.2
Spectral width (or bandwidth) is given by $1/2t_p$, thus

$$\text{spectral width} = \frac{1}{2 \times (1.0 \times 10^{-6} \text{ s})} = 0.5 \times 10^6 \text{ s}^{-1}$$

$$= 0.5 \text{ MHz}$$

Problem Example 3.2
What is the total spread of frequencies required at 2.35 T to cover (a) 10 ppm in a proton spectrum, (b) 200 ppm in a carbon-13 spectrum?

Problem Example 3.3
Calculate spectral widths for proton and carbon-13 as in example 3.2, but for a 200 MHz instrument (4.7 T magnet).

3.8 DATA HANDLING IN FT NMR

In pulsed FT NMR, all of the spectral data are contained in the FID interferogram, which theoretically decays to zero after infinite time. Data are obviously not collected to infinity, but when collection abruptly stops, and the

truncated FID submitted to Fourier Transformation, the signals are slightly distorted by side bands, since some of the essential information has been lost in the shortening process. Various computational smoothing techniques can be applied to minimise these distortions.

The noise content of the FID is greatest at the end of the exponential, and it is possible to give additional weighting to the early part of the interferogram, where spectral information is less distorted by noise. Although this improves the signal-to-noise ratio of the experiment, it results in a slight line-broadening which is regarded as an acceptable trade-off. This *exponential weighting* can be operated in the reverse way to produce sharper lines and thus improve resolution, with a concomitant reduction in signal-to-noise ratio. Another computer process to improve the signal-to-noise ratio is to add a succession of zeros to the end of the acquired FID before FT — a process known as *zero filling*. In the subsequent computation, this has the effect of adding additional interpolated points throughout the FID, with a substantial improvement in line shape and resolution.

3.8.1 Sampling Rate and Fold-back

When a typical FID is converted to digital form, an infinite number of digital points would be needed to specify its complexity completely. Limitations are im-

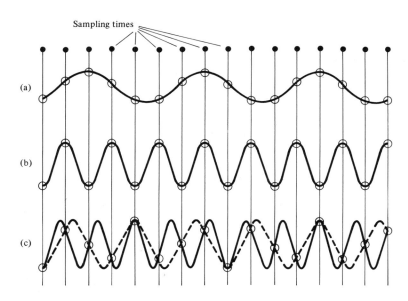

Sampling times

(a)

(b)

(c)

Figure 3.7 Sampling rate and fold-back. The sine curve of frequency (a) is sampled adequately, at five times per cycle. That in (b) is on the limit, at twice per cycle. The higher frequency in (c, continuous line) is inadequately sampled at approximately 1.5 times per cycle, so the computer interprets this in error as an adequately-sampled sine curve of lower frequency (c, dotted line). This lower frequency signal is said to be *folded back* from its correct (higher-frequency) position.

posed by the size of the computer memory, but there is a minimum number of data points below which the record of the FID will be unacceptably patchy.

To specify any sine curve digitally, it must be sampled at least twice in each cycle, thus if the frequency of the sine curve is f Hz, then the sampling rate must be greater than $2f$ Hz. The outcome of too slow a sampling rate is illustrated in figure 3.7; the digitiser is unable to distinguish those inadequately sampled sine waves (with frequencies higher than half the sampling rate) from those lower-frequency sine waves which have been adequately sampled. In figure 3.8 is shown the possible spectral consequences. A signal at high frequency lies outside the spectral range specified, and is sampled at too low a rate; the digitiser/FT interprets this in error as a signal at lower frequency *folded back* or *aliased* from the correct position.

3.8.2 The Fast Fourier Transform – Real and Imaginary Solutions

The computer algorithm used to calculate the Fourier Transform is usually a modified version of a mid-1960s program which simplifies earlier methods by a system of pairing; this results in a shorter calculation, and hence the name Fast Fourier Transform (FFT). It works best when N, the number of data points allocated to define the FID, is a power of 2, such as 2^{12} (4096, approximately four thousand, 4K) or 2^{13} (8192, approximately eight thousand, 8K).

Fourier transformation results in two solutions, corresponding to the cosine and sine transforms; see section 14.5.1. The mathematics of real and imaginary numbers are also involved, and the spectra which constitute these two solutions are respectively the *real* and *imaginary spectra*. They contain the same information and differ only in phase (as do cosine and sine); the cosine solution is the normal absorption spectrum and when this is plotted out it is defined by only half as many data points ($N/2$) as the original FID, since $N/2$ points are used to define the imaginary (sine) solution. Real and imaginary spectra are shown in figure 3.9.

This affects the resolution of the NMR spectrum in a manner which we can quantify. Suppose we record a proton spectrum with a spectral width of 1000 Hz, and allocate 8K of computer memory for the FID. The number of data points finally specifying the proton spectrum will be half of this, that is 4K (or 4096 exactly). The digital resolution will be 0.24 Hz per data point, which is similar to the resolution capabilities of the magnet (as discussed in section 3.2). Once again there are computer sub-programs to enhance the appearance of the spectrum by line smoothing, producing line shapes close to the theoretical Lorentzian.

Problem Example 3.4
A spectrum is recorded with a spectral width of 500 Hz. Calculate the resolution achieved if the data are assigned to (a) 4K, (b) 8K of computer memory.

3.8.3 Phases and Filters

Phase problems in NMR affect the appearance of the spectrum; examples are shown in figures 3.5 and 3.9, but

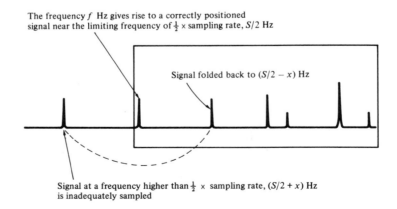

The frequency f Hz gives rise to a correctly positioned signal near the limiting frequency of $\frac{1}{2} \times$ sampling rate, $S/2$ Hz

Signal folded back to $(S/2 - x)$ Hz

Signal at a frequency higher than $\frac{1}{2} \times$ sampling rate, $(S/2 + x)$ Hz is inadequately sampled

Figure 3.8 Fold-back. For a sampling rate of S Hz, the highest frequency sine wave which can be correctly interpreted is $S/2$. A sine wave of a frequency exceeding this, by an amount x Hz, is incorrectly interpreted and, instead of its proper frequency $(S/2 + x)$ Hz being recorded, a signal erroneously appears folded back, or aliased, to $(S/2 - x)$ Hz

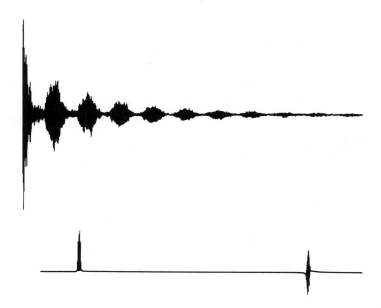

Figure 3.9 The two solutions, real and imaginary of a Fourier transform. The FID is shown above (for the ^{13}C NMR spectrum of ethylbenzene). Note the difference in phase

they can arise in many ways other than by detector tuning or the Fourier transformation of an FID.

High frequency noise is usually filtered out of the NMR signal by means of frequency-selective bypass devices; these filters themselves are responsible for delaying the RF signal, and distortions characteristic of phase errors have to be corrected by various spectrometer control systems, otherwise line shape is not pure absorption mode.

3.8.4 Dynamic Range and Computer Word Length

The computer must be able to store the FID in digital form, and faithfully record the presence of small fluctuations in the presence of large: this is the problem of *dynamic range*.

For a highly discriminatory accuracy of 0.1% in signal intensity (one in 1000) this can be registered in 10 bits of a computer word, since 2^{10} is 1024. If the computer has 12 bit words and several successive spectra have to be added coherently, then data will overflow in this case after four successive additions, since $4 \times 2^{10} = 2^{12}$. In a computer with 16 bit words, 65 summations can be carried out before overflow occurs.

Problem Example 3.5
How many spectra could be added in this way in a computer with 20 bit word length?

Different computer programs adopt different strategies for overcoming this limitation; for example the data may be handled in blocks and dumped onto storage discs before overflow occurs. The word length can also be effectively doubled by using two computer words to register each number, a process known as *double precision.*

The dynamic range of the computer is quite a separate consideration from that of the analogue-to-digital convertor (ADC), and the means of obviating overflow are also different and associated with the strength of the received signal.

3.9 Variable Temperature Probes

There are several circumstances which call for recording a spectrum at high or low temperature. Unstable compounds may decompose at the normal probe temperature (near 30°) and cooling is necessary. Viscous or sparingly soluble samples benefit from higher temperature recording. Kinetic studies are discussed in chapter 8; the need for accurate variable temperatures is central to studies of activation parameters.

The method of altering the sample temperature in the probe is, in principle, straightforward. For high temperatures, a heated stream of air or nitrogen is blown over the sample tube, while for low temperatures cold gas (generated from the evaporation of liquid nitrogen, or by passing through cooling coils immersed in liquid nitrogen) is used.

The real problems are technical, in ensuring that the gas temperature is accurately thermostatted, and that the heating or cooling of the sample causes minimum disturbance to the magnet homogeneity.

The range of temperatures commonly available using these methods is from $-150°C$ to $+200°C$.

The choice of solvents presents other difficulties; the freezing and boiling points of some typical NMR solvents are listed in table 15.19, and these satisfy all but extreme requirements. Since mixtures have lower melting points (freezing points) than pure compounds, at very low temperatures mixed solvent systems can be utilised.

For accurate work, it is necessary to record the sample temperature by some better means other than the instrument thermocouple system. A commonly used method makes use of the fact that NMR signals are often temperature dependent.

In methanol, the CH_3 proton signal in the proton NMR spectrum is constant, while the OH signal moves with changes in temperature (associated with changes in hydrogen bonding). The signal separation is therefore a measure of temperature and such a device is called a *chemical shift thermometer*.

The methanol is usually contained in a capillary tube mounted concentrically within the sample volume of the normal NMR sample tube, so that it records precisely the sample temperature. Much ingenuity has been brought into calibrating the methanol thermometer: one very exact method uses sharply melting solids to cross-check with the signal separation.

For carbon-13 studies, one chemical shift thermometer has been widely used. It depends on the temperature dependence of the carbonyl resonance in acetone-d_6 when complexed with an Yb shift reagent (see section 4.10.2). For phosphorus-31 NMR, the change in ^{31}P resonance of triphenylphosphine oxide, Ph_3PO, referenced to triphenylphosphine, Ph_3P, forms a useful system.

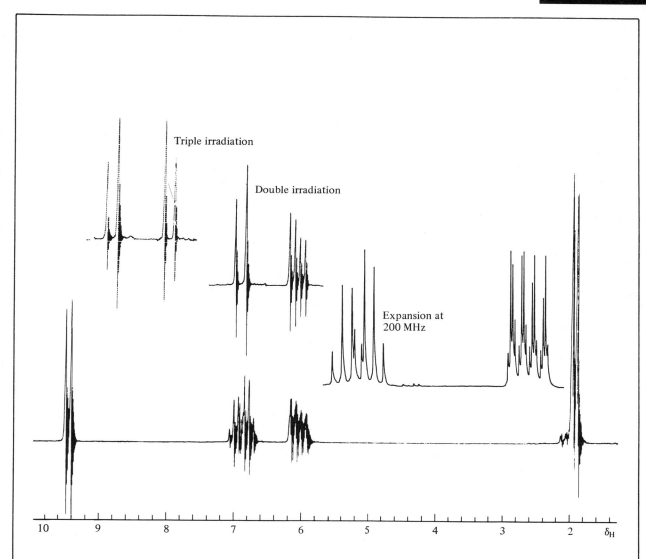

Double and triple irradiation in simplification of the proton NMR spectrum of crotonaldehyde, $CH_3CH=CHCHO$
(main spectrum recorded at 100 MHz, insert at 200 MHz)

The theory of chemical shifts in proton NMR can be rationalised comprehensively, and correlation data are available in tabular form to aid spectral interpretation.

The number of different chemical shift resonances in a proton NMR spectrum derives from the number of non-equivalent protons present in the molecule, but the factors which render protons *chemically* equivalent are not necessarily the same as those which make protons *magnetically* equivalent.

A glance at the proton spectra reproduced in this chapter shows that in most spectra the signals are split (by coupling) into patterns of doublets, triplets, quartets, quintets, septets or even more complex multiplets.

Protons attached to oxygen or nitrogen exhibit characteristics not possessed by those joined to carbon.

4.1 SHIELDING, DESHIELDING AND PROTON CHEMICAL SHIFTS

The origin of chemical shift in NMR lies in the degree to which a magnetic nucleus is *shielded* from the applied field B_0 by the electron cloud surrounding the nucleus. In the most simple circumstance, the more dense the electron cloud, the less effective is the magnetic field experienced by the nucleus and thus the lower is its precessional frequency (since precessional frequency is directly proportional to the magnetic field experienced by the nucleus). In summary shielding leads to a lowering of precessional frequency, that is, to a lower chemical shift value, δ.

Protons are surrounded (shielded) only by s-electrons, which are spherically symmetric in their distribution around the nucleus. These are induced to circulate under the influence of B_0, producing an electric current and an associated magnetic field. The sense of this induced electron circulation is that shown in figure 14.4, so that the analogously induced magnetic component is diamagnetic (acts in opposition to B_0). This *diamagnetic shielding effect* is universally present in protons (as we can never observe the bare nucleus). It is universally present in other nuclei but, unlike the proton, other magnetic nuclei possess p-electrons, which are not spherically distributed; the effect of B_0 on p-electrons is to cause them to circulate in a sense which generates quite powerful magnetic fields, whose influence varies along different directions within the molecule. These differences can be vary large indeed, and the observed chemical shift ranges of other magnetic nuclei are commensurately wider than that of the proton.

Any influence which reduces the electron density will reduce the shielding effect and the nucleus is said to be deshielded; *deshielding* leads to an increase in precessional frequency, that is, to a *higher chemical shift value*, δ.

4.1.1 Electronegativity and Proton Chemical Shifts

Table 4.1 shows the chemical shift values of the methyl protons in a series of simple compounds. The increasing electronegativity in the halogens (I < Br < Cl < F) means that the s-electron density around the protons is

Table 4.1   Chemical shift values of CH_3 protons attached to groups of varying electronegativity

Compound	δ values for CH_3 protons
$CH_3-\overset{\displaystyle CH_3}{\underset{\displaystyle CH_3}{\overset{\displaystyle \mid}{\underset{\displaystyle \mid}{Si}}}}-CH_3$ TMS	0.0 by definition
$(CH_3)_3-Si(CD_2)_2CO_2^-Na^+$ TSP$-d_4$	0 (for the CH_3-Si protons)
CH_3I	2.2
CH_3Br	2.6
CH_3Cl	3.1
CH_3F	4.3
CH_3NO_2	4.3
CH_2Cl_2	5.5
$CHCl_3$	7.3

progressively reduced from methyl iodide through methyl fluoride; increased frequencies, as a consequence of this deshielding effect, are shown in increased δ values.

The introduction of one, two and three chlorine atoms into methane leads to progressive deshielding of the remaining protons and thus to higher δ values (higher resonance frequencies). Chemical shift values for CH_3Cl, CH_2Cl_2 and $CHCl_3$ are shown in table 4.1.

Silicon is more electropositive than carbon and pushes electron density towards the methyl protons. This increased shielding results in a very low precessional frequency for such protons; indeed the protons in TMS have lower precessional frequency than protons in almost all other molecules, and it is partly for this reason that TMS is used as a reference standard (see section 1.6).

4.1.2 Van der Waals Radii and Proton Chemical Shifts

Where molecular geometry constrains two groups to approach more closely than the sum of their van der Waals radii, the electron shells of the groups will mutually repel each other. The result is diminished electron density around the nucleus (deshielding) and a move to higher δ values.

Although these effects are small in proton NMR (usually less than one part per million) they do lead to inaccuracies in the predictability of chemical shifts, and they must be considered in sterically crowded molecules. Valuable conformational information may also be derived from studying such shifts.

4.2 ANISOTROPIC EFFECTS AND PROTON CHEMICAL SHIFTS

Isotropic effects exert their influence uniformly in all spatial directions; anisotropic effects act non-uniformly. The principal anisotropic effects in organic molecules are associated with the ways in which π-electrons react with the applied field, particularly the π-electrons of carbon–carbon and carbon–oxygen multiple bonds.

4.2.1 Aromatic Ring Currents

Aromatic compounds show significant anisotropic effects which are associated with the cyclic delocalisation of the aromatic π-electrons. The model for all aromatic compounds is benzene; in an applied field, B_0, the aromatic sextet of electrons is induced to circulate around the ring, and this electron flow — the *ring current* — in turn generates a magnetic field, its sense being shown in figure 4.1 (compare figure 14.4). From this picture, it is

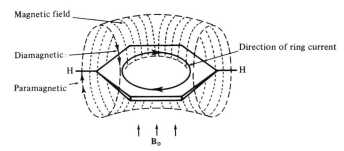

Figure 4.1 Anisotropic effects of the aromatic ring current. Protons around the ring experience increased field, and have high frequency chemical shifts. The zones above and below the ring are shielding in nature, so the opposite effect operates here

apparent that the total effective field acting on the protons consists of B_0 together with a positive contribution from the induced magnetic field. As a consequence of increased effective field, the protons have a higher precessional frequency and come to resonance at δ 7.27, considerably higher than most protons.

The molecules of benzene in solution are rapidly tumbling with respect to the direction of B_0, and the contribution of the ring current effect to the observed chemical shift is averaged out over those molecules oriented as in figure 4.1 and those molecules oriented randomly with respect to B_0.

It is impossible to measure precisely the scale of the ring current effect in isolation; certainly, theoretical treatments abound, but some measure can be gauged from comparison with protons in alkenes in which the unique cyclic delocalisation of aromatic systems is absent. Thus acyclic trienes have protons within the chain with chemical shifts of δ 6.2 and the alkene protons of 1,3-cyclohexadiene come to resonance at δ 5.8.

Since protons of side-chain methyl groups are also influenced by the ring current, the chemical shift in toluene (CH_3 at δ 2.3) bears comparison with a methyl-substituted acyclic polyene (CH_3 at δ 2.0).

In the examples thus far, the anisotropic influence of the ring current has been shown to increase the frequency (δ value) of protons around the periphery of the ring. Above and below the ring, however, the induced magnetic field acts to oppose B_0 (see figure 4.1) and in these zones we should expect to find the contrary effect; this is observed in molecules such as cyclophanes. The δ values at points along the CH_2 chain mirror the geometry of the induced field. The CH_2 above the ring comes to

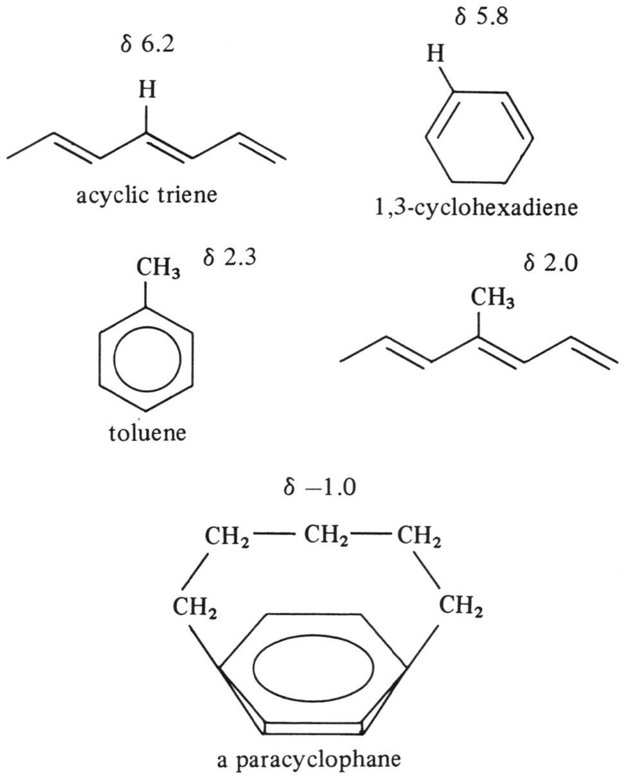

$$\delta\ 6.2$$

$$\delta\ 5.8$$

acyclic triene

1,3-cyclohexadiene

$$\delta\ 2.3$$

$$\delta\ 2.0$$

toluene

(4.1)

$$\delta\ -1.0$$

$$CH_2 \!\!-\!\! CH_2 \!\!-\!\! CH_2$$

$$CH_2 \qquad\qquad CH_2$$

a paracyclophane

resonance near $\delta\ -1.0$, on the low frequency side of TMS.

In summary, circulation of π-electrons produces two kinds of chemical shift effect. In certain zones the shift is to higher frequency; the induced field is parallel to $\mathbf{B_0}$ and the effect is paramagnetic (equivalent to the deshielding discussed in section 4.1). In other zones there is produced a diamagnetic, or shielding effect.

Several chemical criteria can be applied to ascertain whether a molecule possesses any degree of aromaticity; stability, and a propensity for electrophilic substitution reactions, are two such criteria. NMR is the most widely applicable spectroscopic criterion, since aromaticity is associated with cyclically delocalised π-electrons which should be capable of sustaining a ring current, with corresponding influences on chemical shift positions.

Heterocyclic compounds which exhibit the classical chemical behaviour of aromatic molecules (thiophene, furan, pyrrole, pyridine, quinoline) also have NMR spectra which bear witness to the presence of aromatic ring currents. Typical δ values are shown in table 15.4.

Of great interest in Hückel theory are the cyclic polyenes with $(4n + 2)$ π-electrons, and much ingenuity has gone into the synthesis of these models, particularly

the conjugated polyenes with 10, 14 and 18 carbon atoms ($n = 2, 3, 4$). In the molecule of [18]annulene (I) (formulae 4.2) at low temperature, two groups of NMR signals arise from the protons. One signal (at $\delta\ 9.3$) corresponds to twelve hydrogens and another (at $\delta\ -3.0$), that is, on the low-frequency side of TMS, corresponds to six hydrogens. This NMR evidence confirms that the molecule is planar, has eighteen π-electrons sufficiently delocalised to sustain a ring current, and that the twelve peripheral protons lie in the paramagnetic zone while the six inner protons are strongly diamagnetically shielded. At higher temperatures ring inversions take place and blur these distinctions: this phenomenon is treated fully in chapter 8. The ^1H NMR spectrum is shown at the chapter head.

The methyl protons in the pyrene derivative (II) are likewise in the diamagnetic shielding zone of a $(4n + 2)$ π-electron system ($n = 3$) which sustains a ring current. Their resonance position is at the exceptionally low frequency value of $\delta\ -4.2$ (4.2 ppm on the low-frequency side of TMS). The ten electron system in (IV) also sustains a ring current, having $(4n + 2)$ π-electrons, with $n = 2$.

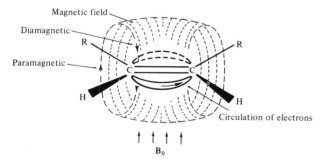

[18] annulene (n = 4)
(I)

pyrene
(II)

dimethyldihydropyrene (n = 3)
(III)

(4.2)

H   H δ −0.5

(IV)   (n = 2)

($4n$ + 2) aromatic systems

4.2.2 Double Bonds in Alkenes

The π-electrons of double bonds create magnetic fields associated with induced electron circulation when the molecule is appropriately oriented with respect to B_0.

For alkenes, the π-electron circulation and direction of the associated magnetic field are shown in figure 4.2. Protons located *in* the plane of the double bond are in the paramagnetic zone of the induced field: they experience a net increase in effective magnetic field, and precess at higher frequency, and chemical shift positions for alkene protons are consequently higher (around δ 4–5) than in corresponding saturated hydrocarbons.

As in the case of aromatic ring currents, the zones above and below the alkene plane are zones of increased shielding (because of the diamagnetic influence of the induced field). Protons held in such an environment have their frequencies reduced and have lower δ values than would otherwise be observed. A classic example of this is the difference in chemical shift between the two geminal methyl groups in α- and β-pinene; the methyl group above the double bond has a lower chemical shift than its twin.

We can summarise the shielding and deshielding zones in alkenes as in figure 4.3(a).

4.2.3 Carbonyl C=O Double Bonds

Around the C=O double bond of carbonyl compounds there is a similar anisotropic influence. The precise geometry is not the subject of universal agreement, but figure 4.3(b) shows the generalised pattern. The protons of aldehydes have chemical shift positions near δ 10 as a result of this effect, and the formyl proton in formate

Figure 4.2 Anisotropic effects of the π-electron circulation in alkenes. Protons of the alkene group are deshielded (experience higher effective field and exhibit high chemical shifts). The zones above and below the plane of the double bond are shielding in nature

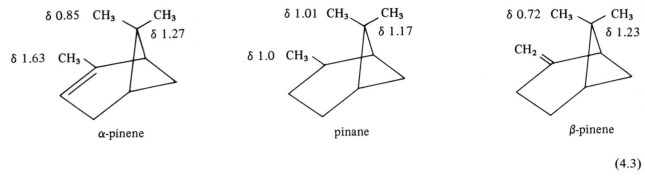

α-pinene   pinane   β-pinene

(4.3)

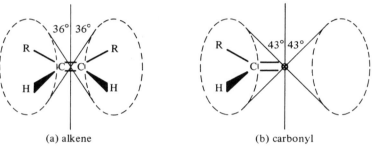

(a) alkene   (b) carbonyl

Figure 4.3 In alkenes (a) and carbonyl compounds (b) the generalised shifts experienced by protons are shown. Within the conical volumes around the axis of the double bond, proton chemical shifts are at high δ values; in all other zones above and below the double bond there is a shielding effect, with chemical shifts at low δ values

esters and formamides is similarly at high frequency near δ 8.

Because of electron delocalisation in amides (such as acetamide, CH_3CONH_2), there is partial double bond character in the C–N bond, and the resultant restricted rotation places the protons on nitrogen in different zones with respect to the anisotropic carbonyl bond. Provided the rotation is sufficiently slow, two proton signals arise: this fact has proved a fruitful source of interesting NMR experiments in measuring rotation rates at different temperatures, and an extensive study is justified later in section 4.3.2 and in chapter 8.

4.2.4 Alkyne Triple Bonds

The axial symmetry of alkyne groups is emphasised in figure 4.4. As a consequence of the continuous cylindrical sheath of π-electrons around the axis, B_0 induces an electron flow around this axis, and the induced magnetic field can be seen to have a diminishing influence on the field experienced by the alkyne proton, which in consequence exhibits low precessional frequency. Alkyne protons come to resonance near δ 2–3.

δ 9.7 δ 10.0 δ 8.0 δ 7.8

aldehydes   formates   formamides

(4.4)

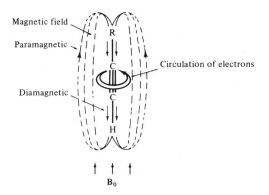

Figure 4.4 Anisotropic effect of the π-electron circulation in terminal alkynes. The proton experiences a field less than $\mathbf{B_0}$ and has a low precessional frequency (low δ value)

4.2.5 Alkanes

The equatorial protons in cyclohexane rings come to resonance about 0.5 ppm higher than axial protons, and this is attributed to anisotropic deshielding by the σ-electrons in the $\beta\gamma$ bonds as shown in figure 4.5. As a consequence of rapid ring-flips at higher temperatures, equatorial and axial labels are constantly being exchanged, so that cyclohexane spectra change in appearance with temperature: these dynamic processes are studied in chapter 8.

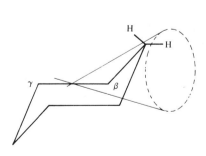

Figure 4.5 Anisotropic effect of the σ-electron circulation in cyclohexanes; the equatorial proton has a higher chemical shift position (by about 0.5 ppm) than the axial proton, since it lies in the deshielding zone with respect to the $\beta\gamma$ bond (δ_{He}, 1.7 : δ_{Ha}, 1.2. Differences observable only at low temperature)

4.3 CHEMICAL AND MAGNETIC EQUIVALENCE IN PROTON NMR

When the Heisenberg Uncertainty Principle was discussed earlier (in section 2.18) the importance of life-times was introduced; we saw that nuclei can occupy particular energy states and that the time spent in each of these states (Δt) was important in determining how accurately we could measure the energy differences between the states (ΔE).

Time-related phenomena are important in NMR in distinguishing those groups of nuclei which are equivalent to one another, and the study of the rates of these dynamic processes will be discussed in chapter 8.

Before using chemical shift data to deduce detailed structural information from the proton NMR spectrum, we must clarify what is meant by 'equivalent'. In the present context we are concerned with *chemical equivalence*: another criterion of equivalence presents itself later (in section 4.7) and this is distinguished by the term *magnetic equivalence*.

4.3.1 Free Rotation and Molecular Conformations

The three protons of a methyl group, such as those in compounds of general formula CH_3CH_2X, are in constantly changing environments because of the rapid rotations around the adjoining $C-C$ bond. We can represent this best in the Newman projections shown.

Newman projections of CH_3CH_2X

(4.5)

Newman projections of 1,2-dibromoethane

The rate of rotation at room temperature is exceedingly fast; each full rotation takes around 10^{-12} s and thus the *residence time* of a hydrogen atom in any one conformational environment is too short (that is, Δt is too small) to allow accurate measurement in their NMR spectra of the energies of these different conformations (ΔE being of necessity large, from Heisenberg's Uncertainty Principle).

The NMR absorption which is observed from such a group of three protons is a *time-averaged* value; all three experience the same averaged-out electronic environment (shielding) and have identical chemical shifts. (Their reactivity in chemical reactions is of course also identical.)

> Protons in identical electronic environments are, in NMR spectroscopy, chemically equivalent, and have the same value of chemical shift.

Protons which have identical chemical shifts (identical frequencies) are often defined as being *isochronous* (*Greek*: iso, the same: chronos, time).

When steric effects slow down the 'free' rotation, it may become possible to identify protons lying in different conformations and in different electronic environments. As an example, at low temperature, the rotation of 1,2-dibromoethane becomes sufficiently sluggish to make protons H_A and H_B distinguishable by their having different chemical shifts: they are thus *chemically nonequivalent*. At room temperature they become chemically equivalent again because of rapid rotation.

Note clearly that this test of chemical equivalence is inseparably associated with time: NMR spectroscopy can distinguish the differences in chemical shift *only* if there is 'sufficient' time to do so. What constitutes 'sufficient' time depends on the difference in energy between the conditions being so distinguished; again, from Heisenberg, if ΔE is a small difference in energy, then Δt has to be large (the life-times being examined must be long). The NMR time scale is frequently of crucial importance: it is discussed in some detail in section 8.4.

Problem Example 4.1
At room temperature cyclohexane shows only one chemical shift signal in its proton NMR spectrum, while at low temperature (around $-100°C$) there are two. Why is this? (See figure 8.4.)

4.3.2 Restricted Rotation in Alkenes and Amides

If we write the structure of vinyl compounds in the form $CH_2=CHX$, it is not made clear that all three protons are chemically non-equivalent. In the expanded formula for vinyl acetate we can see that H_A is *cis* to the acetate

group while H_B is *trans*, each has a different electronic environment and gives rise to a different chemical shift absorption.

Some of the most studied molecules in dynamic NMR are the N-substituted amides such as N,N-dimethylformamide. Because of resonance involving the non-bonding

vinyl acetate

resonance in amides

(4.6)

equilibration in amides
(slow at low temperature)
Me_A and Me_B non-equivalent

electrons on nitrogen, there exists some double bond character in the C—N bond with consequent increase in the energy barrier to rotation — and hence on the rate of rotation. At low temperatures the rate of rotation is sufficiently slow for two chemical shift signals to arise from the chemically non-equivalent methyl groups Me_A and Me_B. At high temperatures, in conditions of rapid rotation, only one time-averaged value arises. The change in the NMR spectrum from two signals to one allows the energy barrier to rotation to be calculated (see chapter 8).

4.3.3 Proton Exchange in Alcohols, Amines, Carboxylic Acids and Keto–Enol Systems

There are many equilibrium processes which affect proton NMR spectra but which are not readily apparent in the test-tube reactivity of the molecules concerned. In O—H groups, the hydrogen atoms migrate from one oxygen atom to another (as shown in formulae 4.7) so that for any particular proton, say H_A, the residence time on any one molecule is limited. In alcohols the time scale is of the order of minutes unless acid or base is present; under acid or base catalysis the reaction is speeded up and residence times drop to less than 0.1 s. For proton H_A,

$$CH_3 OH_A + CH_3 OH_B \rightleftharpoons CH_3 OH_B + CH_3 OH_A$$

proton exchange in alcohols

$$R-N-H_A + R-N-H_B \rightleftharpoons R-N-H_B + R-N-H_A$$

proton exchange in NH groups

$$CH_3 OH_A + H\!-\!O\!-\!H_B \rightleftharpoons CH_3 OH_B + H\!-\!O\!-\!H_A$$

proton exchange between alcohol and water

(4.7)

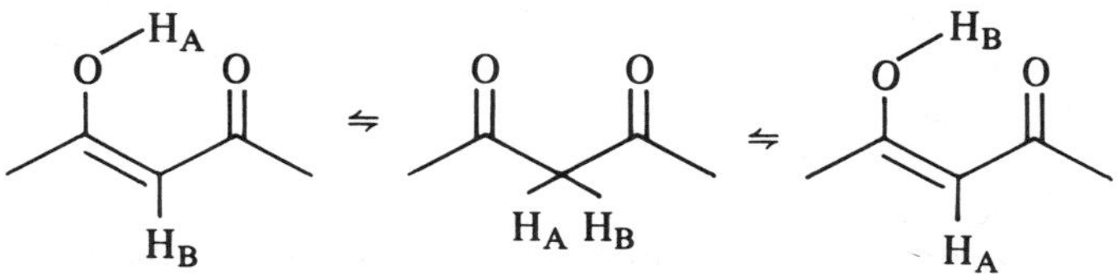

equilibrium exchange of protons among keto–enol
tautomers in the case of 2,4-pentanedione
(acetylacetone, ACAC)

the environment it experiences in each different alcohol molecule is identical, so the exchange does not lead to chemical non-equivalence. The same is true for carboxylic acids, although their dimeric structure (see section 4.5) is a modifying factor.

Comparable exchange occurs with the protons on NH groups.

If water or another proton acceptor is present then proton exchange is more complicated, since H_A will spend time partly on an alcohol molecule and partly on a water molecule. This exchange does lead to chemically non-equivalent protons, and the rate of exchange is again of importance in determining the appearance of the spectrum.

In keto-enol equilibria, we see an extension of this chemical non-equivalence. As shown in formulae 4.7, the protons of the 'active methylene group' are chemically equivalent (while attached to carbon) but these are not chemically equivalent to those in the enol forms.

Labile protons such as those attached to oxygen or nitrogen are also subject to hydrogen bonding, which affects the appearance of the NMR spectra; this is discussed in section 4.5.

Problem Example 4.2
The keto–enol ratio at room temperature for acetylacetone, shown in formulae 4.7, is approximately 15:85. In this mixture, how many different chemically equivalent proton environments will be observable?

4.3.4 Deuterium Exchange

If deuterium oxide (heavy water, D_2O) is added to an alcohol ($R-O-H$) the exchange process is modified and the principal new species generated are $R-O-D$ and $H-O-D$; the proton is no longer on an alcohol molecule but on an $H-O-D$ molecule. Its NMR signal moves characteristically, since it effectively disappears from its previous position (ROH) and a new signal near δ 4.7 arises (for HOD).

The demonstration that a signal is *removed by deuteriation* proves the presence of a labile proton attached to OH, NH or SH groups; these are further discussed in section 4.5.

A corollary of deuterium exchange arises in recording the proton NMR spectra of the many polar compounds (such as carbohydrates) which are insoluble in organic

$$R-O-H + D-O-D \rightleftharpoons R-O-D + H-O-D$$

deuterium exchange in alcohols

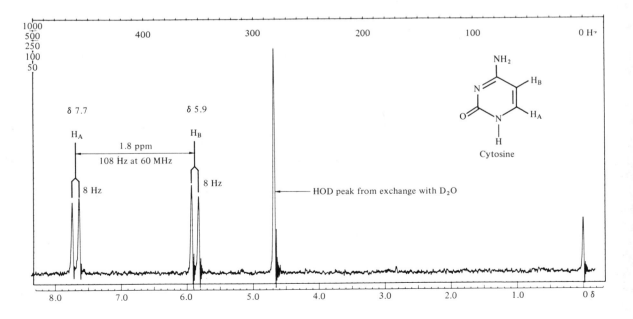

(4.8)

+ HOD   + HOD

base-catalysed deuterium exchange in
reactive methylene groups

solvents, and only soluble in water. Since H_2O cannot normally be used (its strong proton signal swamps the middle of the spectrum) D_2O is used, and deuterium exchange means the specific signals from all OH and NH protons are lost, and arise only in the HOD peak: this peak itself can be troublesome in position and size; pulse sequences which eliminate it are discussed in section 7.2.4. This is seen in the proton NMR spectrum for cytosine in figure 4.6: the H–O–D peak appears characteristically near δ 4.7.

The acidity of CH groups adjacent to carbonyl groups can be used as a means of detecting their presence. Base-

catalysed deuterium exchange removes all of the protons alpha to the carbonyl group specifically, with appropriate changes in the appearance of the spectrum.

4.4 PROTONS ATTACHED TO CARBON ATOMS – CHEMICAL SHIFT ASSIGNMENTS

4.4.1 Use of Correlation Tables 15.1–15.5

Section 1.7 dealt in a rudimentary way with the assignment of proton chemical shifts, and the typical ranges of

Figure 4.6 ^{1}H NMR spectrum of cytosine (one of the bases in DNA and RNA). (60 MHz, in D_2O). Note the HOD exchange peak at δ 4.7: see section 4.3.4

δ values shown in figure 1.8 could profitably be committed to memory.

Considerably more details are listed in tables 15.1–15.6. These δ values are derived empirically from the spectra of real molecules, and they should not be thought of as in any way 'theoretical'. They are mainly averaged values and in most cases they will be accurate to ± 0.2 ppm.

Single line signals do not always arise, and this will be discussed in section 4.7; practice in the use of tabulated data is a first objective.

4.4.2 Protons in Alkane Groups – Tables 15.1, 15.2 and 15.3

The chemical shift positions for CH_3, CH_2 and CH groups depend primarily on the group which is directly attached to the carbon atom, and this can be extracted from table 15.1. There is a minor contribution from functional groups attached to the next-neighbour carbon atom; table 15.2 allows this to be predicted. If a CH_2 group has two functional groups directly attached, table 15.3 shows the summation of the individual effects of these groups on the chemical shift of the CH_2 protons: for three functions attached to CH groups the predictive value is somewhat less accurate, since it depends on the erroneous assumption that the total effect is simply the arithmetic sum of the individual effects.

In all of these computations, we can ignore any substituents which are attached to the γ or to more distant carbon atoms.

Worked Example 4.1
Predict the chemical shift positions for the CH_3 protons in (a) methyl ketones, (b) methyl esters.

Answer 4.1
In methyl ketones (CH_3-COR) the group X is $-COR$, thus the protons appear at a chemical shift position of δ 2.1 (from the first column of numbers in table 15.1). For methyl esters (CH_3-OCOR) the value is δ 3.6; for $CH_3-OCOAr$ it is δ 4.2. Note the small difference between alkyl esters and esters of aryl carboxylic acids.

Problem Example 4.3
Predict the chemical shift positions for the CH_3 protons in (a) methyl ethers (dialkyl ethers), (b) methyl ethers attached to aromatic rings, (c) methyl groups at the end of an alkane chain.

Worked Example 4.2
Predict the chemical shift positions of the CH_2 group protons in (a) ethyl ketones, (b) ethyl esters.

Answer 4.2
In ethyl ketones (CH_3CH_2-COR) the CH_2 protons have an alkyl group on one side (CH_3, or R') and the group $-COR$ on the other side. From the middle column of numbers in table 15.1, which applies to $R'CH_2X$, the chemical shift position for the CH_2 group is δ 2.4. For ethyl esters, X is $-OCOR$ or $-OCOAr$, so the δ value is 4.1 or 4.2 respectively.

Problem Example 4.4
Predict the chemical shift positions of the CH_2 protons in (a) propionate esters (propanoate esters, CH_3CH_2COOR), (b) diethyl ether ($CH_3CH_2OCH_2CH_3$), (c) ethylbenzene ($C_6H_5CH_2CH_3$).

Problem Example 4.5
From table 15.1 (last column of numbers) predict the chemical shift positions for the CH protons in (a) isopropyl alcohol (2-propanol), (b) isopropylbenzene, (c) isobutyric acid (2-methylpropanoic acid).

$$CH_3-COR$$
methyl ketones

$$CH_3-OCOR$$
methyl esters
(of acids with COOH
on an alkyl carbon)

$$CH_3-OCOAr$$
methyl esters
(of acids with COOH
on an aryl ring)

(4.9)

$$CH_3-OR$$
methyl ethers
(dialkyl)

$$CH_3-OAr$$
methyl ethers
(aryl methyl)

isopropylbenzene

$$CH_3-CHCOOH$$
with CH_3 attached to CH
isobutyric acid
(2-methylpropanoic acid)

Worked Example 4.3
Use tables 15.1 and 15.2 to predict the chemical shift positions of the CH_3 protons in (a) ethylbenzene, (b) ethyl esters of carboxylic acids ($RCOO-CH_2CH_3$).

Answer 4.3
The chemical shift of the CH_3 protons depends primarily on the directly attached CH_2 group ($-R$) so from table 15.1 the chemical shift is δ 0.9. The phenyl group which is β to the CH_3 increases the value by 0.35 ppm (table 15.2) giving δ 1.25. For the CH_3 protons in ethyl esters the chemical shift is given by δ 0.9 + 0.4 = δ 1.3.

Worked Example 9.4
Use table 15.3 to predict the chemical shift positions of (a) the CH_2 protons in malonic acid, (b) the CH proton in mandelic acid: see formulae 4.10.

Answer 4.4
For malonic acid the value is 1.2 + 2 × 0.7 ($-COOH$) = δ 2.6. For mandelic acid it is 1.5 + 0.7 ($-COOH$) + 1.3 ($-Ph$) + 1.7 ($-OH$) = δ 5.2.

Problem Example 4.6
Predict the chemical shifts for all of the alkane protons in (a) ethyl acetate, (b) 1-phenylethanol, (c) propylbenzene and (d) benzyl methyl ether: see formulae 4.10.

4.4.3 Protons of Alkene, Alkyne and Aromatic Systems — Tables 15.4 and 15.5

The anisotropic influence on chemical shifts caused by the induced circulation of π-electrons has already been discussed in section 4.2. Table 15.4 lists the approximate chemical shifts for representative examples of alkene protons, alkyne protons, aromatic protons and protons directly bonded to carbonyl groups (formyl protons). While table 15.4 is by no means comprehensive, and other empirical approaches are available, it is extensive enough for the assignment of proton signals in most common molecular types. A study of the table shows the differences in δ values for protons *cis* or *trans* to anisotropic groups.

The acetylenic protons of terminal alkynes are acidic to a measurable extent; this reactivity manifests itself in their ability to form metal salts. In NMR spectroscopy, the alkyne proton can be abstracted by a base such as pyridine. The proton signal moves to a higher frequency and this constitutes an additional piece of confirmatory evidence that such a group is present.

For substituted benzenes, the chemical shift of the ring protons can be calculated from table 15.5. The accuracy is high (around ± 0.2 ppm) for monosubstitution and disubstitution, but where three substituents are present — particularly if they are strongly electron-withdrawing or electron-donating groups — the accuracy occasionally falls to ± 0.5 ppm.

Worked Example 4.5
Predict the chemical shift positions for the alkene protons in vinyl acetate, whose structure is given in formulae 4.6 (page 52).

Answer 4.5
From table 15.4 the values are H_A, δ 4.9, H_B, δ 4.6, H_C, δ 7.3.

malonic acid

mandelic acid

$CH_3COOCH_2CH_3$

ethyl acetate
(ethanoate)

(4.10)

1-phenylethanol

propylbenzene

benzyl methyl ether

Problem Example 4.7
Predict the chemical shift positions of (a) the alkene protons in cinnamic acid ($C_6H_5CH=CHCO_2H$), (b) the aldehyde proton in benzaldehyde (C_6H_5CHO), (c) the aldehydic proton in phenylacetaldehyde ($C_6H_5CH_2CHO$). In (c), assume that the principal influence on the CHO proton is the group directly attached, namely CH_2 or simply R.

Worked Example 4.6
Predict the chemical shift positions for the ring protons in
    (a) nitrobenzene,
    (b) *p*-nitroaniline ($p-H_2N-C_6H_4-NO_2$):
see formulae 4.11.

Answer 4.6
(a) The chemical shift position for benzene is δ 7.27. A nitro group shifts the protons *ortho* to it + 1.0 to δ 8.27; the *meta* protons are shifted + 0.3 to δ 7.57; the *para* protons are shifted + 0.4 to δ 7.67. (b) Because of the symmetry of *para*-substitution, the two protons *ortho* to nitro are chemically equivalent, as are the two protons *ortho* to amino. Protons H_A are influenced by the nitro group (*ortho* to them) and by the amino group (*meta* to them): their chemical shift position is thus 7.27 + 1.0 − 0.15 = δ 8.12. Similarly the H_B protons appear at 7.27 − 0.8 (*o*-NH$_2$) + 0.3 (*m*-NO$_2$) = δ 6.77. (This system is discussed again in section 4.7.1.)

Problem Example 4.8
Predict the chemical shift positions of the ring protons in (a) cinnamic acid, (b) benzaldehyde, (c) benzyl methyl ether. For (c) assume that the principal influence on the ring protons' chemical shifts is the group directly attached to the ring, which is CH_2, which can be evaluated as for CH_3.

4.5 PROTONS IN OH, NH AND SH GROUPS – TABLE 15.6

The striking feature of the chemical shift values given here is the wide range of chemical shift positions which may arise; protons attached to carbon have, in strong contrast, remarkably constant δ values, as we have seen above. Hydrogen bonding is the principal influence in these situations, and it affects all of the spectra involved to a degree. In addition, protons attached to nitrogen have special characteristics associated with the quadrupole moment of the nitrogen atom. Deuterium exchange as an aid to detection of these groups has already been discussed in section 4.3.4.

4.5.1 Hydrogen Bonding and Proton Chemical Shifts

Hydrogen bonding occurs most commonly in compounds containing OH or NH groups, and to a lesser degree in

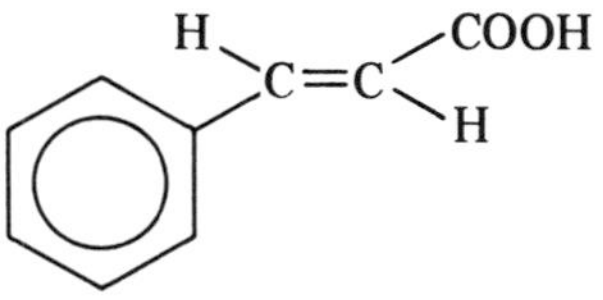

trans-cinnamic acid 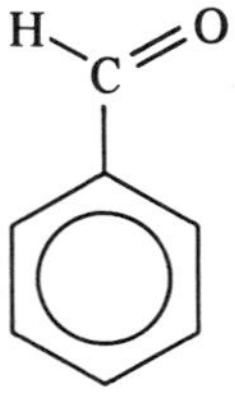   benzaldehyde 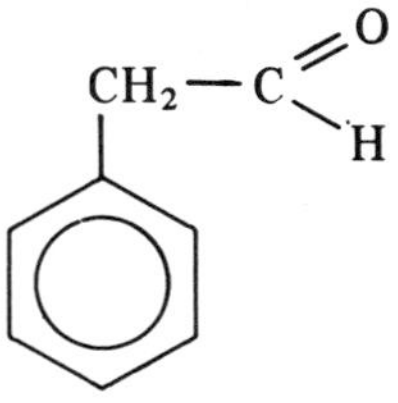   phenylacetaldehyde

(4.11)

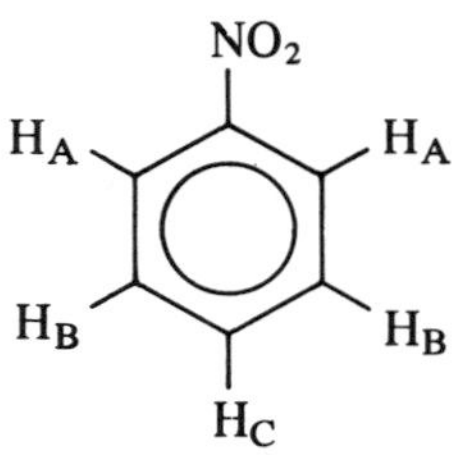

nitrobenzene 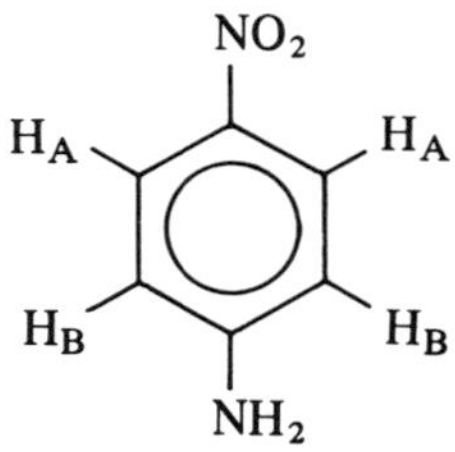   *p*-nitroaniline

SH compounds. The effects on the NMR spectra can be explained most simply in the case of alcohols.

The necessary and sufficient conditions for the formation of a hydrogen bond are: (a) a hydrogen atom must be attached to the atom of a more electronegative element and (b) a second electronegative atom must be in close proximity.

The dipolar attraction between the positively polarised hydrogen and the negatively polarised oxygen of a neighbour molecule leads to dimeric and polymeric association, with consequent lengthening and weakening of the original O—H bond. The electron density around the proton is reduced and this deshielding moves the proton signal to higher frequency.

> Hydrogen bonding leads to deshielding and to an increase in the frequency of the NMR signal of the hydrogen-bonded proton.

If an alcohol is dissolved at high dilution in a non-hydrogen-bonding solvent such as carbon tetrachloride, the consequent reduction in hydrogen bonding moves the OH signal to lower frequency; the range of δ values (0.5–5.0) is mainly dependent on this factor. Raising the temperature of the solution also reduces the hydrogen bonding to a predictable and quantitative extent; this effect is used as an accurate *chemical shift 'thermometer'* in variable temperature NMR experiments, usually with methanol as the 'thermometer'. Variable temperature observations (section 3.9) are necessary in kinetic and dynamic NMR (chapter 8).

Carboxylic acids exist in solution as hydrogen-bonded dimers: the strength of these hydrogen bonds is sufficient to maintain the dimeric association even at high dilution or high temperature, so that the NMR signal is little affected by changing these parameters. The very high frequency of the signal (δ 10.0–13.0) is also a measure of the extent of hydrogen bonding.

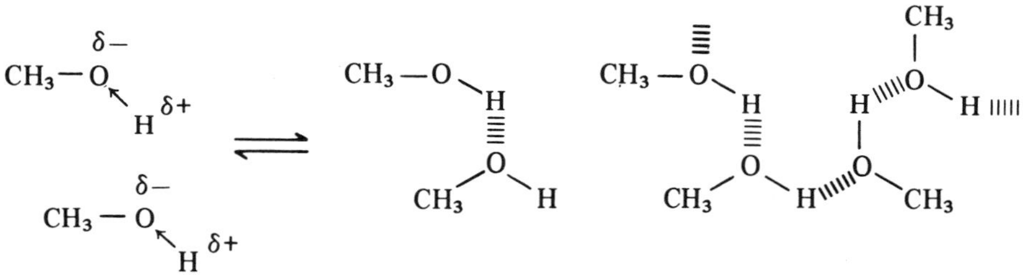

O—H dipoles   dimeric association   polymeric association

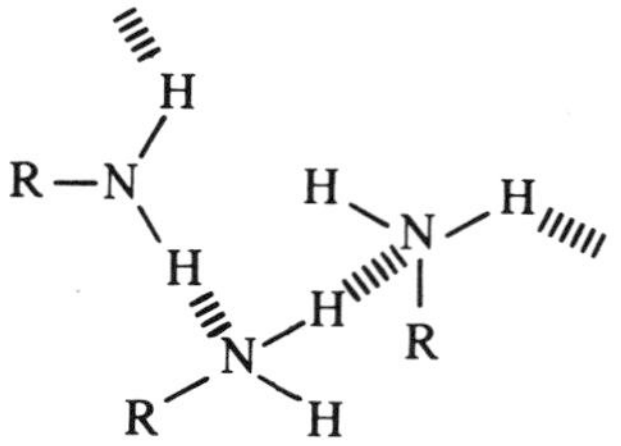

amine hydrogen bonding 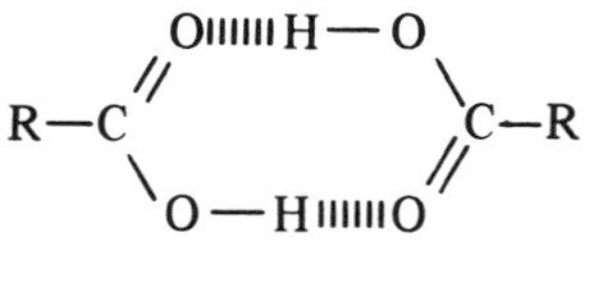   carboxylic acid dimer   (4.12)

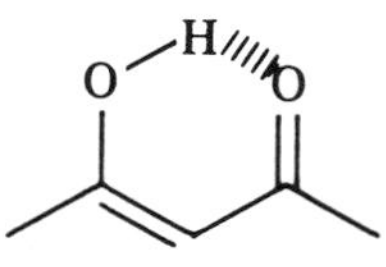

enols

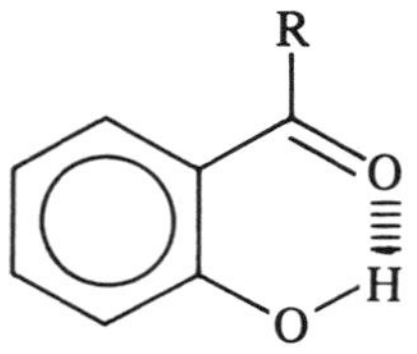

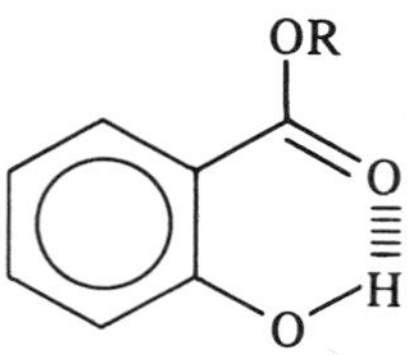

o-hydroxyketones

chelates

salicylate esters

The efficient intramolecular hydrogen bonding in the enols of β-dicarbonyl compounds is reflected in the high frequency of the NMR signal (δ 11–16) of the acidic proton.

In phenols the signal is moved predictably by hydrogen bonding, but if a carbonyl group is present *ortho* to the phenolic OH group (as in *o*-hydroxyacetophenone or in the salicylate esters) then chelation of the OH proton moves the signal to near δ 11. As in carboxylic acids, dilution has no effect on this intramolecular hydrogen bonding.

4.5.2 Quadrupolar Broadening in NH Signals

The NMR signals from protons attached to nitrogen are invariably broad, as noted in table 15.6. This is associated with the fact that for ^{14}N, $I = 1$ and thus nitrogen-14 possesses an electric quadrupole as discussed in section 2.14. The charge distribution within the nucleus is not spherically symmetrical as it is in the proton (and in the nucleus of nitrogen-15).

A full description of this *quadrupolar broadening* is best understood within the context of nitrogen-14 NMR (chapter 11) but much of the broadening is attributable to (1) the way in which a quadrupolar nucleus tends to orient itself *with the molecule* rather than with the applied field, (2) the different magnetic environments experienced by an NH proton as the non-spherically-symmetrical nitrogen nucleus tumbles *with the molecule* whereas the proton's orientation is with respect to the applied field and (3) the consequence that the life-time of each of these different proton environments is short.

From the Heisenberg Uncertainty Principle (see section 2.18) if life-times are short then NMR line widths are large.

Another factor is the influence of the tumbling electric quadrupole of the nitrogen-14 nucleus and the way in which the electrical effects thus generated can accelerate the relaxation processes of the attached proton. Rapid relaxation again leads to short life-times and broadening of the signals.

4.6 SPIN–SPIN COUPLING – SPIN–SPIN SPLITTING

The proton NMR spectra in figures 4.6–4.10 all contain features which are absent from the single line spectra seen up to now; a comparison among them can identify doublets (figures 4.6, 4.7, 4.8 and 4.10), triplets (figures 4.7 and 4.9), quartets (figures 4.8 and 4.9) and higher splittings (such as the septet in figure 4.10). The splitting of these spectral lines is associated with the way in which the spin of one proton couples with that of the near neighbour, hence the alternative names for the phenomenon – *spin–spin coupling* or *spin–spin splitting*. Spin coupling is observed between any sets of magnetic nuclei, and not solely among protons; thus protons couple with carbon-13 nuclei and with fluorine-19 nuclei and so on. This topic was introduced briefly in section 1.9.

Proton–proton coupling is defined as *homonuclear*, as is ^{13}C–^{13}C coupling, while, for example, ^{13}C–^{1}H, ^{13}C–^{19}F, ^{19}F–^{31}P couplings are all *heteronuclear*. The following discussions apply to nuclei with spin $I = \frac{1}{2}$, and other magnetic nuclei are met in section 4.8.

4.6.1 Predicting Multiplicity from the (n + 1) Rule

To predict empirically the number of lines which will appear in the NMR signal for any group of protons in these simple cases, it is necessary to count the number of protons on neighbouring carbon atoms.

> The multiplicity of a signal in simple proton NMR spectra is given by ($n + 1$), where n is the number of coupling protons on neighbour atoms.

Thus in the proton NMR spectrum of cytosine shown in figure 4.6 (p.54), proton H_A couples with H_B; each has one neighbour, and each signal is split into a doublet. (The OH and NH protons are deuterium-exchanged, producing the HOD signal at δ 4.7, as discussed in section 4.3.4.)

In 1,1,2-trichloroethane the CH_2 protons have one neighbour so ($n + 1$) = 2 and a doublet is observed. For the CH proton ($n + 1$) = 3 and a triplet appears, and so on (see figure 4.7). Note that, because of their strong quadrupole moment (see 4.8.2) the chlorines do not affect coupling.

In all of the spectra in figures 4.6–4.10 this simple multiplicity rule holds, and these are said to be *first order spectra*. In many cases (and this is the norm rather than the exception in proton NMR) complicating factors lead to the breakdown of the ($n + 1$) rule, and spectra of this type are said to be *second order*. The same simple rules apply to the NMR spectra of other nuclei with $I = \frac{1}{2}$ (such as ^{13}C, ^{19}F and ^{31}P) but additional complications arise for nuclei with $I > \frac{1}{2}$, when the number of lines is given by the more general formula $2nI + 1$ (see section 4.8).

Worked Example 4.7

Explain, using the ($n + 1$) rule, the observed multiplicity in the proton NMR spectra shown in figures 4.8, 4.9 and 4.10.

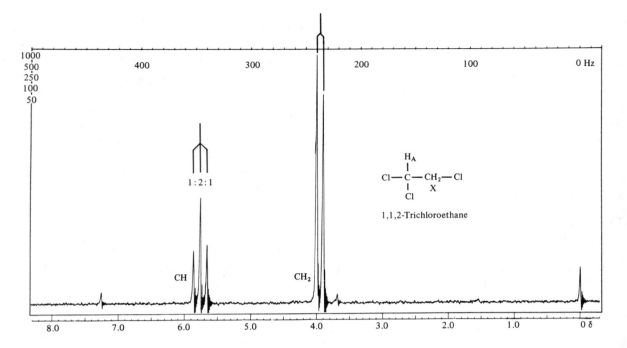

Figure 4.7 ^{1}H NMR spectrum of 1,1,2-trichloroethane (60 MHz, in CDCl$_3$). Note the small peak at δ 7.3 from traces of CHCl$_3$ in the CDCl$_3$ solvent

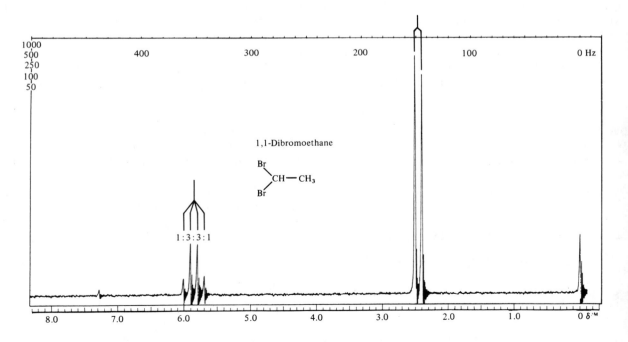

Figure 4.8 ^{1}H NMR spectrum of 1,1-dibromoethane (60 MHz, in CDCl$_3$)

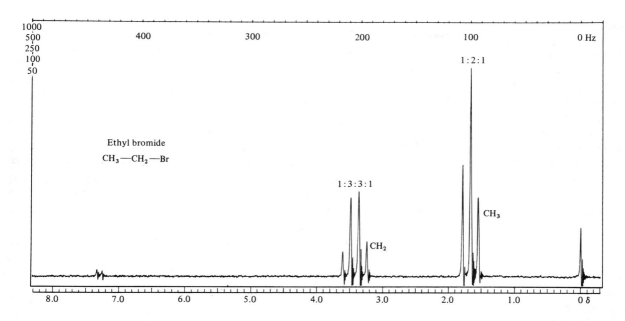

Figure 4.9 ^{1}H NMR spectrum of ethyl bromide (60 MHz, in CDCl$_3$)

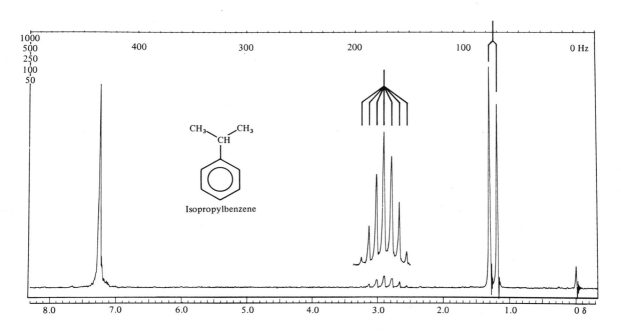

Figure 4.10 ^{1}H NMR spectrum of isopropylbenzene (60 MHz, in CDCl$_3$)

Answer 4.7

The CH_3 group in 1,1-dibromoethane is split only by the single proton on the adjacent carbon atom, and thus the CH_3 signal is a doublet; conversely the CH_3 protons split the single proton into a quartet $(n + 1) = (3 + 1)$. In the ethyl bromide spectrum the triplet must arise from being split by two neighbours, and the quartet is produced by coupling to three neighbours; the CH_3 signal is the triplet and the CH_2 signal is the quartet. In isopropyl-benzene, the methine (CH) proton is split by all six of the methyl protons and gives rise to a septet; mutually, the single methine proton splits the six-hydrogen signal from the two chemically equivalent methyl groups into a doublet.

Problem Example 4.9

Predict the appearance of the proton NMR spectrum of isopropyl acetate $(CH_3 COOCH(CH_3)_2)$; use correlation tables 15.1 and 15.2 to predict the chemical shifts, and the $(n + 1)$ rule to predict the multiplicities. State also the total integrated areas under each of the chemical shift positions, corresponding to the number of protons in each. The spectrum is shown in figure 1.13.

Problem Example 4.10

An ester of formula $C_5 H_{10} O_2$ gave a proton NMR spectrum as follows: doublet (integrated area corresponding to 6H) at δ 1.1; singlet (integration 3H) at δ 3.6; septet (integration 1H) at δ 2.2. Draw the spectrum to scale. What is the structure of the ester?

4.6.2 The Coupling Constant, J – Table 15.7

The spacing between the lines in each doublet in figure 4.6 is a measure of the degree to which H_A and H_B interact. Interestingly, this interaction is completely independent of the value of the applied magnetic field B_0, and is always measured in hertz as *the coupling constant, J*.

The spectrum for cytosine (figure 4.6) was recorded at 60 MHz (with $B_0 = 1.4$ T) so we can recall section 1.6 and calculate the coupling constant between the alkene protons as 8 Hz, so $J = 8$ Hz.

In figure 4.6 (p. 54), 8 Hz corresponds in chemical shift terms to 0.13 ppm; the spectrum of cytosine recorded at 200 MHz (4.7 T) shows exactly the same coupling constant, $J = 8$ Hz, although in this spectrum 8 Hz would correspond in chemical shift terms to 0.04 ppm. These two spectra are compared in figure 4.11.

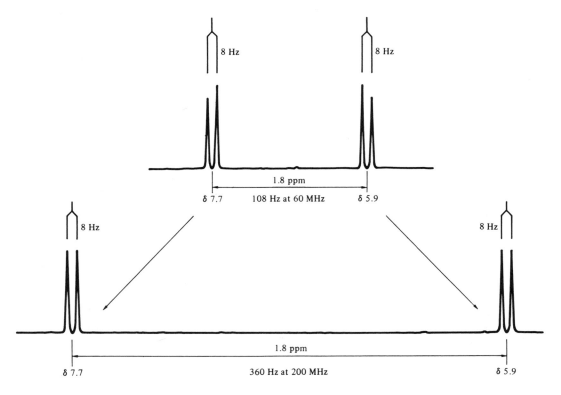

Figure 4.11   Representation of the ^{1}H NMR spectrum of cytosine at 60 MHz (1.4 T, above) and at 200 MHz (4.7 T, below). The coupling constant, J, is unaffected by changes in field strength

Table 4.2 Some representative values of proton coupling constants

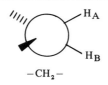

−CH₂−

geminal coupling $^2J_{HH}$
(through 2 bonds)

at 109.5°, 12 Hz
with strain, 6–18 Hz

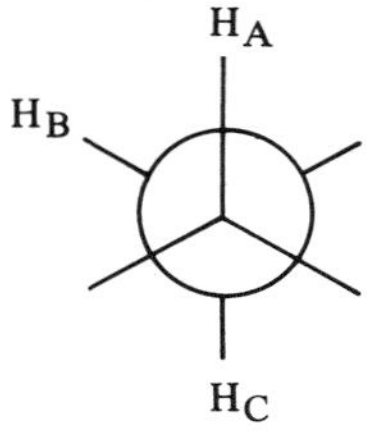

−CH−CH−
　|　　|

vicinal coupling $^3J_{HH}$
(through 3 bonds)

at 60°, 2–5 Hz
at 180°, 9–12 Hz
with free rotation, 6–8 Hz

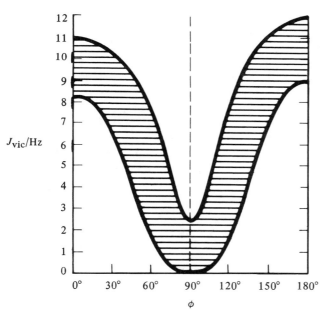

Variation of vicinal coupling constant, J_{vic}, with dihedral angle ϕ. (graphical presentation of Karplus's equations)

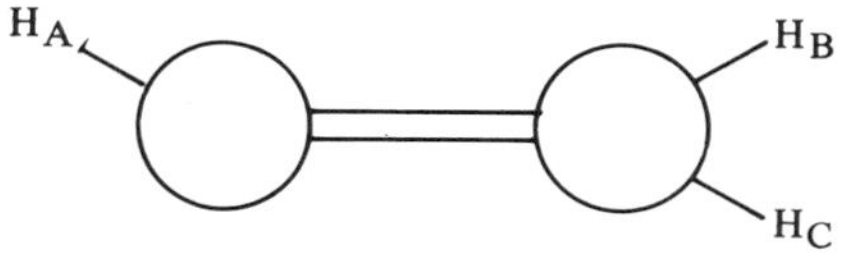

Alkenes

J_{AB} *cis*　　5–14 Hz
J_{AC} *trans* 11–19 Hz
J_{BC} *gem*　　0–7　Hz

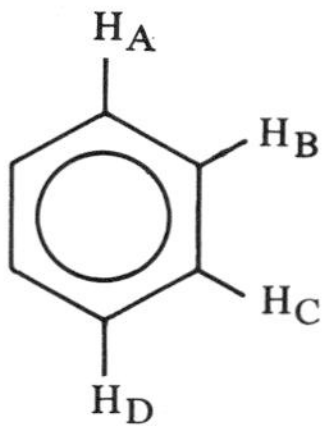

Benzenes

J_{AB} *ortho*　7–10 Hz
J_{AC} *meta*　　2–3 Hz
J_{AD} *para*　　0–1 Hz

Chemical shifts may be measured in hertz (and these will depend on B_0) or in ppm or δ units (when they will be field-independent). Coupling constants are always measured in hertz and are always field-independent.

Problem Example 4.11

Measure the coupling constant in the spectrum of 1,1,2-trichloroethane (figure 4.7). Note that the spacing in the doublet (J) is repeated twice in the triplet.

Some simple coupling constants are shown in table 4.2 and more extensive data are given in table 15.7.

Although the listed values of J are correct for most molecules, steric and electronic effects have a marked influence on the observed coupling constants; the magnitudes of these effects are not easily predicted for unknown or newly encountered compounds. As was expressed for the estimation of δ values, an empirical approach is most reliable, particularly if a series of similar compounds is under examination.

There are some usable generalisations. (Note: ^2J and ^3J represent coupling through two and three bonds, respectively: see section 4.6.4.)

In unstrained CH_2 groups, the geminal $^2J_{HH}$ is near 12 Hz: to observe this directly, the protons must be magnetically non-equivalent, such as the *gem* protons in styrene oxide (see figure 4.18).

In freely-rotating alkane chains, the vicinal $^3J_{HH}$ is 6-8 Hz. In restricted rotation (and in cycloalkane groups) the value depends on the dihedral angle according to the graph shown in table 4.2. This derives from semi-empirical calculations by Karplus (see section 14.5.1) but electronegative substituents render the predictions less accurate, and this graphical presentation indicates the expected ranges within reasonable limits.

In alkenes, *cis* $^3J_{HH}$ is less than the **trans** value: this is highly reliable, even though potential for ambiguity arises if the observed value of J is around 11 Hz.

In substituted benzenes, the *ortho*, *meta* and *para* coupling constants are so reliably distinctive that the deduction of the orientation of substituents on the ring is straightforward.

4.6.3 Theory of Spin–Spin Coupling – I

The explanation of spin–spin splitting can be set at several levels, but the present interpretive purpose will be well enough served by the least rigorous treatment, which succeeds in very many cases. Quantum mechanical theory is covered in section 6.1.

We need to explain initially how protons H_A and H_B in cytosine give rise to two doublet signals as shown in figure 4.6 and, diagrammatically, in figure 4.12. Note

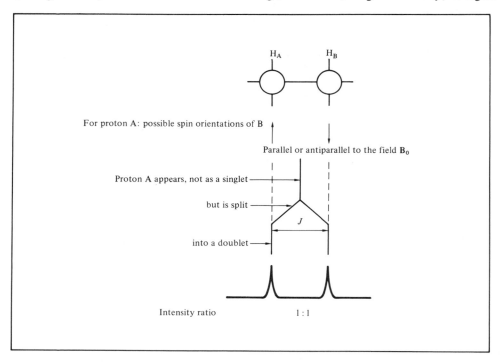

Figure 4.12   Representation of the doublet splitting observed when proton H_A is spin coupled to one neighbouring proton H_B

that H_A and H_B must be chemically non-equivalent and thus have different chemical shift positions, δ_A and δ_B respectively.

The precessional frequency of H_A is governed by the effective magnetic field acting upon it, and the principal influence is obviously $\mathbf{B}_0$, which for a 100 MHz proton spectrum will be 2.35 T. Proton H_B can modify this in a small way however, since approximately 50 per cent of the H_B nuclei are *aligned* with $\mathbf{B}_0$ (and thus augment it slightly) while the remaining 50 per cent of the H_B nuclei are *opposed* to $\mathbf{B}_0$ (and reduce it slightly). Protons H_A then experience *two different effective fields* ($\mathbf{B}_0 + H_B$ and $\mathbf{B}_0 - H_B$); H_A comes to resonance therefore at *two different frequencies*, and two lines appear on the spectrum. One line of the doublet is at a higher frequency than the origin chemical shift position, δ_A, the other line being at a lower frequency.

The same mutual effect causes proton H_B to appear as a doublet. Expressed anthropomorphically, H_B 'sees' H_A in two orientations — aligned or opposed to the field $\mathbf{B}_0$ — so H_B experiences two values of effective field ($\mathbf{B}_0 + H_A$ and $\mathbf{B}_0 - H_A$) and comes to resonance at two frequencies (doublet signal).

Note that the separation of the lines in the doublets (that is, the coupling constant J) depends on the size of the magnetic moments, and this is not altered by $\mathbf{B}_0$, so that J *is independent of* $\mathbf{B}_0$.

The probabilities of the magnetic moments in all of these circumstances being aligned or opposed is very nearly equal as we saw in the discussion on Boltzmann theory in section 2.16. For this reason the line intensities in the doublets should all be equal; from the spectrum we can see that this is only approximately correct, and the departures from equal intensity are characteristic; they will be encountered again in section 4.9.

A system of doublets generated by two protons whose chemical shifts are well spaced (as are the letters A and X in the alphabet) is named an AX coupling system. In the cytosine molecule, the two coupling protons have chemical shifts sufficiently close at 60 MHz to cause the small intensity distortions observed, and it might strictly be named an AB system. In truth, these distortions are very slight and this spectrum is virtually as uncomplicated as an AX case.

4.6.4 AX_2, AX_3 and A_2X_3 Coupling Systems

In figure 4.7, the proton NMR spectrum for 1,1,2,-trichloroethane, one proton (H_A) is coupling with two protons (H_X); this is named an AX_2 system. (In labelling nuclei A, B or C, the preferred nomenclature awards

A to the highest frequency signal and so on; thus an A_2X system would have a high frequency doublet and low frequency triplet.)

The H_X signal is a doublet because, as in section 4.6.2, each H_X 'sees' H_A in only two possible ways, aligned or opposed.

The H_A signal is a triplet because there are three ways in which the nuclear spins of the two H_X protons can be combined, as shown in figure 4.13. Both the X protons, X and X', can be aligned with the field $\mathbf{B}_0$, or both can be opposed to the field; these give rise to the high frequency and low frequency lines of the triplet respectively. Alternatively, X can be aligned and X' opposed, causing no net change in the effective field experienced by H_A. The same result ensues if X is opposed and X' is aligned, and the middle line of the triplet is associated with these two spin combinations. Since this is twice as likely to arise as the both-aligned or both-opposed states, the relative line intensities are, as shown, 1:2:1.

In figure 4.7, the total integrated area of the triplet (one H_A proton) and the total area of the doublet (two H_X protons) are in the overall ratio of 1:2.

For an AX_3 coupling system (figure 4.8) the explanation of the observed multiplicity is an extension of the above. In particular, the quartet signal for H_A arises because of *four* possible spin combinations of the *three* H_X protons. Thus H_A 'sees' the three H_X all aligned ($\uparrow\uparrow\uparrow$) or all opposed ($\downarrow\downarrow\downarrow$): these give the high and low frequency lines of the quartet respectively. Additionally H_A will 'see' two H_X aligned and one H_X opposed, and there are three different ways to arrange this ($\uparrow\uparrow\downarrow$ or $\uparrow\downarrow\uparrow$ or $\downarrow\uparrow\uparrow$) so that the probability of this arising is three times greater than the all-aligned or all-opposed combinations. Lastly, H_A 'sees' one H_X aligned and two H_X opposed, in three different ways ($\uparrow\downarrow\downarrow$ or $\downarrow\uparrow\downarrow$ or $\downarrow\downarrow\uparrow$).

The line intensities within the quartet mirror the probability with which each spin combination can arise, and are therefore in the ratio 1:3:3:1.

For the A_2X_3 coupling system in figure 4.9 the multiplicity can again be correlated with the number of possible spin combinations which each group of equivalent protons 'sees' on the adjacent carbon atom. The same is true for the spectrum in figure 4.10.

Strictly, just as the spectrum in figure 4.6 is properly named AB (rather than AX) because of the slight distortion of first order appearance, spectra 4.7–4.9 would be designated respectively AB_2, AB_3 and A_2B_3 in nature. The departure from ideality is so slight however that no serious transgression is involved in the use of AX_2, AX_3 and A_2X_3.

The coupling interaction among nuclei which we have

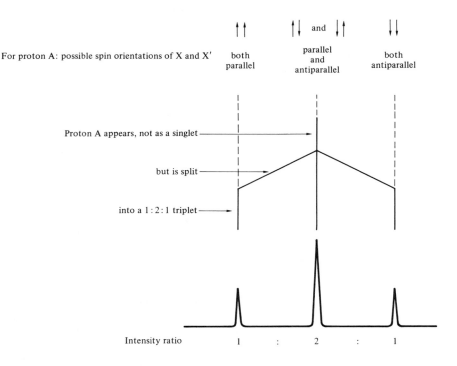

For proton A: possible spin orientations of X and X′

| both parallel | parallel and antiparallel | both antiparallel |

Proton A appears, not as a singlet ⟶

but is split ⟶

into a 1:2:1 triplet ⟶

Intensity ratio   1   :   2   :   1

Figure 4.13 Representation of the triplet splitting observed when proton H_A is spin coupled to 2 neighbour protons H_X

seen here is not transmitted through space, but *via* the spins of the electrons in the intervening bonds (see section 6.1). We can usefully indicate how many bonds intervene by use of a superscript, so the a ^3J splitting is transmitted through three bonds (as are all of the examples in the spectra discussed thus far). Coupling between geminal nuclei such as in a $-CHF-$ group involves two bonds, and is designated by $^2J(HF)$ or as $^2J_{HF}$ and so on.

4.6.5 Coupling of Protons to Other Nuclei with Spin $= \frac{1}{2}$

The proton and fluorine-19 NMR spectra of trifluoroethanol are shown in figure 4.14; the proton spectrum was recorded at 60 MHz and the fluorine spectrum at 56.4 MHz, with B_0 equal to 1.4 T.

Simple $(n + 1)$ rules of multiplicity apply, and the proton signal for the CH_2 group is split into a quartet by the three vicinal fluorines with $^3J_{HF} = 9$ Hz, while the fluorine signal for the CF_3 group appears as a triplet (two vicinal protons) with the same coupling constant.

This heteronuclear coupling between two groups of magnetically and chemically non-equivalent groups of

nuclei is no more than an extension of the proton-proton homonuclear cases. Numerous further examples arise in later chapters dealing with the NMR spectra of nuclei other than proton.

While the proton is nearly 100% abundant, carbon-13 appears naturally to the extent of only 1.1%. This means that only a low probability exists for observing in proton spectra the coupling due to ^{13}C: if observable, then the coupled proton signal appears as a weak doublet, with line separation of $^1J_{CH}$, set astride the major proton singlet line which arises from the 98.9% of molecules which contain only carbon-12. Historically, these so-called *carbon-13 satellite peaks* yielded the first information on carbon–proton coupling constants. Practically, they can only be identified in simple molecules which yield sufficiently simple proton spectra, with very intense singlet signals.

Worked Example 4.8
Predict the multiplicity in the carbon-13 NMR signal of (a) $^{13}CHCl_3$, (b) $^{13}CFCl_3$, (c) $(^{13}CH_3)_3$ ^{15}N.

Answer 4.8
(a) The carbon-13 nucleus is coupled directly to one proton, so its signal will appear as a doublet, with split-

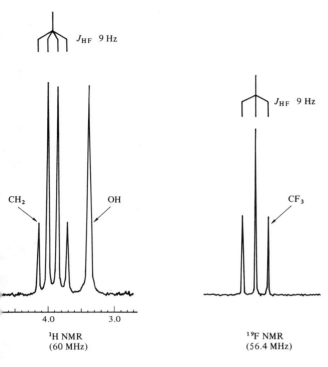

J_{HF} 9 Hz

J_{HF} 9 Hz

CH$_2$ OH   CF$_3$

4.0   3.0

^{1}H NMR
(60 MHz)

^{19}F NMR
(56.4 MHz)

Figure 4.14 Proton (left) and fluorine-19 NMR spectra of trifluoroethanol, CF_3CH_2OH. Coupling to OH is not shown

ting equal to $^1J_{CH}$. (b) The carbon signal will again be a doublet, with coupling constant $^1J_{CF}$. (c) The three carbons have the same chemical shift, so this signal will be split by $^1J_{CH}$ into four lines with additional splitting (doublet) by $^1J_{CN}$, since ^{15}N has $I = \frac{1}{2}$.

Problem Example 4.12
Predict the multiplicity in (a) the proton and phosphorus-31 NMR spectra of trimethylphosphite, $(MeO)_3P$, (b) the carbon-13 and fluorine-19 NMR spectra of $^{13}CF_3-^{13}COOH$, assuming $^1J_{CF}$ to be larger than $^2J_{CF}$, and that the carboxyl proton does not couple. For (a), see figure 10.3 (p.180).

4.7 GENERAL FEATURES OF SIMPLE COUPLING SYSTEMS

It will be convenient here to introduce some definitions which permit us to predict with confidence the multiplicity observed in the spectra, and to exemplify how these rules are applied or modified in more complex systems. A fuller exposition of theory is to be found in chapter 6.

4.7.1 Magnetic Equivalence in Proton NMR

In all of the spectra in figures 4.8–4.10 we saw that the three CH_3 protons coupled equally with the protons on the adjacent carbon atom and the signals from these vicinal protons appeared as quartets. The methyl protons do not split one another however, otherwise these spectra would have been more complex than they are. The methyl protons were defined in section 4.3 as being *chemically equivalent* because of their rapid rotation, and they all have the same chemical shift.

The observed fact that they all couple equally with the vicinal protons leads us further to define them as *magnetically equivalent*.

It occasionally arises in considering the symmetry of molecules that two protons A and B have the same chemical environment and the same chemical shift and yet couple differently to a third proton C; that is, the coupling constant J_{AC} is different from J_{BC}. In such a molecule, A and B are *chemically equivalent* but *magnetically non-equivalent*.

(4.13)

(The conventional choice of labels here is not particularly helpful, since the words 'chemical' and 'magnetic' appear in so many different contexts unrelated to the present one. It may be useful to remember that chemical equivalence means *chemical shift equivalence* while magnetic equivalence means *coupling equivalence*. Several examples are needed to make this clear.)

In the conformation (I) both A protons have the same chemical environment, as do both B protons.

(*Note*: The proton NMR spectrum of this specific conformer could only be recorded at low temperature, since at room temperature rapid rotation around the C—C bond converts the system to A_2B_2.)

Although each constitutes a chemically equivalent pair, A and A′ couple differently with B (see table 4.2). A and A′ are therefore magnetically non-equivalent, as are B and B′. The notations A and A′ signify that both A protons are *chemically equivalent*, but the prime mark distinguishes that A and A′ are *magnetically non-equivalent*. Both protons labelled B are chemically equivalent (but chemically non-equivalent to A) and the pair B and B′ are magnetically non-equivalent.

Figure 4.15 shows the proton NMR spectrum for *p*-nitro-*N*-methylaniline (II). Once again the ring protons can be labelled A, A′, B, B′ with the same significance as above since, for example, A couples with B (*ortho* to it) differently from B′ (*para* to it). The aromatic region of the spectrum is superficially similar to an AB coupling system, except for the (characteristic) additional lines within each doublet.

The protons of a methylene group adjacent to a chiral carbon atom as in the conformations (III), (IV) and (V) (formulae 4.13) can be seen by inspection always to be chemically non-equivalent. Such a pair of protons are said to be *diastereotopic*; they have the same relation-

ship to each other as any pair of vicinal groups on adjoining chiral carbon atoms in diastereoisomers. Protons which are chemically non-equivalent must also be magnetically non-equivalent. The converse is not always true as we saw in formula I: protons can be magnetically non-equivalent and yet chemically equivalent.

Problem Example 4.13

Label the protons in the following, to indicate the groups of chemically equivalent and magnetically equivalent protons. (a) chlorobenzene, (b) crotonaldehyde, (c) cyclobutene.

(4.14)

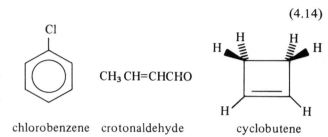

chlorobenzene   crotonaldehyde   cyclobutene

4.7.2 Successive Branching and Pascal's Triangle

A valuable general method of predicting multiplicity in first order spectra is to consider each splitting succes-

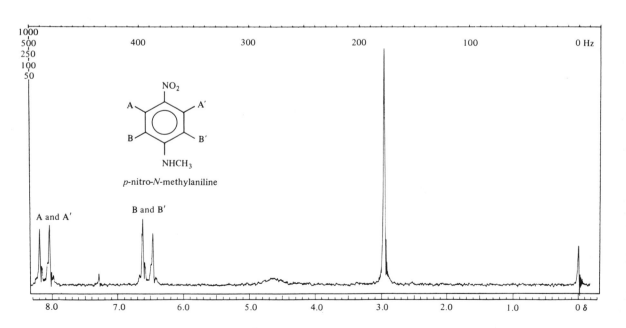

Figure 4.15 ^{1}H NMR spectrum of *p*-nitro-*N*-methylaniline, showing approximate AB system for the ring protons. Protons A and A′ are chemically equivalent but magnetically non-equivalent (as are B and B^1) (60 MHz, in CDCl$_3$, CH$_3$ at δ 2.9 and NH at δ 4.65)

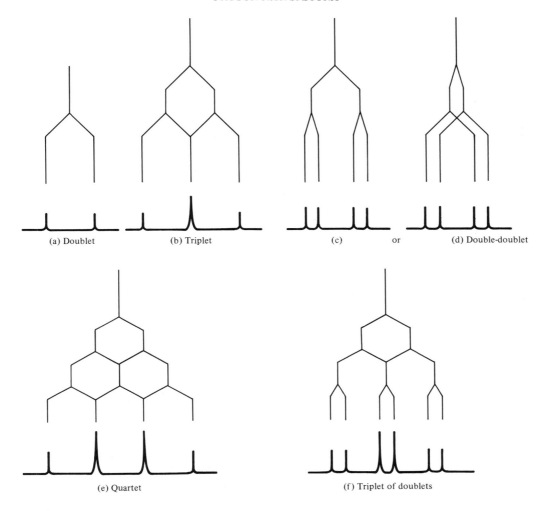

Figure 4.16 Multiplicity predicted by successive branching in first-order spin coupling. The final appearance depends on the relative sizes of successive coupling constants

sively, and to build up a branching diagram showing each successive coupling to scale.

Thus if nucleus X is split by one adjacent proton, it will give rise to a doublet as indicated in figure 4.16(a).

If X is further split by a second proton, each line of the doublet will be further split in two. Provided the first and second coupling constants are equal, then situation (b) arises, in which two inner lines overlap to produce a 1:2:1 triplet (compare figure 4.7).

If the two J values are unequal, then a system of four lines arises in double–doublet formation. It is inconsequential in drawing these whether or not the first splitting is shown large and the second as small, as in (c); the same end result arises if the small coupling is drawn first and then the large splitting, as in (d). (Nuclei do not distinguish a sequence of splittings — they are experienced simultaneously.)

If X is split by three neighbour protons successively, and provided $J_1 = J_2 = J_3$ as in (e), then the familiar 1:3:3:1 quartet arises (compare figures 4.8 and 4.9). This of course is the same end-product as is predicted by the $(n + 1)$ rule for splitting by CH_3 groups, but such a quartet is produced only if all couplings are equal, that is, if the three protons are magnetically equivalent. If this is not so, then several possible multiplicities will arise, of which the triplet of doublets is one example (f).

The $(n + 1)$ rule only applies when n is a group of magnetically equivalent nuclei.

Although the three magnetically equivalent protons

of a methyl group do not split one another's signals, the nuclei are nevertheless coupled *via* the intervening electrons; this feature is taken up again in section 4.9.

Line intensities in the multiplets predicted by the $(n + 1)$ rule can be shown to have relative values which are the same as the coefficients in the binomial expansion, and they are easily remembered from Pascal's well-known triangle.

						1						singlet
					1		1					doublet
				1		2		1				triplet
			1		3		3		1			quartet
		1		4		6		4		1		quintet
	1		5		10		10		5		1	sextet
1		6		15		20		15		6		septet

The difference in line intensity between inner and outer lines, in sextets, septets and beyond, is so great that the outer lines may scarcely be discernible in the spectrum. The septet in figure 4.10 is typical; in this case the maximum intensity ratio is 20:1 and the multiplet could be mistakenly interpreted as a quintet.

Problem Example 4.14
Use graph paper to draw out the consequent splitting pattern for a nucleus X coupling successively with protons A, B and C when the coupling constants are (a) $J_{AX} = 10$ Hz, $J_{BX} = 5$ Hz and $J_{CX} = 0$ Hz; (b) $J_{AX} = 10$ Hz, $J_{BX} = 10$ Hz and $J_{CX} = 2$ Hz; (c) $J_{AX} = 5$ Hz. $J_{BX} = 10$ Hz and $J_{CX} = 20$ Hz. State all of the line intensities.

Problem Example 4.15
As in problem example 4.14, consider nucleus X undergoing spin splitting with (a) two fluorine nuclei, when $J_{FX} = 50$ Hz; (b) two fluorine nuclei with $J_{FX} = 50$ Hz and then with one proton, when $J_{HX} = 10$ Hz. State the relative line intensities.

4.7.3 Long Range Coupling

It was stated earlier (in section 4.6.4) that coupling occurs *via* the spins of the electrons in the intervening bonds, the number of bonds being indicated by ^1J (the coupling constant for nuclei directly bonded as in a ^{13}C-^{19}F- group), ^2J (for example between geminal protons, H-C-H) and ^3J (for example between vicinal protons, H-C-C-H). Four or five bond couplings in saturated compounds are rare and invariably do not complicate the spectra but they do arise in π-bonded systems, such as allyl groups and aromatic rings. Table

15.7 shows the dimensions of typical J_{HH} values. In those cases where ^4J and ^5J proton–proton couplings are found, it is described as *long range*. Several factors favour the occurrence of long range coupling; the ^4J coupling between equatorial protons in cyclohexanes is found in molecules where the W-shaped zig-zag of bonds (the heavy bonds in table 15.7) is near to being co-planar. Where two protons are linked by several alternative bond-chains (as in the bicyclo-[1.1.1] pentane molecule) the J value is surprisingly large.

These unusual molecules apart, it is useful to list a few common examples of protons which do not show measurable splittings because of the number of intervening bonds. At very high resolution, small couplings (that is, much less than 1 Hz) may be discernible, but for practical purposes these will have virtually no effect on the line shape of routine spectra recorded in a 10 ppm scan.

(a) Across quaternary carbons, as in *tert*-butyl derivatives, $(CH_3) C-CH-$;
(b) across ether links, as in $CH_3 OCH_3$;
(c) across carbonyl groups of ketones, as in $CH_3 COCH_3$ (aldehydes show ^3J coupling);
(d) across carboxylic acids, esters or amides, as in $CH_3 COOH$, $CH_3 COOCH_3$ or $CH_3 CONH_2$;
(e) from side chains into aromatic rings, as in alkylbenzenes such as toluene $C_6 H_5 CH_3$. (Observed couplings vary from 0.4 to 0.9 Hz.)

4.7.4 Coupling in Proton Exchange Processes

The $^3J_{HH}$ vicinal coupling over the H-C-O-H chain in alcohols is influenced by the facts of proton exchange discussed in section 4.3.3. It is a time-dependent phenomenon, and for coupling to be observed as in figure 4.17 (bottom) the proton must have a long residence time on any particular alcohol molecule. If the O-H bond is broken frequently (acid-catalysed fast exchange as in figure 4.17, top) and the electrons of the bonds are subject therefore to frequent reorganisation, then Δt is too short to enable the 6 Hz ^3J coupling to be measured.

The frequent breaking of the bonds and the stifling of the coupling mechanism should be regarded as *decoupling* of the OH proton from its neighbours.

It is useful and consistent to consider this decoupling in terms of one nucleus 'seeing' another nucleus in particular magnetic orientations. In the system H-C-O-H, the CH proton will be split by the OH proton if the CH proton 'sees' the OH proton in a fixed environment for a sufficiently long time, that is, if the OH exchange is slow. If the exchange is fast, then the CH proton will 'see' a

$$CH_3-\overset{\overset{\displaystyle CH_3}{|}}{\underset{\underset{\displaystyle CH_3}{|}}{C}}-\overset{\overset{\displaystyle CH_3}{}}{\underset{|}{C}}-\;\;\textcircled{H}$$

***tert*-butyl**

$$CH_3-O-\overset{\textcircled{H}}{\underset{|}{C}}-$$

ether

$$CH_3-\overset{\overset{\displaystyle O}{\parallel}}{C}-\overset{\textcircled{H}}{\underset{|}{C}}-$$

ketone

$$CH_3-\overset{\overset{\displaystyle O}{\parallel}}{C}-O-\textcircled{H}$$

carboxyl
fast exchange: see section 4.7.4

$$CH_3-\overset{\overset{\displaystyle O}{\parallel}}{C}-O-\overset{\textcircled{H}}{\underset{|}{C}}-$$

ester

$$CH_3-\overset{\overset{\displaystyle O}{\parallel}}{C}-\overset{\textcircled{H}}{\underset{|}{N}}-$$

amide

(4.15)

side-chain

Note: $CH_3-O-\textcircled{H}$

alcohol

time-dependent: see section 4.7.4

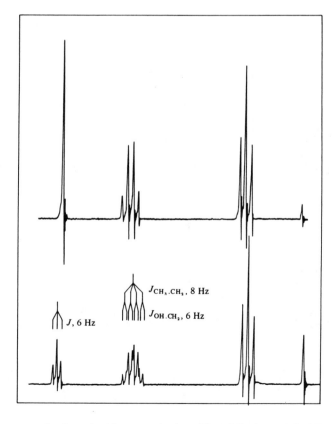

Figure 4.17 ^{1}H NMR spectrum of ethanol. Above: sample with acidic impurities. Bottom: pure sample showing $-OH-CH_2-$ coupling (100 MHz, neat sample). CH_3, δ 1.2; CH_2, δ 3.7; OH variable (see p. 58)

succession of changing partners, none of which stays long enough for the coupling to be measured. Expressed thus, the decoupling is analogous to the technique discussed in section 4.10.3.

Carboxyl protons do not show coupling because of their fast exchange rates.

Problem Example 4.16

Figure 1.5 is the proton NMR spectrum of *tert*-butyl alcohol. What changes would be observed in the spectrum if to the sample were added (a) a small amount of acid, (b) a small amount of D_2O, (c) a small amount of both acid and D_2O?

Problem Example 4.17

Predict the chemical shift positions and signal multiplicities in the proton NMR spectrum of 1-nitropropane, given that the two $^3J_{HH}$ values are equal.

4.7.5 AMX Coupling Systems

Figure 4.18 shows the proton NMR spectrum of styrene oxide, and in this all three protons of the oxirane ring couple with one another to produce a characteristic twelve-line spectrum. Since the chemical shifts are widely

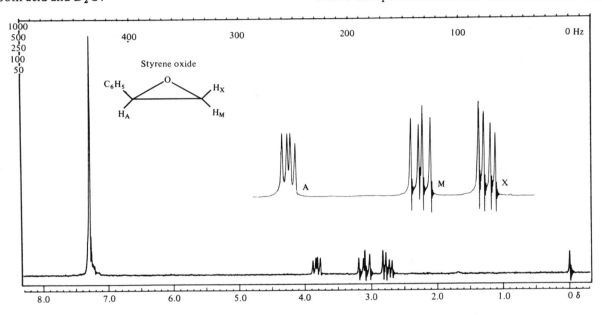

Figure 4.18 ^1H NMR spectrum of styrene oxide (with scale expansion, ring protons only). (Main spectrum 60 MHz, insert 90 MHz, in $CDCl_3$)

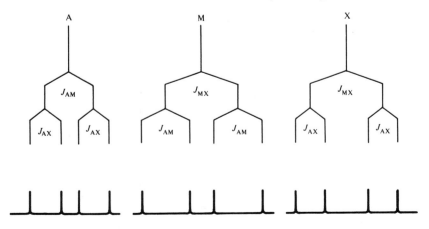

Figure 4.19   Coupling constants in an AMX system. Successive branching shows the typical twelve-line appearance (if $J_{AM} \neq J_{AX} \neq J_{MX}$)

separated, this is labelled an **AMX** system, and it can be treated by a first order analysis, using successive branching as shown in figure 4.19.

The signal for H_A is split into a doublet by proton H_M, and each line of this doublet is split by proton H_X into a doublet, giving a four-line double doublet. The H_A signal is constructed thus from two couplings, with coupling constants J_{AM} = 4 Hz and J_{AX} = 2.5 Hz.

In the H_M signal we can identify again the coupling constant J_{AM} together with the coupling to H_X, with J_{MX} = 6 Hz. Finally, the double doublet signal for H_X contains both J_{AX} and J_{MX}.

All AMX systems consist of twelve-line spectra, in three groups of four. There are three coupling constants in all, and each is found in two of the four-line groups.

Problem Example 4.18

Figure 4.20 is the proton NMR spectrum of *p*-chlorostyrene. Use tables 15.4 and 15.5 to predict the chemical shift positions of the protons, and from the spectrum extract the three coupling constants of the AMX system.

4.8 Coupling to Nuclei with Spin $I > \frac{1}{2}$

Two crucial considerations affect the appearance of NMR spectra involving the coupling to nuclei with spin greater than $\frac{1}{2}$. (a) The observable multiplicity is greater than for spin = $\frac{1}{2}$ nuclei and (b) all nuclei with spin = 1

or more possess an electric quadrupole moment.

The most instructive examples are the simplest, and these involve spin coupling between a proton and a nucleus with spin = 1, such as nitrogen-14 or deuterium, ^2H.

Fundamental theories relating to this section are covered in chapter 2, sections 2.12–2.15.

4.8.1 Predicted Multiplicity for Spin = 1 Nuclei

In section 2.12 it was noted that in a magnetic field, B_0, nuclei such as ^{14}N and ^2H can adopt three possible spin orientations, corresponding respectively to + 1, 0, and −1 components of the spin angular momentum, and consequently also to the orientations of the magnetic moment vector.

For a deuterium-substituted methylene group (H–C–D) we can consider how many ways the proton 'sees' the deuteron, and since there are three possible alignments of the deuterium nucleus, these will affect the magnetic environment of the proton to three different extents and the proton will precess at three different frequencies.

The proton appears as a triplet; but the probabilities of deuterium being +1, 0, and −1 are almost exactly equal (from Boltzmann's Law, discussed in section 2.16) so the proton triplet consists of three lines of equal intensity.

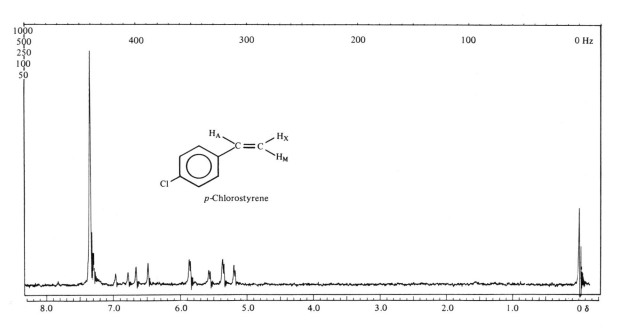

Figure 4.20 ^1H NMR spectrum of *p*-chlorostyrene, $ClC_6H_4CH=CH_2$ (60 MHz, in $CDCl_3$)

Worked Example 4.9

What multiplicity will arise in the NMR signal of a carbon-13 nucleus attached to one deuterium nucleus?

Answer 4.9

The carbon nucleus 'sees' the deuterium in three possible orientations with respect to B_0, with an equal probability of each arising; the carbon signal is therefore a 1:1:1 triplet. This coupling arises in $^{13}CDCl_3$, and several spectra in chapter 5 show such triplets; it would be instructive to seek them out.

Problem Example 4.19

Modify the rules of successive branching (section 4.7.2) to predict the multiplicity and relative line intensities in the carbon-13 signal of a $^{13}CD_2$ group.

> Multiplicity in first order spectra can be found using the formula $(2nI + 1)$.

The same formula obviously applies to nuclei with $I = 3/2$ such as chlorine-35 and -37, but splitting is not normally observed for reasons to be expounded in section 4.8.2.

It is a fact that the ratio $J_{HH}:J_{HD}$ is 6.5 (following a general property that coupling constants between nuclei are proportional to the product of their magnetogyric ratios) so that information about proton couplings can be derived by deuterium substitution. This is particularly useful where protons are magnetically equivalent, such as in most CH_2 or CH_3 groups.

4.8.2 Effects of Quadrupole Moments on Observed Splitting

The predicted multiplicity in the proton NMR signal of a H–C–D group or of an N–H group is three lines, equally intense, separated by a coupling constant J_{HD} or J_{HN} respectively.

From Heisenberg's Uncertainty Principle these separations (ΔE) will be resolved in the spectrum provided 'sufficient' time (Δt) is available for the distinction to be made.

Nuclei with electric quadrupole moments will only retain specific orientations with respect to the applied magnetic field B_0 if their magnetic moments are strong and if their electric quadrupole moments are weak. If their magnetic moments are weak and their electric quadrupole moments are strong, then we saw in section 2.15 that such nuclei will prefer to take up specific orientations with respect to the molecules within which they are fixed. Since in solution these molecules are tumbling with respect to B_0, then a proton (fixed with

respect to B_0) may 'see' a quadrupolar nucleus tumbling so rapidly that specific magnetic orientations have very short life-times, that is, small values of Δt.

If this is so, then the proton signal will not be resolved into a triplet, although some vestigial coupling may cause broadening of the signal.

Two extremes and an infinity of intermediate possibilities have been identified, with time-dependence holding the key in the value of Δt.

Figure 4.21(a) indicates the splitting commonly

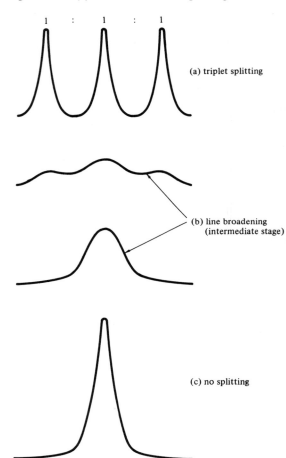

(a) triplet splitting

(b) line broadening (intermediate stage)

(c) no splitting

Figure 4.21 Appearance of the proton NMR signal when coupling to nuclei with spin $> \frac{1}{2}$. The clear 1:1:1 triplet (spin = 1 nuclei) in (a) is seen in –CHD– systems, but in –NH– groups the *triplet splitting* contributes more to line broadening, as in (b). For coupling to nuclei with strong quadrupoles, such as in –CHCl– groups, *quadrupolar tumbling* completely decouples the halogen from H and no splitting is observed, (c). For rapid *proton exchange* in –NH– groups, again no splitting is observed, (c)

observed in coupling to deuterium, whose quadrupole moment is weak. Such clear splitting can only rarely be observed for coupling to nitrogen-14, unless the molecular environment around nitrogen is so symmetrical that no (or almost no) electric field gradients exist; the tetrahedral ammonium ion is such a case.

In the case of chlorine-35 and 37, the quadrupole moment is strong, and a covalently-bonded chlorine atom always exists in a strongly dipolar environment with a pronounced electric field gradient. Chlorine nuclei therefore are so immutably oriented with respect to the tumbling molecules that specific magnetic orientations (with respect to B_0) are exceedingly short-lived and no splitting of the signal of nearby nuclei is observed. The NMR signal of any nucleus coupled to chlorine is unperturbed as in figure 4.21(c).

Nitrogen-14 is intermediate: a common appearance of proton signals in N—H groups is as in figure 4.21(b) (see also figure 4.15: the broad NH proton signal is at δ 4.65).

It must be recalled that for N—H protons the additional factor of proton exchange (see section 4.3.3) must be considered, as this too leads to signal broadening.

Several factors are at work here in determining the ultimate appearance of the spectrum, and a few generalities can be set out.

Alkylamines (with nitrogen attached to saturated carbon as in $-CH_2NH-$) are sufficiently basic to catalyse rapid proton exchange. No NH coupling is observed, and the signal is reasonably sharp.

Arylamines (with nitrogen directly attached to the ring as in Ar—NH—) show slow proton exchange and H couples with N; but because of strong electric field gradients, quadrupole tumbling decouples H and N partly, so the signal appears broadened as in figure 4.15. Similar factors operate in aromatic nitrogen heterocycles such as pyrrole.

Amides have the additional possible complexity of restricted rotation (see section 4.3.2). Being non-basic, proton exchange is slow. The electric field gradients vary a great deal from compound to compound, so different degrees of quadrupolar decoupling take place; primary amides usually show broad signals, but secondary amides sometimes show broad and sometimes sharp NH signals.

Ammonium salts (including substituted alkylammonium salts, $R\overset{+}{N}H_3$, $R_2\overset{+}{N}H_2$, $R_3\overset{+}{N}H$ and $R_4\overset{+}{N}$) in strong aqueous acid have slow proton exchange or none $(R_4\overset{+}{N})$. In unsymmetrical salts the signal may be moderately sharp because of quadrupolar decoupling. In simple primary amine salts, the quaternary nitrogen is tetrahedral and fairly symmetrical, so electric field gradients

are small: quadrupolar decoupling is at its minimum then. Thus in $CH_3\overset{+}{N}H_3$, the NH protons show 1:1:1 triplets ($^1J_{NH}$ = 50 Hz) with each peak further split into 1:3:3:1 quartets ($^3J_{HH}$ = 5 Hz): this simplicity is rarely observed.

Worked Example 4.10

At natural abundance, predict the influence of (a) ^{14}N, (b) ^{15}N on the proton NMR signal of the group —NH—.

Answer 4.10

(a) The ^{14}N nucleus will either split (triplet) or broaden the proton signal, depending on molecular symmetry and temperature. (b) The ^{15}N will split the proton signal into a doublet, since ^{15}N has $I = \frac{1}{2}$. However the number of molecules possessing a $-^{15}NH-$ group is 0.37% of those with ^{14}N (see table 1.1); the doublet signal will therefore be present at such low intensity as to be effectively unobserved.

Problem Example 4.20

The proton NMR spectrum of ethyl bromide is shown in figure 4.9. Explain why no splitting corresponding to $^2J_{HBr}$ is observed.

4.9 NON-FIRST ORDER SPECTRA

True first order spectra are rare in proton NMR although those distortions which we have noted up to now were capable of being ignored for practical purposes. Loss of first order status arises when the separation in resonance frequencies between the nuclei ($\Delta\nu$) approaches the line separation caused by coupling (J) and this is illustrated for the AX and AB cases in figure 4.22.

In these examples, we will express the difference in chemical shift positions in hertz ($\Delta\nu$). When this is greater than $6J$, the multiplets are well separated and distortion in line intensities is very slight; the origin chemical shift position for the coupling nuclei may be taken as the centres of the doublets, but closer proximity of the signals produces more marked distortion in the line intensities, with the inner lines heightened. The line positions (energies of the transitions) are also changed, so that the origin chemical shift positions no longer correspond to the mid-points of the doublets, but can be calculated as shown in the figure; the calculation shows each δ value to lie roughly at the 'centre of gravity' of each doublet.

If the value of $\Delta\nu$ in hertz is less than J, then overlapping of the lines may occur, and ultimately if $\Delta\nu$ is zero, the nuclei are by definition chemically equivalent as in most simple CH_2 groups. Although these two

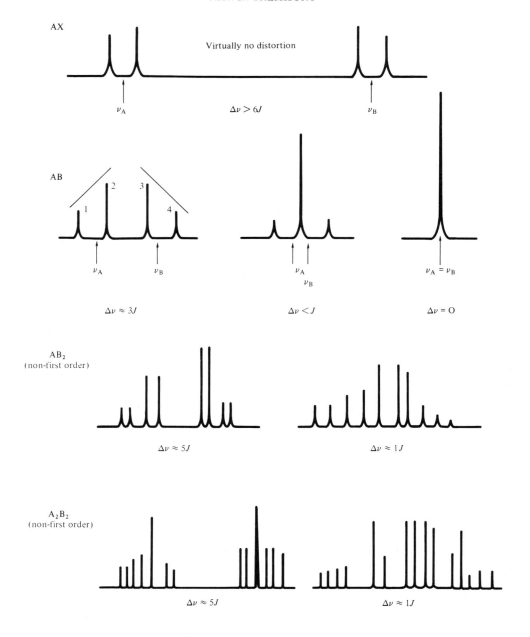

Figure 4.22 Effect of the ratio $\Delta\nu{:}J$ on the appearance of spin coupled spectra. Note the 'roof' effect in AB systems, and the additional lines which arise in AB_2 and A_2B_2 non-first order spectra. (For AB cases the origin chemical shift positions can be calculated from $\nu_A - \nu_B = [(\nu_1 - \nu_4)(\nu_2 - \nu_3)]^{1/2}$)

nuclei do couple, there is no observable effect on the spectrum, which appears as a singlet.

Worked Example 4.11

Calculate $\Delta\nu$ in hertz for the AX system in both proton NMR spectra of cytosine in figure 4.11, and since $J = 8$ Hz (see section 4.6.2) calculate for each case the ratio $\Delta\nu{:}J$ and comment on the difference.

Answer 4.11

In both spectra, $\Delta\nu$ is 1.8 ppm (field-independent) which corresponds to 108 Hz at 60 MHz and to 360 Hz at 200 MHz. The ratios $\Delta\nu{:}J$ are 13.5 and 45 respectively.

COMMENT

Increased B_0 means increased $\Delta\nu{:}J$ ratio, and more likelihood of first order conditions applying.

Problem Example 4.21

Calculate the ratio $\Delta v:J$ for the aromatic system in figure 4.15.

Problem Example 4.22

Calculate the ratio $\Delta v:J$ in the proton and fluorine NMR spectra of trifluoroethanol, in figure 4.14, taking δ_H and δ_F as 60 MHz and 56.4 MHz respectively.

Even more complexities arise in spectra produced by the mutual coupling of several protons with close-lying chemical shift positions. The nomenclature is self-explanatory, and includes systems described such as ABX, ABC and so on, with multipliers as necessary. In the simplest cases it is possible without elaborate computer software to perform calculations to assign δ and J values (see chapter 6) and collections of assigned spectra (for example Wiberg and Nist mentioned in Further Reading) are available for comparison, which is quite fruitful. Beyond that, computer programs are available to simulate spectra for many-spin systems (see chapter 7) and this now is the method of choice where precise spectral analysis is required; for interpretive analytical purposes this is not always justified. A brief indication of the scale of the problem is implied in the diagrammatic spectra in figure 4.22.

What must remain clear in dealing with non-first order spectra is that line positions are often substantially moved (depending on the $\Delta v:J$ ratio) and δ and J values cannot be extracted directly from the observed spacings.

4.10 SIMPLIFICATION OF COMPLEX SPECTRA

We have seen that several factors influence the complexity of an NMR spectrum; full analysis must therefore take into account the effects of (a) coupling constants and the ratio $\Delta v:J$, (b) proton exchange and dynamic processes in general and (c) temperature (which in turn is important to (b)). Spectra can only be simplified if the nature of the complexity has been assessed from the standpoint of these effects, which will more often than not be present in conjunction with one another.

The measurement of rate processes in dynamic molecules is discussed in chapter 8, and more sophisticated techniques for the analysis and manipulation of NMR data are given in chapter 7 for which the additional theory of chapter 6 is a prerequisite. The use of deuterium exchange discussed in section 4.3.4 is also germane.

4.10.1 Increased Field Strength

Since the ratio $\Delta v:J$ increases with increased magnetic field strength (see section 4.6.2) spectra recorded at

higher field will more closely approach first order appearance, and multiplets which overlap at lower B_0 may be drawn apart at high B_0. Figure 4.23 shows how much more easily analysed is a proton spectrum recorded at 200 MHz.

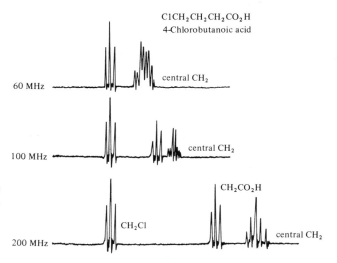

Figure 4.23 Representation of the ^{1}H NMR spectrum of 4-chlorobutanoic acid at 60, 100 and 200 MHz

There is, of course, a price penalty to pay: capital investment and running costs for high field spectrometers operating at say 500 MHz are considerably greater than for a small 60 MHz instrument. Justification comes from the ability to resolve NMR spectra from very complex molecules such as enzymes (see chapter 7), but spectra which are already simple (such as those in figures 4.6–4.10) will be no simpler for being recorded at 500 MHz.

4.10.2 Chemical Shift Reagents

Transition metals with an unpaired electron are strongly paramagnetic and a variety of effects is associated with their presence in a sample whose NMR spectrum is being recorded.

Chromium (III) is used to accelerate relaxation processes (see chapter 6) and, like chromium, most of the first-row transition metals cause some line broadening.

The paramagnetism of the lanthanide metals, especially europium (Eu) and praseodymium (Pr), has a pronounced anisotropic effect on the local field experienced by nearby magnetic nuclei, and this produces quite marked changes in the NMR line positions of these. Figure 4.24 shows the extent to which the chemical shift

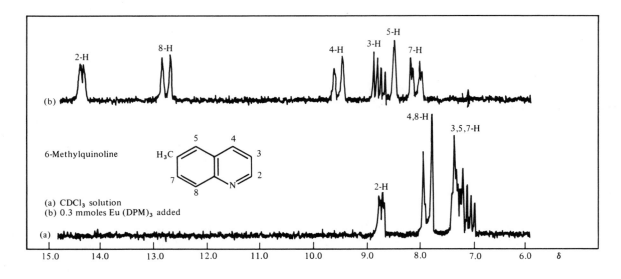

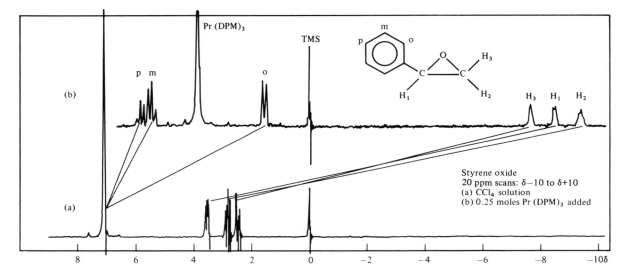

Figure 4.24 Effect of shift reagents on the ^{1}H NMR spectra of 6-methylquinoline (above) and styrene oxide (below). Europium moves the signals to higher frequency, and praseodymium has the opposite effect (60 MHz, in CDCl$_3$)

values are moved when a europium complex is added to a sample of 6-methylquinoline; note that accurate peak assignment can be made on the (almost) first order system generated.

Eu and Yb usually move the signals to higher δ values, while Pr and Dy usually have the opposite effect. This is illustrated by the effect of a Pr complex on the proton NMR spectrum of styrene oxide, also shown in figure 4.24. Note in this spectrum the line broadening of the alkyl protons, compared with figure 4.18.

These *chemical shift reagents* operate by associating, through the metal orbitals, with non-bonding electrons in the substrate, so that they are only effective with molecules belonging to such functional classes as amines, alcohols, ethers, aldehydes, ketones, esters, nitriles and epoxides. Mixed with the silver analogues, and thus making use of the affinity of silver(I) for π-electrons, spectral shifts in weakly nucleophilic alkenes and aromatics can be induced.

The simple ionic salts of Eu and Pr are sparingly

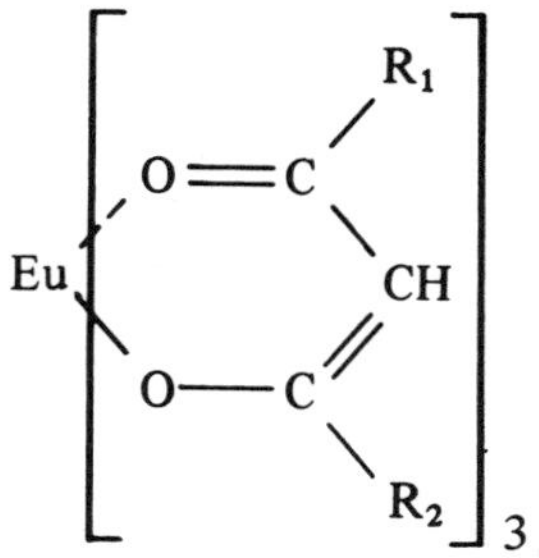

metal enolate 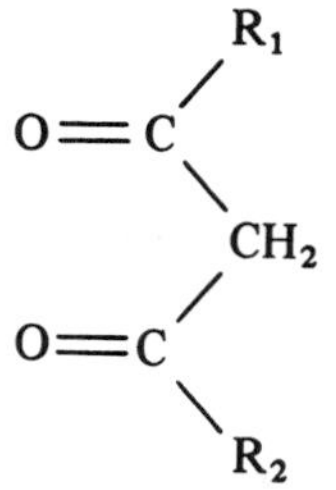   keto

$R_1 = R_2 = -CMe_3$ dipivaloylmethane $Eu(DPM)_3$
    IUPAC name:
        2,2,6,6-tetramethyl-2,5-heptanedione $Eu(THD)_3$
$R_1 = -CMe_3$ $R_2 = -C_3F_7$ (4.16)
        heptafluorodimethyloctanedione $Eu(FOD)_3$
$R_1 = R_2 = -C_2F_5$
    decafluoroheptanedione $Eu(FHD)_3$

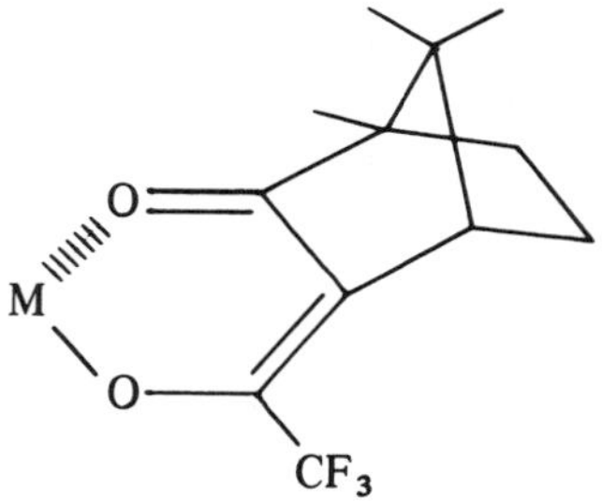

optically active 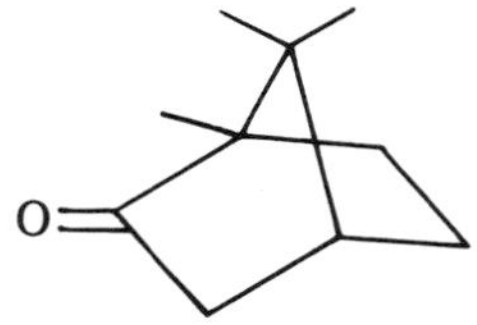   camphor

Other metals: Ag, Dy, Gd, Ho, La, Pr, Yb

soluble in typical NMR solvents, and a range of soluble derivatives is available commercially, all derived by tris-complexation with enolic β-dicarbonyl compounds as shown in formulae 4.16. Eu(FOD)$_3$ is widely used because of its solubility, its resistance to hydrolysis by atmospheric moisture, and because it itself gives rise to only two proton signals in the spectrum.

Practically, the choice of shift reagent used depends to an extent on trial and error and on availability, but much theoretical effort has gone into understanding their mode of action. There is an associated phenomenon in radical chemistry in which the direct coupling between the unpaired electron of the radical and the nuclear spin causes changes in the NMR resonance frequency of the nucleus suffering the coupling. In ESR spectra, this causes the hyperfine splitting of the signal, and has been named *contact shift*. The ability of Eu to change chemical shifts because of the paramagnetism associated with its unpaired electron is a through-space effect (which falls off inversely with the cube of the distance between the Eu atom and the nucleus concerned). This has been named *pseudo-contact shift* to distinguish it from the so-called true contact shift above. Although the preferred generic term is shift reagent, these compounds are nonetheless often named lanthanide shift reagents or contact shift reagents.

Chiral chemical shift reagents, derived from chiral diketones (such as the camphor derivative shown in the formulae) have been used to investigate the proton NMR spectra of chiral molecules by causing different shifts in the two optical isomers.

4.10.3 Spin Decoupling — Double and Triple Irradiation

Considerable spectrum simplification can be brought about by decoupling one nucleus from another: the simplest cases were mentioned in section 1.9, and quite elaborate procedures will be introduced in chapters 6 and 7. Routine carbon-13 spectra (see chapter 5) are recorded with the coupling to protons eliminated.

The technique for decoupling nucleus A in order to simplify the NMR signal for nucleus B is general, whether A and B are of the same element (*homonuclear decoupling*) or not (*heteronuclear decoupling*). It is usefully explained by recalling that A is split by B because A can 'see' B in different magnetic orientations; the splitting will only be maintained if the life-time of B in any one spin state is sufficiently long (Δt again) for the coupling to be measured. Any factor which shortens the life-time of these spin states will eliminate the splitting (as in section 4.7.4).

Irradiation of nucleus B by a separate RF source tuned to the B resonance frequency will cause the B nuclei to undergo both upward and downward transitions between the energy levels as discussed in sections 2.17, and 1.9. If this *double irradiation* is sufficiently intense, the transitions will become rapid — and the life-times of specific spin states (magnetic orientations) will be correspondingly shortened. Nucleus A, formerly coupled to B, will now be unable to differentiate separate orientations of B (since Δt will be too short) and the coupling will be eliminated. The A signal will then appear as if nucleus B were non-magnetic.

Figure 1.13 shows the effects of spin decoupling on the proton NMR spectrum of isopropyl acetate (isopropyl ethanoate, $CH_3 COOCH(CH_3)_2$. At (a) is shown the normal spectrum: the acetyl CH_3 protons appear as an uncoupled singlet, while the isopropyl group shows the characteristic doublet (methyl protons) and septet (methine proton) with the weak outer lines of the septet lost in the base-line (see section 4.7.2). Decoupling is shown in two ways.

Irradiation at the precise frequency of the methyl protons decouples these from the CH proton; the CH signal collapses to a singlet. This is shown at (b). Note that the second, double irradiating, RF source (B_2) forms a beat pattern with the primary RF source (B_1) around the irradiation frequency.

The converse experiment is shown at (c), and involves double irradiation at the CH frequency with B_2: note the beats with B_1. This causes the methyl doublet to collapse to a singlet, since the methyl protons now 'see' only a rapidly changing neighbour proton, and resolution of the splitting is not possible.

Worked Example 4.12
Figure 4.14 shows the proton and fluorine-19 NMR spectra of trifluoroethanol. What frequency is needed to simplify the proton spectrum by removing the fluorine coupling? Describe the experiment which will give rise to a single line in the fluorine spectrum.

Answer 4.12
If proton is being observed at 60 MHz (field strength 1.4 T) then the fluorine resonance is at 56.4 MHz: this is the frequency required for double irradiation. (The decoupler frequency will clearly have to be exactly adjusted, around the approximate figure of 56.4 MHz, to match precisely the frequency of the fluorines in trifluoroethanol.)

If the sample is irradiated with a 60 MHz source, while the fluorine spectrum is being recorded at 56.4 MHz, the proton coupling will be removed, and the fluorine triplet will collapse to a singlet.

Problem Example 4.23
In the spectrum of ethyl bromide (figure 4.9) at what position would the irradiating frequency be placed in order to reduce the quartet to a singlet?

Where three magnetically non-equivalent nuclei are coupling together as in the ^1H–^{13}C–^{19}F group, it is possible by introducing an additional coil around the sample tube to observe one nucleus, for example the carbon-13 at 25 MHz, while decoupling the proton (by irradiation at 100 MHz) and simultaneously decoupling the fluorine (by using a third RF source at 94 MHz). This method is named *triple resonance*.

Worked Example 4.13
(a) What multiplicity is observed in the fluorine-19 94 MHz NMR spectrum of the group $-^1H-^{13}C-^{19}F-$
                                                                /\
if the sample is double irradiated at 25 MHz? (b) What will be observed in the carbon-13 NMR spectrum of the same group if it undergoes triple irradiation, with the two decoupler frequencies at 100 MHz and 94 MHz respectively?

Answer 4.13
(a) If carbon-13 frequency is 25 MHz and fluorine-19 is 94 MHz, then the proton frequency is 100 MHz. The carbon-13 coupling is being eliminated by double irradiation, so only the proton splitting (doublet) will remain in the fluorine-19 spectrum. (b) The carbon-13 signal will be split (doublet) by fluorine-19 and again (doublet) by proton, so that the undecoupled spectrum will be a double doublet. Triple irradiation at 100 MHz and 94 MHz decouples the carbon-13 nucleus from both proton and fluorine, and it will appear as a singlet.

Problem Example 4.24

The proton NMR spectrum of crotonaldehyde (CH$_3$CH=CHCHO) is shown at the chapter head, together with inserts which show the effects, respectively, of double irradiation at the methyl resonance, and triple irradiation at both the methyl and aldehyde resonances. Interpret these observations.

Problem Example 4.25

Estimate the alkene coupling constant in the crotonaldehyde spectrum (from the triple irradiation experiment) and decide from table 15.7 whether the molecule is *cis* or *trans*.

4.11 ADDITIONAL PROBLEMS

1. One of the isomers of C$_3$H$_6$Cl$_2$, dichloropropane, has a proton NMR spectrum consisting of a triplet (δ 3.7) and a quintet (δ 2.2). Which isomer is this?

2. One of the isomers of C$_3$H$_6$ClNO$_2$, chloronitropropane, has a proton NMR spectrum consisting of a triplet (δ 5.8), an approximate quintet (δ 2.3) and a triplet (δ 1.1). Which isomer is this?

3. Salicylic acid is *o*-hydroxybenzoic acid. When sul-phonated, the main product is sulphosalicylic acid, but the problem is deciding the position of the sulphonic acid group. The proton NMR spectrum shows, for the three ring protons, signals at δ 7.15 (doublet, J = 10 Hz), 8.0 (double-doublet, J = 2 Hz and J = 10 Hz) and 8.4 (doublet, J = 2 Hz). Write out all possible isomers of sulphosalicylic acid, and from chemical shift and coupling evidence deduce the true structure.

4. The proton NMR spectrum of *p*-nitrophenylferrocene is shown in figure 4.25. Analyse the spectrum. (Consider firstly the *para* substituted benzene ring; recall that the signal at δ 7.3 arises from chloroform in the CDCl$_3$. The *symmetrical* (*unsubstituted*) cyclopentadiene ring gives rise to a singlet. Decide the number of magnetically equivalent protons on the *substituted* cyclopentadiene ring; because $\Delta\nu$:J is small, the multiplicity is not first order.)

5. Deduce the structure of the compound, C$_8$H$_{11}$N whose proton NMR spectrum is shown in figure 4.26. The signal at δ 1.6 is removed by deuteration.

6. The proton NMR spectrum of 1,2-dibromobutane was recorded at 30°C and it is shown in figure 4.27. Explain its complexity.

7. Deduce the structure of the compound C$_8$H$_9$OBr, whose proton NMR spectrum is shown in figure 4.28.

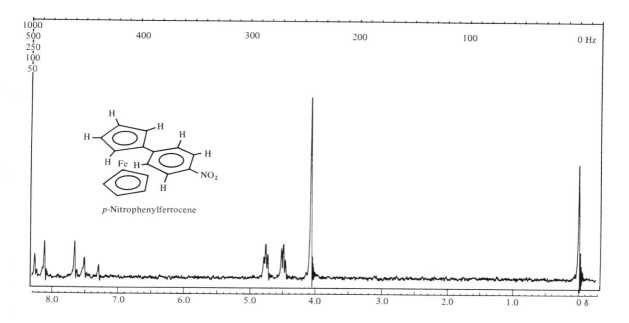

Figure 4.25 Proton NMR spectrum of *p*-nitrophenylferrocene (60 MHz, in CDCl$_3$)

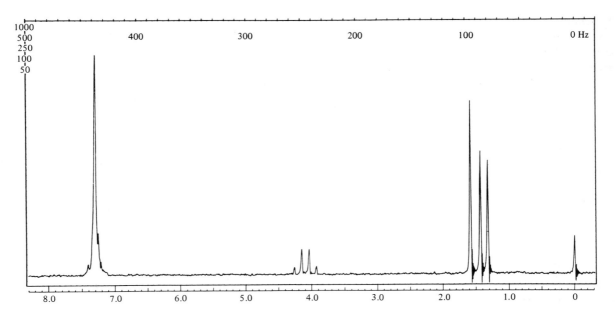

Figure 4.26 Proton NMR spectrum of compound $C_8H_{11}N$ in additional problem 5 (60 MHz, in $CDCl_3$)

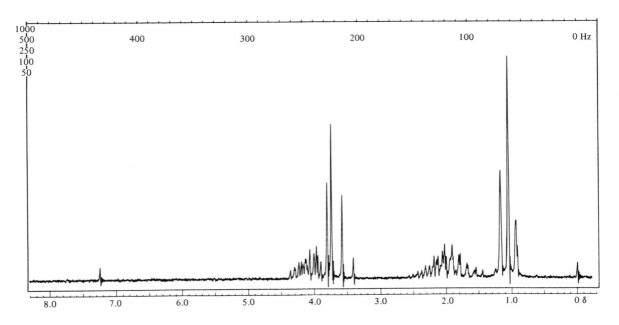

Figure 4.27 Proton NMR spectrum of 1,2-dibromobutane at $30°C$ (60 MHz, in $CDCl_3$)

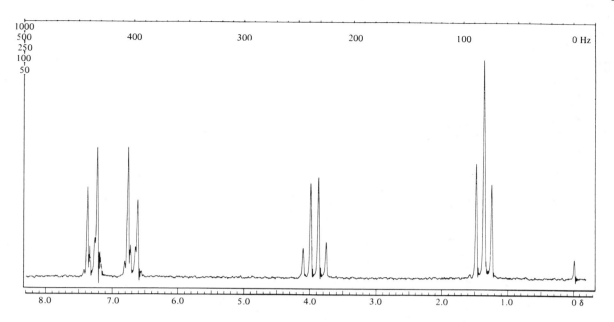

Figure 4.28 Proton NMR spectrum for compound C_8H_9OBr in additional problem 7 (60 MHz, in $CDCl_3$)

5

Carbon-13 NMR Spectra

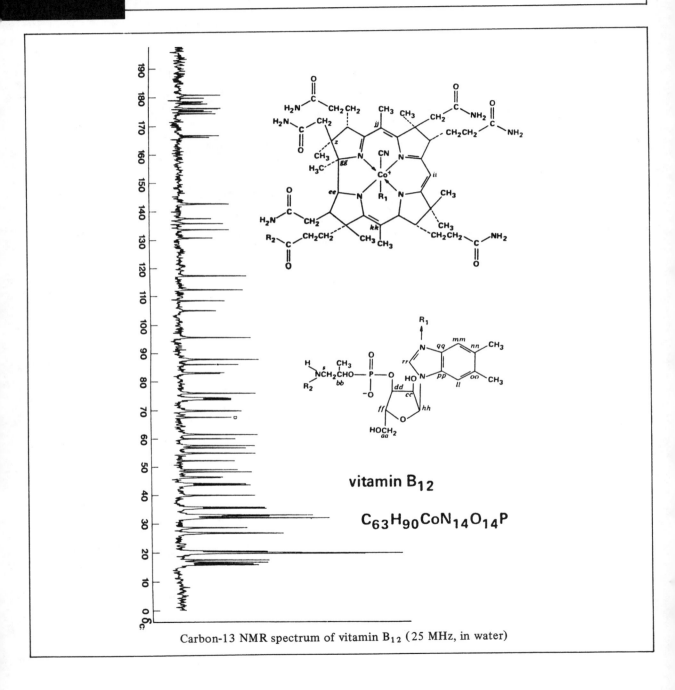

vitamin B$_{12}$

C$_{63}$H$_{90}$CoN$_{14}$O$_{14}$P

Carbon-13 NMR spectrum of vitamin B$_{12}$ (25 MHz, in water)

The chemical shift range of carbon-13 resonances is so wide (more than 200 ppm for simple functional classes) that most compounds show a separate signal for each different carbon environment in the molecule; this is dramatically illustrated in the spectrum for vitamin B_{12} at the head of the chapter, and more modestly in the menthol spectrum in figure 5.2.

The carbons of CN and CO groups (ketones, esters, amides) give resonance lines and can thus be directly detected, whereas their presence can only be inferred from proton NMR. The same is true for quaternary carbons, including carbons in aromatic rings with substituents attached: these likewise give rise to characteristic NMR signals.

Interpretation of carbon-13 NMR spectra will be covered extensively in this chapter, showing the detailed structural information which can be deduced from chemical shift and coupling multiplicity. The use of empirical data tables can lead the analyst to a comprehensive picture of the carbon skeleton of the molecule.

Low sensitivity is always a problem in recording carbon-13 NMR spectra and this practical aspect will be addressed first.

5.1 RECORDING CARBON-13 NMR SPECTRA

Most of the spectra in this chapter have been simplified by the routine elimination of all coupling to hydrogen nuclei in the molecule (see section 1.9). Several benefits accrue from this, not only in simplification but also in increased sensitivity.

5.1.1 Natural Abundance and Isotopomers

The total natural abundance of carbon-13 (without enrichment) is 1.1% of the total carbon present, so that each carbon position in the molecule has a 1.1% probability of being carbon-13.

Thus for acetic acid, two isotopomers are important — $^{13}CH_3COOH$ and $CH_3^{13}COOH$ — and each signal is at an intensity appropriate to 1.1% of the total sample. The natural abundance carbon-13 NMR spectrum is shown in figure 5.1(a). The two carbons in the molecule give two signals in the spectrum; note, in passing, the low intensity of the signal from COOH.

For a C4 molecule such as 1-butanol, each signal in the carbon-13 spectrum arises from one of four possible isotopomers present in the mixture, each isotopomer containing one carbon-13 nucleus at different positions in the molecule; the total strength of each signal again corresponds to 1.1% of ^{13}C.

$$^{12}C-^{12}C-^{12}C-^{13}C-OH \qquad ^{12}C-^{12}C-^{13}C-^{12}C-OH$$

$$^{12}C-^{13}C-^{12}C-^{12}C-OH \qquad ^{13}C-^{12}C-^{12}C-^{12}C-OH$$

1-butanol isotopomers with one ^{13}C atom

$$(5.1)$$

For a complex molecule containing 100 carbon atoms, there exist 100 different isotopomers with one carbon-13 atom, and to record a spectrum of this compound requires 50 times as much of that compound as the amount of acetic acid needed for a spectrum of the same signal strength.

Although the probability of two carbon-13 nuclei appearing on adjacent positions in the molecule is very low indeed, we can recognise in the case of 1-butanol that three possible isotopomers are doubly invested in this fashion with carbon-13, and we will return to this

$$^{12}C-^{12}C-^{13}C-^{13}C-OH \qquad ^{12}C-^{13}C-^{13}C-^{12}C-OH$$

$$^{13}C-^{13}C-^{12}C-^{12}C-OH$$

1-butanol isotopomers with two adjacent ^{13}C atoms

$$(5.2)$$

observation in section 5.5.2 and also in section 7.7.4. Isotopomers with two non-adjacent carbon-13 atoms have no usefulness in NMR: those with more than two carbon-13 atoms are at vanishingly low concentration.

Enrichment of the carbon-13 content can only be regarded as feasible at synthetically accessible sites in the molecule, and although many interesting biosynthetic studies use this process, it is not universally practicable. As an example, acetic acid with carbon-13 enrichment on the carboxyl carbon is easily synthesised, and the carbon-13 NMR spectrum of this molecule is shown in figure 5.1(b). Note the quartet splitting caused by coupling to the CH_3 protons. The signal for the CH_3 carbon atom (not shown, but at lower frequency and thus off scale) will be at natural abundance and of very low intensity.

5.1.2 Magnetic Moment and Magnetogyric Ratio

The carbon-13 nucleus has only a weak magnetic moment, and consequently a small magnetogyric ratio; the

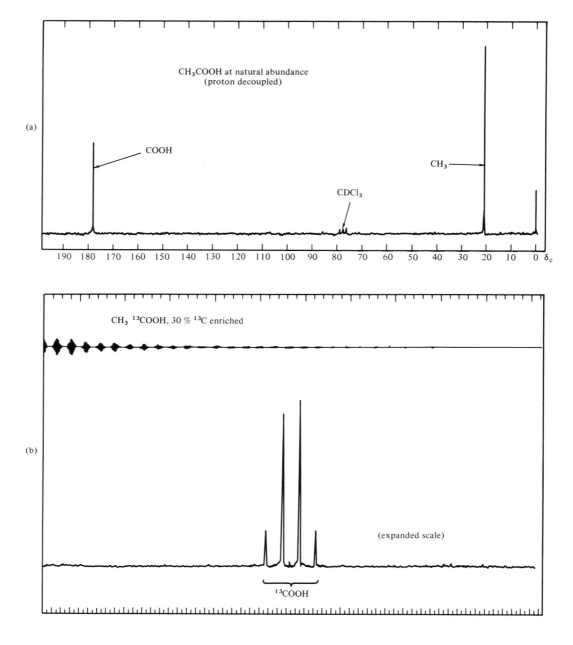

Figure 5.1 (a) Natural abundance carbon-13 NMR spectrum, with proton coupling removed (25 MHz, in $CDCl_3$). (b) The carbon-13 NMR signal from the COOH carbon in $CH_3{}^{13}COOH$, about 30% enriched. The three protons split the carbon-13 resonance into a quartet (25 MHz, in $CDCL_3$)

relationship between these two parameters was discussed in sections 2.6 and 2.8. Since sensitivity in the NMR experiment depends on the magnetic moment, carbon-13 nuclei give weak signals. Compared with proton signals, carbon signals are in the sensitivity ratio $(\gamma_C : \gamma_H)^3$ which, as we saw in section 3.6.2, is approximately 1/64.

When the low natural abundance of carbon-13 is additionally taken into account, hydrogen sensitivity is greater than carbon sensitivity by approximately 6000. With such a sensitivity penalty to overcome, carbon-13 NMR spectra are routinely recorded by pulse irradiation, signal summation, and Fourier Transform; the experimental details of pulse FT NMR were discussed in section 3.5.

5.1.3 Coherent and Broad Band Decoupling – $^{13}C-\{^1H\}$ NMR Spectra

When decoupling was introduced earlier (in section 1.9 and in section 4.10.3), a specific nucleus A was double irradiated to simplify the NMR signal of a coupling nucleus B: the use of such an exactly tuned RF decoupling frequency is named *coherent decoupling*. As an example, looking at figure 5.1(b), irradiation of the methyl protons in $CH_3{}^{13}COOH$, with the decoupler RF near 100 MHz at the CH_3 proton frequency, would collapse the observed quartet for the carbon-13 signal (at 25 MHz) to a singlet.

Maximum simplification in carbon-13 spectra is achieved by simultaneously decoupling all of the protons from all of their coupling carbon partners, but to do so requires a decoupling signal which contains *all* of the appropriate proton frequencies. For example, in 1-butanol the proton frequencies are spread over about 5 ppm, and to irradiate them all requires a *broad band decoupling* source. If the carbon-13 spectrum is to be observed at 25 MHz, the proton decoupler is set at 100 MHz and modulated by mixing in other frequencies to create a spread of side bands around the central 100 MHz beam. One technique involves modulation of the decoupling RF by 'white noise' – familiar as the hiss on audio tapes – so that the decoupler is 'noise modulated', and the resultant carbon-13 NMR spectrum is then *proton noise decoupled*. Since many other modulation devices are used to spread the decoupling frequencies more efficiently than noise modulation, the result is best referred to as a *broad band proton decoupled spectrum*. Proton decoupling by the broad band method is readily achieved because of the relatively narrow bandwidth over which proton resonances arise (less than 20 ppm). Broad band decoupling of other nuclei requires a sufficient bandwidth to span all frequencies, but the practical problems are considerable.

The spread of chemical shift frequencies for any nucleus is dependent on field strength. Thus, for protons with chemical shift range around 20 ppm, at 100 MHz (2.35 T) this corresponds to a frequency spread of 2000 Hz: at 200 MHz (4.7 T) 20 ppm corresponds to 4000 Hz, so the broad band decoupler must be capable of generating this RF band width uniformly over the range and with sufficient RF power. For other nuclei the problems are more daunting because of the wider spread of chemical shifts: typically, these are 300 ppm for ^{19}F,

700 ppm for ^{31}P and 900 ppm for ^{15}N. Broad band fluorine decoupling at 2.35 T must operate over 300 ppm at 94 MHz (the ^{19}F frequency); for ^{19}F in a 4.7 T instrument, 300 ppm at 188 MHz corresponds to broad band decoupling over 56 400 Hz (56.4 kHz). While broad band decoupling of other nuclei is feasible in restricted and favourable circumstances, it is seldom routine, since the power of the decoupling irradiation may be as high as 50 W, with attendant problems of heat dissipation.

A convenient notation for broad band decoupled spectra is to specify the observed nucleus and indicate in curly brackets the nucleus which is being broad band irradiated. Thus a $^{13}C-\{^1H\}$ spectrum is a fully proton decoupled carbon-13 NMR spectrum. All coupling to proton is eliminated and only single line carbon resonances remain. Figure 5.1(a) is a $^{13}C-\{^1H\}$ NMR spectrum. (The notation includes decoupling in general.)

The irradiation of the proton resonances to decouple them from carbon induces the protons to accelerate their upward and downwards energy changes. When these changes are slow (no decoupling) Δt is long, and the splittings are fully resolved. At high decoupling power, the changes are rapid and Δt is short: singlet carbon-13 lines appear.

A useful intermediate stage occurs when *low power decoupling* of the protons is applied, because the signals from carbons with proton attached begin to broaden (Δt becoming shorter) and adjustment of the decoupler power can produce a spectrum in which all CH_3, CH_2 and CH signals are sufficiently broadened to allow only the unbroadened quaternary carbon to be recognised above the base line. The method therefore constitutes another means of identification of quaternary carbon atoms, complementary to those given in sections 5.1.4 and 5.2.

The increase in signal intensity brought about by the loss of signal multiplicity – *multiplet collapse* – can be favourably exemplified from figure 5.1(b); the quartet lines are in the ratio 1:3:3:1 but the proton decoupled spectrum, figure 5.1(a), adds these together to give a single line of relative intensity eight.

The clarity of single line spectra leads to easier analysis and in figure 5.2 the proton and carbon-13 NMR spectra of menthol emphasise this difference: the additional factor of greater chemical shift range further enhances the value of the carbon-13 spectrum. With ten non-equivalent carbon atoms in the molecule, menthol gives a ten-line ^{13}C NMR spectrum.

When a carbon-13 nucleus is coupled to a proton, as in a $^{13}C-H$ group, each affects the magnetic energy levels of the other, and decoupling of the protons creates dis-

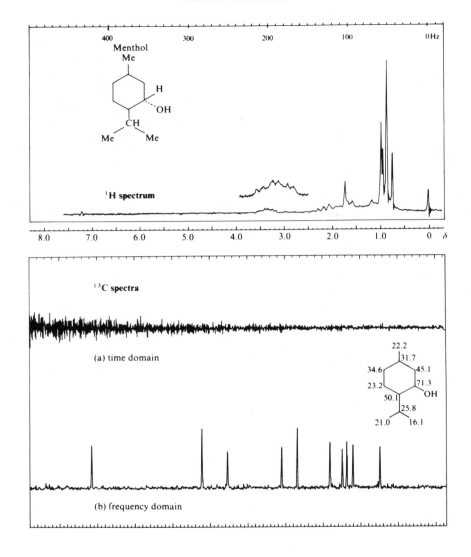

Figure 5.2   Comparison between the ^{1}H and ^{13}C NMR spectra of menthol, showing the relative simplicity in the ^{13}C spectrum because of the greater range in chemical shifts and because all coupling to proton has been removed (^{1}H at 60 MHz, in CDCl$_3$. ^{13}C at 25 MHz, in CDCl$_3$)

tortions in the populations of the carbon energy levels. The result, in this case, is an increase in the probability of upwards transitions for the carbon-13 nuclei and hence a more intense signal arises than would be found with no decoupling. The effect is a special case of a phenomenon first observed in 1953 by Albert W. Overhauser, then working at the University of Illinois. He noted that the conduction electrons of metals interact with the atomic nuclei to perturb their relaxation processes and thus alter the populations of the available energy levels. In NMR spectroscopy, changes brought about in the energy populations of one nucleus by the decoupling of

a neighbouring nucleus is named the *nuclear Overhauser effect* or NOE.

When more detailed theories of coupling have been explained, it will be possible to quantify the influences of the NOE for several different nuclei: see section 6.9. Other population changes will be discussed in chapter 7.

5.1.4 Off Resonance Decoupling

While broad band decoupled carbon-13 NMR spectra bring the advantage of clarification to the spectroscopist, all of the valuable coupling information is lost, and a compromise method called *off resonance decoupling* may be used to restore partially the most significant couplings. Essentially, it is a deliberately inefficient double irradiation of the proton frequencies: thus the decoupler is offset from (say) 100 MHz by a small amount, typically a few hundred hertz, and the result in the observed carbon-13 spectrum at 25 MHz is that weak C–H couplings are decoupled and strong couplings remain, albeit somewhat distorted. In practice, the direct one bond ^{13}C–H couplings, ^1J(CH), are the only residual splittings seen, while ^2J(CCH) and ^3J(CCCH) couplings (being weak) are removed.

The residual splittings retain their multiplicity information, so that a CH_3 carbon appears as a quartet, a

CH_2 carbon as a triplet, CH as a doublet and quaternary carbon as a singlet.

Figure 5.3 shows off resonance proton decoupled carbon-13 spectra for eugenol (the major constituent of oil of cloves). Each was recorded with slightly different offsets of the decoupling irradiation and this systematic approach allows the best compromise offset to be found. Although the shapes of the doublets and triplets are far from being first order, there is no ambiguity in recognising the multiplicity.

Direct ^1J(CH) coupling constants are around 120 Hz, while clearly the observed splittings in figure 5.3 are much less than that. This is indeed an advantage, since doublets with close lying chemical shifts and large

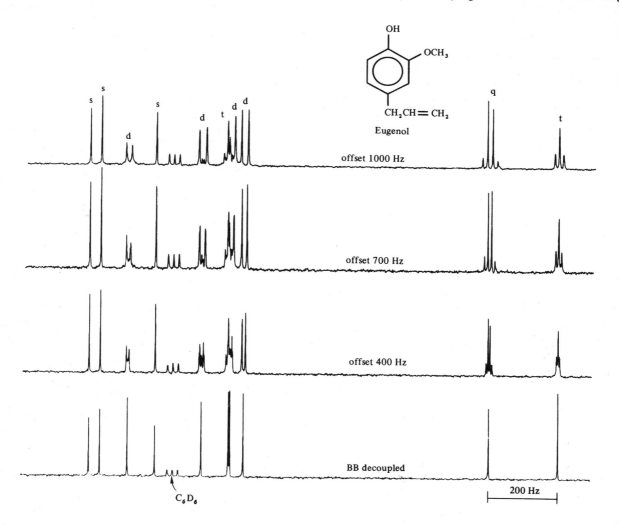

Figure 5.3 ^{13}C NMR spectra of eugenol. The broad band proton decoupled spectrum is shown at the bottom; off resonance decoupled spectra show how the observed splittings depend on the decoupler frequency offset (20 MHz, in C_6D_6, with proton decoupling near 80 MHz)

couplings would give rise to overlapped signals and lead to problems in assignment. The observed splittings (the reduced coupling constant, J_R) and the true coupling constants (J) are related to each other as a function of the decoupler offset and power ($\Delta\nu$ and $\mathbf{B}_2$); the approximate relationship being

$$J_R = \frac{J(\Delta\nu)}{\gamma\mathbf{B}_2}$$

It is therefore possible to calculate $^1J(CH)$ from off resonance decoupled spectra, but not to extract J values directly. (Changes in J_R with offset can be seen in figure 5.3.)

It will be useful to later discussions if we note here that the offset decoupling RF differs from each separate proton frequency because of the different proton chemical shifts. That is to say, the reduced coupling (J_R) seen in each carbon signal contains precise information about the chemical shift value of the proton(s) to which that carbon is attached. This information can be extracted and made available in 2D form as an aid to structure identification, and the details are given in section 7.7.

5.2 RELAXATION EFFECTS IN CARBON-13 NMR SPECTRA

Although a more exact account of relaxation processes fits best into chapter 6, it is desirable here to consider qualitatively how carbon-13 NMR spectra are affected.

Line intensities in NMR spectra depend on several factors but two concern us here. The net consequence of absorption of energy at resonance is that nuclei in the lower energy level pass to the upper energy level: absorption will ultimately cease unless there is a commensurate relaxation of nuclei from the upper energy level to the lower, and this was pictured diagrammatically in figure 2.8. It happens that, while relaxation of protons is fast, relaxation of carbon-13 nuclei is slow, and in the pulse FT experiment for carbon it is necessary to wait for a delay period after each pulse before repeating the irradiation, to avoid the problems of saturation discussed in sections 3.5.2 and 6.7.2.

In most organic molecules, the relaxation of the carbon-13 nuclei arises through interaction with dipolar forces created by attached protons, so the CH_3 and CH_2 protons have, in general, faster relaxation characteristics than quaternary carbons, which lack this efficient proton-dominated relaxation. It follows that it is easy to saturate the signal from quaternary carbons: it is merely

a question of reducing the delay time between successive pulses. The shorter the delay, the weaker becomes the signal from quaternary carbon atoms, and this is illustrated in the series of quinoline spectra shown in figure 5.4. This process can be operated deliberately as a means of identifying such environments in the molecule, and it serves as a complement to the similar use of off resonance decoupling and low power decoupling.

Where slow relaxation is problematic (some quaternary and carbonyl carbons have very slow relaxation and give very weak signals) the use of relaxation agents is widespread in helping to overcome this. The theory was discussed in chapter 4. The commonest agent is the chromium (III) tris-complex with acetylacetone ($CH_3COCH_2COCH_3$, or ACAC) and it is usually phoneticised as crack-ack, $Cr(ACAC)_3$.

Quantitative information is not as easily extracted from carbon-13 spectra as from proton spectra. Apart from the discrepancies in relaxation rates, the influence of the NOE (see section 5.1.3) leads to preferential signal enhancement of those carbons attached to proton, so that proton decoupled carbon-13 spectra usually exhibit line intensities which are very uneven: Figure 5.1(a) is typical in this respect. Examples of this occur in the problem exercises, where it can be turned to advantage in signal assignment. Among the advanced techniques discussed in chapter 7 is a programme which minimises the influence of the NOE (see section 7.1.3).

5.3 CHEMICAL SHIFTS IN CARBON-13 NMR SPECTRA

Figure 1.8 shows the approximate δ ranges for common carbon environments, measured in ppm from TMS; recognition of these overall spectral regions always represents the first step in assigning carbon chemical shifts. Finer distinctions can be made with the Summary Chart (figure 15.1), preceding tables 15.8–15.18.

The information in figure 1.8 is easily (and profitably) committed to memory, while the chart is a convenient survey for more detailed reference. As ever, exceptional shifts arise in species which possess unusual electronic or steric features, and indeed this can be a sensitive probe for these anomalies. The charge-bearing carbons of carbocations appear in the range $\delta = 200$–300, and carbanions also are outside common ranges. Even such a simple molecule as CI_4, tetraiodomethane, gives a carbon signal near $\delta = -300$ (that is about 300 ppm to the low frequency side of TMS).

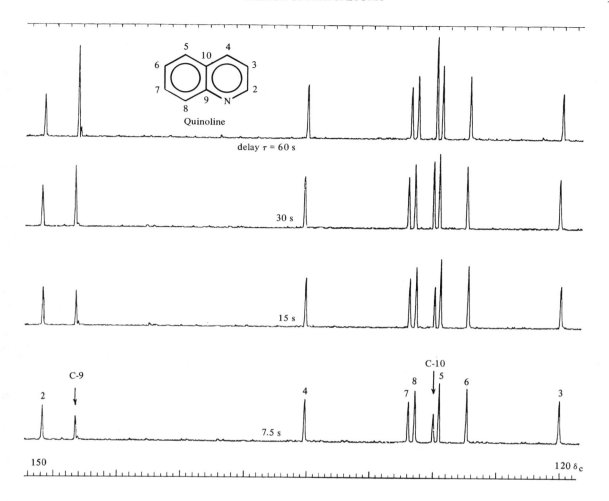

Figure 5.4 ^{13}C NMR spectra of quinoline. At fast pulse repetition rates (short delay times, τ) the quaternary carbon signals show lowered intensity (25 MHz, in CD_3COCD_3)

5.3.1 Theory of Carbon-13 Chemical Shifts

Disappointingly, a full rationale of chemical shift influences is not possible in carbon-13 NMR, in spite of its pivotal importance and a monumental amount of study. Fortunately though, and largely as a result of these studies, empirical relationships have been comprehensively documented, and for the most part these can be relied upon in complex spectral interpretation. The additive effects of substitution on shift positions is summarised in tables 15.8–15.16, and these will be used as the basis of prediction.

In the alkane hydrocarbons, and in alkyl groups within other classes, there is a progressive move to a higher frequency with additional carbon substitution, as, for example, if methyl groups progressively replace hydrogen atoms in $CH_3CH_2CH_2CH_3$.

The directly substituted carbon, the α-carbon, and the carbons adjoining the α-carbons, have their chemical shifts moved about 6–9 ppm to higher frequency — a deshielding effect.

$$
\begin{array}{ccc}
 & \overset{\displaystyle 22}{\underset{|}{C}} & \overset{\displaystyle 29}{\underset{|}{C}} \\
\underset{13}{C}-\underset{25}{C}-\underset{25}{C}-\underset{13}{C} & \underset{22}{C}-\underset{30}{C}-\underset{32}{C}-\underset{11}{C} & \underset{29}{C}-\overset{30}{\underset{|}{C}}-\underset{37}{C}-\underset{9}{C} \\
 & & \underset{29}{C}
\end{array}
$$

^{13}C δ values in alkanes \hfill (5.3)

The γ-carbons have their chemical shifts moved about 2.5 ppm to a lower frequency — a shielding effect.

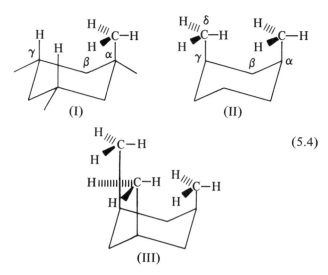

(5.4)

This γ-effect is obviously intriguing, and many studies have noted a correlation with van der Waals interaction between hydrogen atoms on the carbon atoms involved. The 1,4-carbon systems affected are shown in formulae 5.4 for an axially-substituted cyclohexane (I).

Since γ-shifts to higher frequency are not unknown, this explanation cannot generally hold. Also, as an additional anomaly, further crowding by axial substitution as in (II) and (III) (and that is δ-substitution) leads to shifts to higher frequency, or deshielding. Although the reasons for these shifts cannot solely be due to steric crowding, the consistency with which they are observed can lead to valuable detailed analysis of the conformations of molecules such as the steroids.

Table 15.12 shows that the shifts induced in a cyclohexane ring by further alkyl substitution depend on whether the additional group is axial or equatorial, and again this is of consistent value in structure elucidation.

These progressive changes in chemical shift associated with additional carbon substitution also apply to alkene carbons and aromatic ring carbons, and the values are given in tables 15.9, 15.11 and 15.13.

Alkynes are less frequently met but a few typical examples are given in table 15.10.

Introduction of other substituents (that is, other than simple alkyl substitution) also follows simple additive rules, and the data are listed in the tables. Some theoretical comfort can be derived from table 15.12 by noting that electronegative groups tend on the whole to produce shifts to higher frequency, by the expected deshielding which they bring. Note for example the α-shift of F, Cl, Br and NO_2. The γ-effect is also present, but again no full explanation is available. Also, multiple substitution by F and Br does not produce simple additive changes in δ values.

The anomalous influence of iodine (producing an α-shift in alkanes of −7.2 ppm and in aromatic carbon of −32 ppm) is also mystifying, but the effect is found with other atoms of high atomic number, and no completely agreeable theory accounts for these shifts — which are simply grouped together under the set name of the *heavy atom effect*. This of course is merely offering a means of identification but not of explanation.

Progressive iodine substitution into methane moves the carbon resonance through δ −22, −55, −141, to −294. For the analogous bromomethanes the values progress through δ 9, 20, 11 and 30.

Substitution by deuterium is most frequently encountered in the deuteriated solvents used in NMR, such as $CDCl_3$ and C_6D_6. It is worth recording here that this isotope substitution shifts the carbon resonance slightly relative to the corresponding hydrogen analogue; the effect is typically around 0.2 ppm, and is not therefore usually troublesome. Isotope shifts are a general phenomenon, so that a ^{13}C resonance will differ slightly in frequency when the ^{13}C atom is attached either to an adjacent ^{12}C ($^{13}C-^{12}C-$ bond) or to an adjacent ^{13}C ($^{13}C-^{13}C-$ bond). This factor has to be taken into account in the double quantum experiments discussed in section 7.7.4. Other isotope shifts (notably those caused by ^{18}O) are discussed in the specialist texts listed under Further Reading.

5.4 CHEMICAL SHIFT ASSIGNMENTS IN CARBON-13 NMR SPECTRA

The most satisfactory method of assigning signals in a decoupled ^{13}C NMR spectrum involves the use of the data tables 15.8–15.16 to predict the chemical shift position of each carbon atom in the structure. This presupposes that the structure is known (the simplest circumstance) but if the structure is unknown or in doubt it may be necessary to perform the operation on several alternative structures until a best-fit is achieved. This Aunt Sally approach is a perfectly legitimate way to solve many NMR problems and is considerably easier than direct deduction from chemical shift data back to the structure.

5.4.1 Summarised Procedure – Use of Correlation Tables 15.8–15.16

(a) Count the number of signals in the spectrum: this is the number of chemically non-equivalent carbon atoms in the molecule.

(b) Use the chart (figure 15.1) to ascertain the approximate spectral position of common environments.

(c) Estimate the chemical shifts for the carbon skeleton of the parent (see section 5.4.2) using the best model or models from tables 15.8, 15.9, 15.10 and 15.11, ignoring for the moment all functional substituents, even though they may contain carbon (C=O, CN).

(d) Consider whether conformational effects, restricted rotation, tautomerism or other possible exchange process may be operative in the molecule: these may give rise to more signals (or fewer) than a cursory inspection can indicate.

(e) Compute the influence of substituents on these parent chemical shifts, using tables 15.12 and 15.13. Assign carbonyl carbons (table 15.14), multiple-bonded carbons (table 15.15) and isolated methyl groups (table 15.16).

5.4.2 Identifying the Parent Model

Suppose we wish to predict the ^{13}C chemical shift position for the following (formulae 5.5).

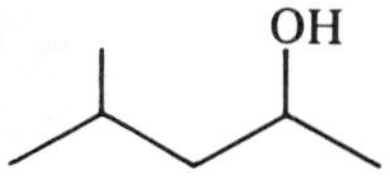

(I) 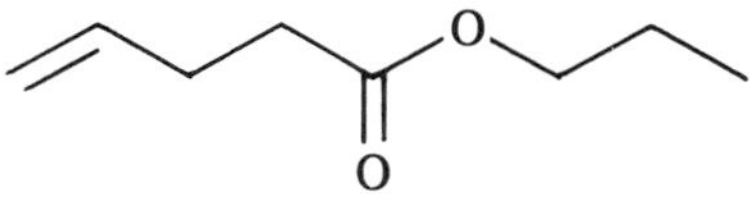 (II) 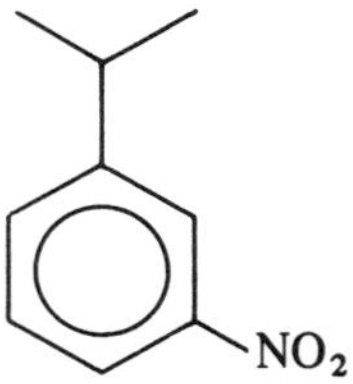 (III) (5.5)

We must first dissect each molecule.

For (I): This is considered as two parts; the model (a) and the substituent (b). We calculate the hydrocarbon parent (a) first, and *then* calculate the influence of (b) on (a) (see formulae 5.6).

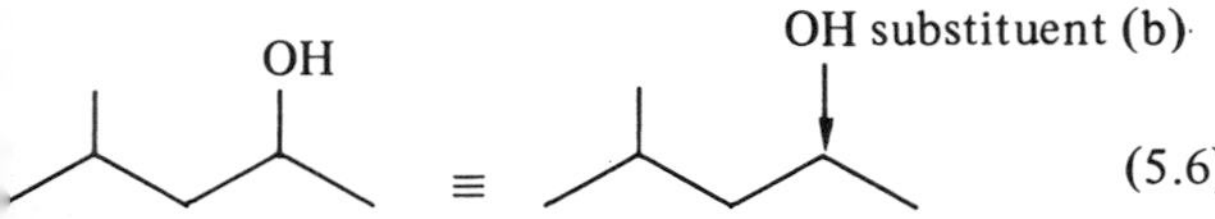

(5.6)

hydrocarbon parent (a)

Chemical shifts for this model (a) can be deduced from table 15.8. See problem examples 5.3 and 5.4.

For (II): This has two hydrocarbon parents, (a) and (b). Into each of these we substitute the ester function (c) (noting that the carbonyl end has a different influence from the oxy end) (see formulae 5.7).

Model (b) is an alkane (table 15.8) and model (a) is an alkene: chemical shifts for (a) can be deduced from table 15.9. (Note however that substitution of the ester carbonyl into (a) takes place at an alkane carbon, and we will use table 15.12 to compute the effects of this.) See problem example 5.1.

hydrocarbon parents

(II) ≡

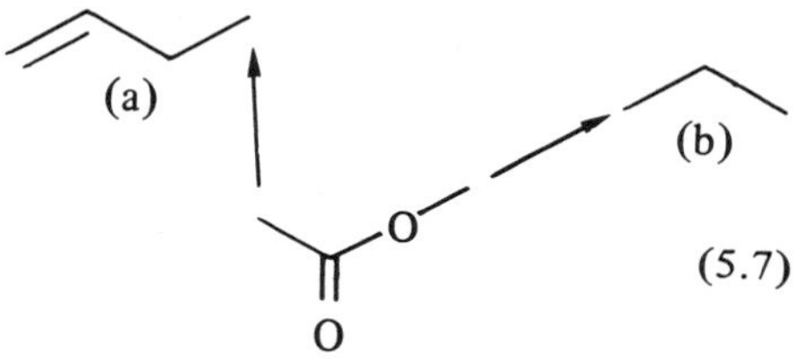

(5.7)

substituent (c)

For (III): The parent hydrocarbon here is isopropylbenzene (cumene) and the substituent is NO_2. Since table 15.11 does not list isopropylbenzene and its chemical shifts, we must further dissect this molecule until we can reconstruct it as a composite of models which are listed. Propane is listed under alkanes in table 15.8 and benzene has six equivalent carbons at δ 128 (table 15.11) (see formulae 5.8).

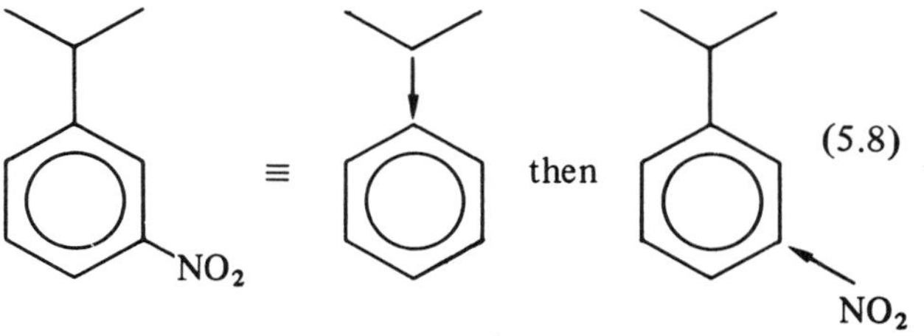

≡ then (5.8)

In detail, the conjunction of propane with benzene will involve two calculations, (a) the influence on propane chemical shifts when a phenyl group is substituted into the molecule, and (b) the influence on benzene chemical shifts when an alkyl group (isopropyl) is substituted into the molecule. See worked example 5.2.

This separate identification of model and substituent will be extended into complex molecules through several worked examples for each major class of model — alkanes, alkenes, alkynes and aromatics.

5.4.3 Alkane Chemical Shifts — Table 15.8

Empirical prediction of the chemical shifts for alkane (sp^3) carbons in hydrocarbons is usually successful to an accuracy of a few ppm. For the simple alkane series of hydrocarbons, the accuracy is very high (within one ppm), but this is not too surprising when it is recalled that the empirical data in the table were originally derived from just these alkanes.

The examples of common molecules listed are obviously eclectic, but serve the purpose of gaining experience in the principles of the method. For comprehensive treatment see Further Reading.

It must be clear that table 15.8 is used for predicting only the hydrocarbon skeleton of an alkane molecule (or of an alkyl group in a functionalised molecule). The influence of further substituents must be considered *after the hydrocarbon shifts have been deduced*: this makes use of table 15.12, and examples will follow later.

To predict the carbon-13 chemical shifts of molecules not shown in the table, the calculation from the tabulated data requires a little practice.

Worked Example 5.1

Predict the carbon-13 chemical shift positions for methylbutane. The observed values are shown for comparison, to the nearest ppm (formulae 5.9). State what

Answer 5.1
(a) Figure 15.1 shows that alkane shifts are about δ 0–80
(b) There are four different (non-equivalent) chemical shift environments present, namely (C-1 and C-5), C-2, C-3 and C-4. (c) *Carbons 1,5* These are CH_3 carbons, so the constant is 6.80. The number of α-carbons attached to them is one (C-2) which is CH, so the increment for this is + 17.83. The β-carbon (C-3) is not counted since its contribution is subsumed in the value 6.80. There is only one γ-carbon (C-4) for which the contribution is −2.99, and there is no δ-carbon.
Chemical shift for C-1 and C-5 = 6.80 + 17.83 − 2.99 = δ 21.84
(d) *Carbon 2* This is a CH carbon, constant 23.46. There are three α-carbons attached, but no increment is to be added for the two CH_3 groups and only the influence of the α-CH_2 (C-3) needs to be added; there is no γ- or δ-carbon.
Chemical shift for C-2 = 23.46 + 6.60 = δ 30.06
(e) *Carbon 3* This is a —CH_2— carbon; the α-CH_3 group (C-4) does not contribute but the α-CH— (C-2) does; there is no γ- or δ-carbon.
Chemical shift for C-3 = 15.34 + 16.70 = δ 32.04
(f) *Carbon 4* This is a —CH_3 carbon; the α-carbon is —CH_2— (C-3) there are two γ-carbon atoms (C-11 and C-5), and no δ-carbon.
Chemical shift for C-4 = 6.80 + 9.56 + 2 (− 2.99) = δ 10.38
(g) The off resonance multiplicities will be quartets for (C-1 + C-5) and C-4, a triplet for C-3 and a doublet for C-2.

Worked Example 5.2
Predict the ^{13}C chemical shift values for 2,2,4-trimethyl pentane. The observed values are shown for comparison (formulae 5.10).

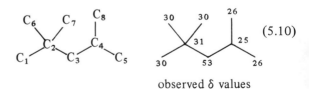

(5.9)

observed δ values

(5.10)

observed δ values

multiplicity is shown by each signal in an off resonance ^{13}C–{^{1}H} spectrum. To calculate each chemical shift, it is simply a matter of taking a constant (a base value) and computing the additive influence of additional carbon substitution.

Answer 5.2
(a) The chart in figure 15.1 shows alkane carbons about δ 0–80.
(b) There are five different chemical shift environments present, (C-1 + C-6 + C-7), C-2, C-3, C-4 and (C-5 + C-8)

c) *Carbons 1, 6 and 7* CH_3 carbons each with one α-carbon ($-\overset{\textstyle |}{\underset{\textstyle |}{C}}-$), one γ-carbon, and two δ-carbons.

Chemical shift $= 6.80 + 25.48 + (-2.99) + 2(0.49) = 31.27$

d) *Carbon 2* $-\overset{\textstyle |}{\underset{\textstyle |}{C}}-$ carbon; only the $-CH_2-\alpha$-carbon is computed (not the CH_3 groups); there are two γ-carbons and no δ-carbon.

Chemical shift $= 27.77 + 2.26 + 0.68 = \delta\ 30.17$

e) *Carbon 3* $-CH_2-$ carbon; one $-\overset{\textstyle |}{\underset{\textstyle |}{C}}-\alpha$-carbon and one $-CH-\alpha$-carbon; no γ- or δ-carbons.

Chemical shift $= 15.34 + 21.43 + 16.70 = \delta\ 53.47$

f) *Carbon 4* $-\overset{\textstyle |}{CH}-$ carbon; only the $-CH_2-\alpha$-carbon is considered (not the two $-CH_3$ α-carbons); there are three γ-carbons and no δ-carbons.

Chemical shift $= 23.46 + 6.60 + 3(-2.07) = \delta\ 23.85$

g) *Carbons 5 and 8* $-CH_3$ carbons; the α-carbon is $-\overset{\textstyle |}{CH}-$; there is one γ-carbon and three δ-carbons.

Chemical shift $= 6.8 + 17.83 - 2.99 + 3(0.49) = \delta\ 23.11$

Problem Example 5.1

Predict the carbon-13 chemical shift positions for 2-methylpentane. The observed spectrum is shown in figure 5.5: assign the peaks. Note the intensity of the signal at δ 23.

5.4.4 Alkene Chemical Shifts — Table 15.9

In the absence of a successful rationale of chemical shift influences, the prediction of δ values for alkene carbons rests heavily on empirical data. In the hydrocarbons, alkene carbons give signals in the range δ 80–145, and representative examples are shown in table 15.9. As with the alkanes, a successful method for estimating shifts in other alkenes not shown will be illustrated by worked and problem examples. Extensive compilations are available in the literature (see Further Reading).

Table 15.9 is used only for the effect of carbon chain substituents on δ values: other effects will be practised later in relation to the use of table 15.13.

Worked Example 5.3

Predict the carbon-13 chemical shift values for the alkene carbons in 2-pentene, and compare them with the experimental values given in table 15.9. (The procedure again starts from a base value (δ 123) and computes the influence of further carbon substitution. Note that, for

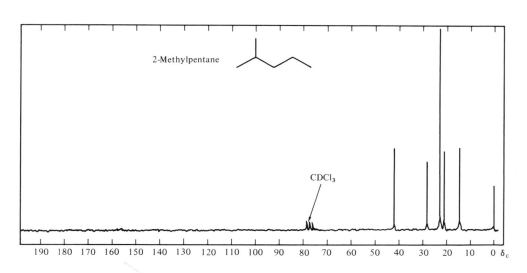

2-pentene   2-methyl-2-butene

(5.11)

each alkene carbon in turn, the influence of the *nearest* substituents (α, β, γ) differs from the influence of the more *distant* substituents (α', β', γ').)

2-Methylpentane

CDCl$_3$

190 180 170 160 150 140 130 120 110 100 90 80 70 60 50 40 30 20 10 0 δ_c

Figure 5.5 ^{13}C NMR spectrum of 2-methylpentane (25 MHz, in CDCl$_3$)

Answer 5.3

(a) The expected range for C=C carbons in hydrocarbons is, from figure 15.1, δ 80–145.

(b) *Carbon 2* The base value for alkenes is δ 123. To this is added + 10 (for C-1, an α-carbon), −8 (for C-4, an α′ carbon) and −2 (for C-5, a β′-carbon).
Chemical shift for C-2 = 123 + 10 − 8 − 2 = δ 123.

(c) *Carbon 3* This carbon has one α-carbon (C-4) one β-carbon (C-5) and one α′-carbon (C-1).
Chemical shift for C-3 = 123 + 10 + 7 − 8 = δ 132

Problem Example 5.2

Predict δ values for the sp^2 carbons in 2-methyl-2-butene. Experimental values are given in the structure in table 15.9.

Many attempts have been made to systematise further the influence of structure on shifts, and although these are successful within the detailed contexts in which the correlations were established, their predictive value in new situations is unreliable and little of novelty would be gained in introducing them here. For example, in the spectra of acyclic alkenes, the *cis* isomer differs from the *trans* by approximately one ppm (*cis* having the lower δ value). Since predictability is not accurate to within one ppm, this difference would only be useful if both isomers were available and their spectra compared.

For cycloalkenes the empirical approach also works well, unless there is considerable strain because of ring size. There comes a point, in counting carbons in one direction round the ring, when there is overlap with the count in the opposite direction. The rule here is to carry on counting, as the following example illustrates.

Worked Example 5.4

Predict δ values for the alkene group in norbornene, whose structure is given in table 15.9, with observed δ values. The method for counting carbons is shown in formulae 5.12.

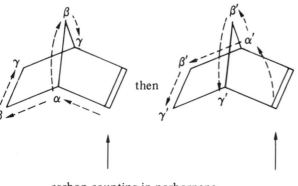

carbon counting in norbornene

(5.12)

Answer 5.4

Because of symmetry, the alkene carbons are equivalent Each has one α, two β and two γ substituents, and thus each also has one α′, two β′, and 2 γ′ substituents.
Chemical shift = δ 135 (observed, δ 136)

The success of the method should be assessed by performing like calculations for the alkenes whose chemical shifts are given in table 15.9. By doing this, some idea will be given of the error range which typically applies.

Table 15.9 allows calculation of the expected δ values only for the sp^2 carbons in the alkenes: the sp^3 carbon chemical shifts must clearly be predicted as for alkanes, using table 15.8, and the alkene group will then be regarded as a substituent in the alkane residue. Examples of this method are given later in section 5.4.8.

5.4.5 Alkyne Chemical Shifts – Table 15.10

The relationships between structure and chemical shift in alkynes are very similar to those in alkenes, and the method of applying the empirical predictions follows exactly that discussed in section 5.4.4. As before, a few representative alkynes are shown in table 15.10, and this small selection serves the present purpose well enough.

5.4.6 Aromatic and Heterocyclic Chemical Shifts – Table 15.11

The range of δ values found in aromatic systems (whether carbocycles or heterocycles) is relatively narrow and widely separated from the alkane range, so that it is easy, as in proton NMR, to distinguish these broad functional groups from their carbon-13 NMR spectra. The aromatic and alkene ranges do however overlap, as seen in the chart of figure 15.1.

A few typical aromatic systems are shown in table 15.11, but no successful method is available for predicting such δ values. The additive influence of further substitution is, however, well documented and predictable; this will be discussed in section 5.4.8.

Quite obviously, it would be impossible to include even a small fraction of the heterocyclic molecules known and studied by carbon-13 NMR spectroscopy: the few examples given are selected because of their simplicity, and because they are familiar to all chemists. Glucose is included for interest (and since it is heterocyclic): note the steric effect on chemical shifts in the two anomeric forms.

The perhydro heterocycles (such as THF) have sp^3 carbons whose spectroscopic properties mirror those of the alkanes in table 15.8, but they are included in table 15.11 as a match for their heteroaromatic counterparts.

4.7 Influence of Functional Substituents on Alkane Chemical Shifts — Table 15.12

nowing the values of the chemical shifts in the alkane p³) carbons of the molecule (table 15.8 and section 4.3) it is possible thereafter to predict quite reliably ow these δ values are moved by functional groups intro-uced into the molecule.

Unusual steric or electronic influences will make the redictions less confident and simple substitution by Br r I can produce unexpected values. Where the influence f only one functional substituent is involved the agree-ent with observed values is good: if two functional roups are present they may interact or simply form ydrogen bonds, and this leads to malestimates in such pecies as β-diketones, hydroxy acids and thiol acids.

A worked example illustrates the method, in three eps, (a), (b) and (c).

orked Example 5.5

redict the ^{13}C chemical shift values for the four iso-eric butyl alcohols, C_4H_9OH.

The four butyl alcohols are as shown in formulae .13.

) In figure 15.1 the chart shows carbon attached to xygen (C—O) in the range near δ 40–80, with the other nsubstituted alkane carbon atoms about δ 0–80.

(b) Chemical shifts for the carbon skeleton without the OH group are first deduced. For this, we need two carbon skeletons: the chemical shift values are given in table 15.8 but they could equally have been computed as in the previous examples.

(c) Influence of substituents (using table 15.12)

1-Butanol

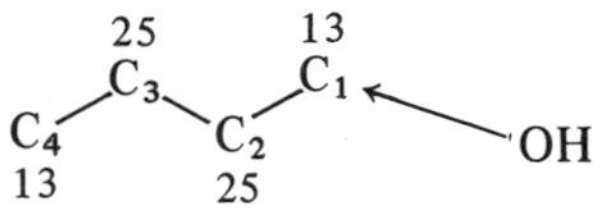

$$(5.15)$$

Carbon 1 Influence of OH on a CH_2 group α- to it is +50. Chemical shift = 13 + 50 = δ 63
Note that the α-shift caused by the OH group (+ 50) is here considered to influence the attacked carbon as a CH_2 carbon, even although we use, as the base, the δ value for the hydrocarbons, in which this carbon is in a CH_3 group.
Carbon 2 Influence of −OH on a β-carbon is + 9. Chemical shift = 25 + 9 = δ 34
Carbon 3 Influence of −OH on a γ-carbon is −3. Chemical shift = 25 − 3 = δ 22

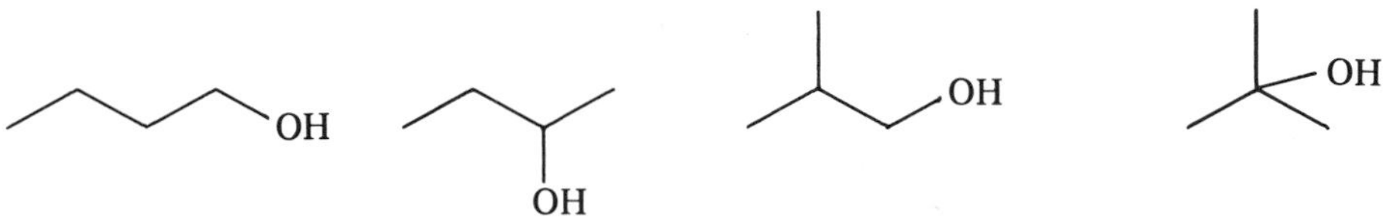

$$(5.13)$$

| 1-butanol (*n*-butyl) | 2-butanol (*sec*-butyl) | 2-methyl-1-propanol (isobutyl) | 2-methyl-2-propanol (*tert*-butyl) |

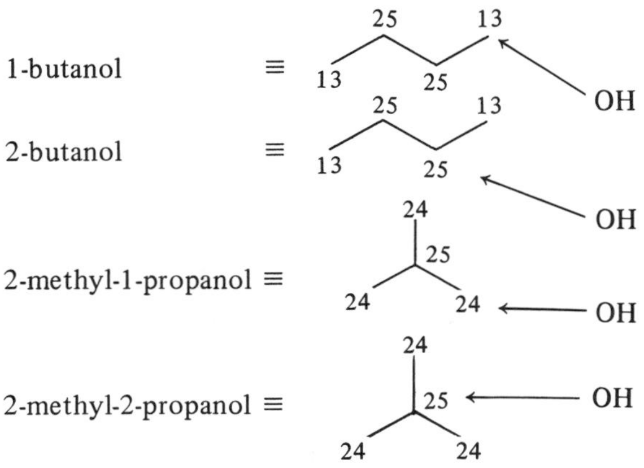

$$(5.14)$$

Carbon 4 Influence of −OH on δ-carbon is zero
Chemical shift = δ 13
(Observed δ values, 60, 37, 22, 16)

2-Butanol (sec-butyl)

$$\begin{array}{cc} \overset{25}{C_3} & \overset{13}{C_1} \\ C_4 & C_2 \\ 13 & 25 \end{array} \quad \text{OH}$$ (5.16)

C-1 Chemical shift = 13 + 9 (β −OH) = δ 22
C-2 Chemical shift = 25 + 45 (−OH on −CH−) = δ 70
C-3 Chemical shift = 25 + 9 (β −OH = δ 34
C-4 Chemical shift = 13 − 3 (γ −OH) = δ 10
(Observed δ values, 23, 69, 32, 10)

2-Methyl-1-propanol (isobutyl)

$$\begin{array}{c} \overset{24}{C_4} \\ \overset{25}{C_2} \\ \overset{C_3}{24} \quad \overset{C_1}{24} \end{array} \longleftarrow \text{OH}$$ (5.17)

Chemical shifts
C-1   24 + 50 (α −OH on −CH₂−) = δ 74
C-2   25 + 9 (β −OH)   = δ 34
C-3, C-4   24 − 3 (γ −OH)   = δ 21
(Observed δ values, 70, 31, 19)

2-Methyl-2-propanol (tert-butyl)

$$\begin{array}{c} \overset{24}{C_4} \\ \overset{25}{C_2} \longleftarrow \text{OH} \\ \overset{C_3}{24} \quad \overset{C_1}{24} \end{array}$$ (5.18)

Chemical shifts
C-1, C-2, C-3   24 + 9 (β −OH) = δ 33
C-2   25 + 40 (α −OH on −CH−) = δ 65
(Observed δ values, 31, 69. See also figure 1.4)

Problem Example 5.3
Predict the ¹³C chemical shift values for 4-methyl-2-pentanol. The observed spectrum is shown in figure 5.6 assign the peaks. Use the δ values calculated in problem example 5.1 for the alkane base, and recall that the shift in this molecule will be appropriate for a secondary alcohol (+ 45). The assignments for the three methyl groups shown on the spectrum were confirmed using chemical shift reagent, Eu(DPM)₃ (see section 4.10.2

Problem Example 5.4
Figure 5.7 is the carbon-13 NMR spectrum of an unequ mixture of 2-methyl-1-butanol and 3-methyl-1-butano Predict the δ values for both of these, assign the peak and thus show which alcohol predominates.

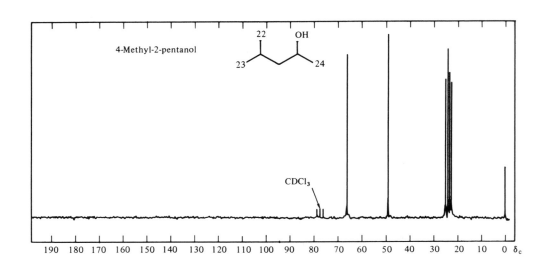

Figure 5.6 ¹³C NMR spectrum of 4-methyl-2-pentanol (25 MHz, in CDCl₃)

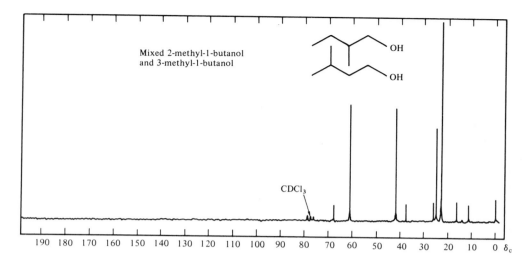

Figure 5.7 ^{13}C NMR spectrum of an unequal mixture of 3-methyl-1-butanol and 2-methyl-1-butanol (25 MHz, in CDCl$_3$)

Problem Example 5.5
Predict the δ values for (a) the alkane carbons in iso-propylbenzene and (b) the propyl ester group discussed in section 5.4.2. In each case use the propane chemical shifts shown in table 15.8 as base.

5.4.8 Influence of Functional Substituents on Alkene and Aromatic Chemical Shifts — Table 15.13

Use of table 15.13 is self-explanatory, since it follows on from the deductions which were made for alkane chemical shifts in the previous section.

The shifts listed for alkenes are of course only appropriate for the double bond carbons of the alkene: if alkane groups are present, then these carbons will be shifted as indicated in table 15.12.

Note also that alkene δ values will be affected by substitution at points further along the carbon chain (as in allyl alcohol, CH$_2$=CH–CH$_2$–OH) but systematic correlations have not been compiled. In any event, the major influence on the alkene carbons will be the *direct* substituent (in the case of allyl alcohol the CH$_2$ group) and this approach is usually satisfactory. In summary, if a substituent is identifiable as CH$_2$X, it should simply be treated as CH$_3$.

The same principles hold in predicting shifts in aromatic δ values. The table gives surprisingly good predictions for trisubstituted benzenes, even although the data are mainly based on measurements of the spectra of monosubstituted benzenes. Where deviations from pre-

dicted values are found, the reason is often associated with hydrogen bonding or steric effects: compounds related to salicylic acid show such deviations because of the strong intramolecular hydrogen bond between the OH group and the *ortho* carbonyl group.

Worked Example 5.6
Predict the carbon-13 δ values for the unsaturated acid part of the ester discussed in section 5.4.2.

Answer 5.6
The alkene group has only one substituent (–CH$_2$CH$_2$COOR) which must be approximated to CH$_3$. The two alkene carbons therefore are predicted from table 15.13 (and from table 15.9) to appear at δ 133 and δ 115. For the CH$_2$CH$_2$ part of the acid moiety we use ethane as the base: table 15.8 gives δ 5.7 for this. From table 15.12, these alkane carbons will be shifted respectively + 20 and + 2 (by COOR) and + 7 and + 22 (by CH=CH$_2$) giving δ 5.7 + 20 + 7 = δ 32.7 and δ 5.7 + 2 + 22 = δ 29.7

Worked Example 5.7
Predict the carbon-13 δ values for the ring carbons in *m*-nitroisopropylbenzene, discussed in section 5.4.2.

(5.19)

Answer 5.7
The isopropyl group is R, but branched at the point of attachment (giving a greater shift than the unbranched R substituent).

	Base	Isopropyl	Nitro	Total (δ)
C-1	128	+ 21	+ 1	150
C-2	128	0	− 5	123
C-3	128	0	+ 20	148
C-4	128	− 2	− 5	121
C-5	128	0	+ 1	129
C-6	128	0	+ 6	134

Problem Example 5.6
The carbon-13 NMR spectrum for vinyl acetate ($CH_3COOCH=CH_2$) shows four signals at δ 20, 97, 142 and 168. Confirm from table 15.13 that the middle two are the signals from the alkene carbons.

Problem Example 5.7
The carbon-13 NMR spectra for vanillin (the flavour constituent of vanilla) and methyl salicylate (oil of wintergreen, and the dominant flavour constituent of root beer) are shown in figures 5.8 and 5.9 respectively. Assign as many ring carbons as possible, and compare with the listed assignments. (Quaternary carbons give weaker signals: see section 5.2.)

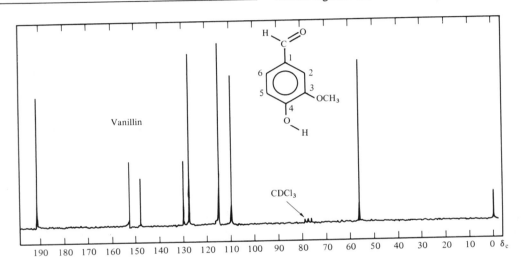

Figure 5.8 ^{13}C NMR spectrum of vanillin (25 MHz, in $CDCl_3$)

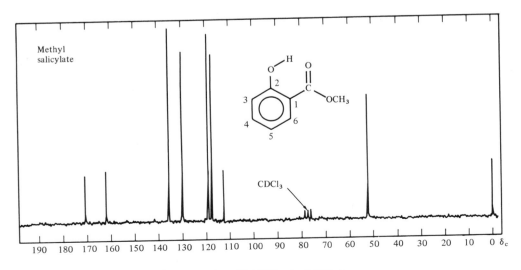

Figure 5.9 ^{13}C NMR spectrum of methyl salicylate (25 MHz, in $CDCl_3$)

vanillin

methyl salicylate

(5.20)

5.4.9 Carbonyl Group Chemical Shifts – Table 15.14

The ability to observe directly the NMR characteristics of carbonyl carbons is a major strength of carbon-13 NMR in chemistry. Additionally, the carbonyl resonance is at very high frequency, so that it is well separated from interferences and confusions. The ultimate merit lies in the narrow ranges within which different classes appear (see table 15.14) so that quite fine distinction can be made, in the knowledge that the influence of unaccounted factors will be minimal.

The ranges quoted in the table are capable of further subdivisions according to substitution and conjugation effects, and detailed study has amassed quite comprehensive information on carbonyl shifts: compendia of data are listed in Further Reading. The present purpose is more limited, and adequately served by the values in table 15.14.

Introduction of alkyl groups on the carbons directly bonded to CO usually shifts the CO signal by 2–3 ppm.

The influence of ring size in cyclic ketones is important but not well understood, though ring strain will obviously play a part: cyclopropanone gives a CO signal at δ 155.

Conjugation with the CO group has an effect on the carbonyl resonance of moving it to lower frequency; interestingly in esters, the same effect arises even if the 'conjugation' is in the alcohol-derived part of the ester (such as in vinyl esters).

Perhaps surprisingly, the anions of carboxylic acids are not much shifted in range from the free acids, in spite of the fact that the C—O bonding in carboxylate anions is weaker (because of the resonance system) than the true C=O bond in the acids. Theory fails to offer a convincing explanation.

Problem Example 5.8
Go back to worked example 5.6, and problem examples 5.6 and 5.7 and predict the δ values for the carbonyl carbons present.

5.4.10 Miscellaneous Multiple-bonded Carbon Chemical Shifts – Table 15.15

The shifts listed here are presented largely without comment, but they are needed to complete a useful data base in the tables. They also help to emphasise the value of carbon-13 NMR in directly observing such environments spectroscopically.

5.4.11 Methyl Group Chemical Shifts – Table 15.16

An isolated methyl group (isolated in the NMR sense) is such a common feature of organic molecules that a compilation of their δ values is helpful.

Apart from methyl amines and the rather simple circumstance of methyl substitution of a double bond, when the δ value varies widely, the range of chemical shift is very narrow (and reliably so).

Clear unambiguous distinctions can be made for example between acetates and methyl esters: this is also easy with proton NMR, using table 15.1.

Problem Example 5.9
Go back to problem examples 5.6 and 5.7 and complete the spectra interpretations by assigning the isolated methyl group in each molecule.

5.5 COUPLING CONSTANTS IN CARBON-13 NMR SPECTRA – TABLE 15.17 – SATELLITES

Carbon-13 nuclei couple with other magnetic nuclei and in this they follow the rules laid out for proton coupling in chapter 4. Thus the $(2nI + 1)$ rule (sections 4.6.1 and 4.8.1) and the defined concept of magnetic equivalence (section 4.7.1) apply for carbon-13 splittings.

Although broad band proton decoupled spectra are the most frequently recorded for carbon-13 NMR study, the coupling constants J_{CH} and J_{CD} are themselves of value in structural work. Coupling of carbon-13 to carbon-13 (homonuclear coupling) is not commonly observed, but must be considered, and coupling to other spin $\frac{1}{2}$ nuclei will also be exemplified.

> Where carbon-13 resonances are split by coupling to another nucleus, then the converse mutual splitting must also be present in the NMR signal of that other nucleus, with the same value of coupling constant seen in both spectra.

This important point is easily missed, since at natural abundance only 1.1% of the carbons are carbon-13, and 98.9% are carbon-12 and so give no NMR signal.

As an example, chloroform ($CHCl_3$) gives a carbon-13 signal and a proton signal. The carbon signal arises from the 1.1% of molecules containing carbon-13, and 100% of these contain proton so that the carbon-13 signal is split by $^1J_{CH}$. The proton signal arises from the 100% of molecules with ^1H, only 1.1% of which contain carbon-13: the proton NMR spectrum therefore consists of an intense singlet (from the 98.9% of $^{12}C-H$ groups) and a weak doublet split by $^1J_{CH}$ (from the 1.1% of $^{13}C-H$ groups). Each line of the doublet has an intensity of 0.55% of the large singlet intensity.

The positions of the two lines symmetrically on either side of the main signal give rise to the name *carbon-13 satellites*.

Carbon-13 satellites occur then in the NMR spectrum of any nucleus that is spin coupled to carbon, but they will only be observed at high sensitivity and associated with a strong signal.

Accurate measurement of chemical shifts sometimes shows a slight isotope effect in these satellite signals due to the different isotopomers involved ($^{13}CHCl_3$ and $^{12}CHCl_3$), but to a close approximation the satellites sit symmetrically astride the uncoupled signal.

5.5.1 Coupling of Carbon-13 to Hydrogen and Deuterium

Most applications of carbon-13 NMR in chemistry centre around broad band proton decoupled spectra ($^{13}C-\{^1H\}$ spectra) although off resonance proton decoupling (section 5.1.4) is valuable in providing multiplicity information.

Figure 5.1(b) is an example which shows clearly the quartet splitting in $CH_3{}^{13}COOH$ due to $^2J_{CH}$, but such clarity is only possible with isotope enrichment. Commensurately, the proton NMR spectrum of this molecule will show a clear doublet for the CH_3 group, with the same $^2J_{CH}$ value.

For natural abundance molecules of any complexity, proton coupling produces very extensively split signals, since long range couplings also arise: consider the effect on carbon resonance of the methyl group in $CH_3CH_2CH_2X$ if it is successively split by $^1J_{CH}$ into a quartet, $^2J_{CH}$ in triplets and $^3J_{CH}$ into triplets. The amount of valuable chemical data contained in such a signal is considerable, but its extraction and presentation is a major problem. One approach uses a computer program to display the information in 'two-dimensional' form, and this is briefly described in section 7.7.

A few selected values of J_{CH} are given for interest in table 15.17. There is a consistent relationship between the value of $^1J_{CH}$ and the s-character of the carbon, ranging from around 250 Hz for alkyne C—H to around 125 Hz for alkane C—H. Increased substitution by

electronegative groups (such as fluorine) also increase the J value.

Since most carbon-13 NMR spectra are recorded in solution with a deuterated solvent, solvent molecules such as $CDCl_3$ (deuteriochloroform), C_6D_6 (hexadeuteriobenzene or benzene-d_6) and CD_3COCD_3 (acetone-d_6) give rise to a carbon signal in the spectrum. The multiplicity can be predicted from $(2nI + 1)$, and the characteristic $CDCl_3$ triplet appears at δ 77 in many spectra in this chapter.

Slow relaxation, multiplicity and the absence of NOE all conspire to make the solvent signal weak in routine recordings. Slight isotope shifts again arise between the hydrogen and deuterium analogues, but these are small (0.2 ppm).

5.5.2 Homonuclear Carbon Coupling

As we saw in section 5.1.1 the conjunction of two carbon-13 nuclei on adjacent sites is of low probability at natural abundance, but nevertheless such isotopomers are present. This is conceptually important, because it leads to the deduction that for all carbon-13 signals in routine spectra there must exist carbon-13 satellite peaks on each side of the principal peak.

Detection and analysis of these satellites gives information about which carbon atoms are bonded to which, since the same coupling constant $^1J_{CC}$ will appear in each related pair of signals. Since the recording and presentation of the information is computer processed, we will delay further discussion until chapter 7.

Many $^1J_{CC}$ values have been obtained from synthetically enriched molecules, and a few representative examples are given in table 15.17.

5.5.3 Coupling of Carbon-13 to Other Nuclei

Provided coupling to protons is removed, then molecules containing other spin $\frac{1}{2}$ nuclei give fairly simple carbon-13 spectra, especially if only one atom of the 'other' nucleus is present in the compound, since each coupling carbon signal will appear as a doublet (from the simple $(n + 1)$ rule for spin $\frac{1}{2}$ nuclei).

Figure 5.10 shows the carbon-13 NMR spectrum for trifluoroacetic acid, CF_3COOH, and each of the two carbon signals is split into quartets. The one bond coupling $^1J_{CF}$ is 284 Hz and the coupling to the carboxyl carbon, $^2J_{CF}$, is 44 Hz, so the signals are readily assigned (and chemical shift values also agree). The $CDCl_3$ triplet appears as usual at δ 77.

Because the carbon-13 and fluorine-19 chemical shift positions are so far apart (20 MHz and 75 MHz in these

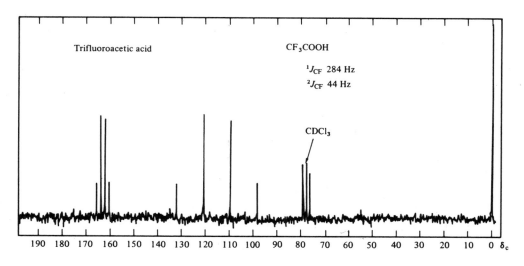

Figure 5.10 ^{13}C NMR spectrum of trifluoroacetic acid, CF_3COOH (25 MHz, in $CDCl_3$). $CDCl_3$ triplet at δ 77

spectra) relative to the coupling constants (284 Hz and 44 Hz) the ratio $\Delta \nu : J$ is very large indeed so these multiplets are truly first order. This is a general rule in heteronuclear coupling.

Worked Example 5.8

Describe the appearance of the ^{19}F NMR signal for the fluorines in trifluoroacetic acid.

Answer 5.8

The signal will consist mainly of a singlet, but a satellite doublet will be present (very low intensity) from the isotopomer $^{13}CF_3COOH$ ($^1J_{CF}$ = 284 Hz) and a second satellite doublet arises from the other important isotopomer $CF_3{}^{13}COOH$ ($^2J_{CF}$ = 44 Hz).

Problem Example 5.10

Figure 5.11 is the ^{13}C–$\{^1H\}$ NMR spectrum for triphenylphosphine selenide, $Ph_3P=Se$, analogous to the oxide, Ph_3PO. Both ^{31}P and ^{77}Se have $I = \frac{1}{2}$ but while ^{31}P is 100% abundant, ^{77}Se is present only at 7.6% and no C–Se couplings are noted. Given the C–P coupling constants shown in the figure, assign the signals for the ring carbons. (The ^{31}P and ^{77}Se NMR spectra for this compound are in figures 10.4 and 13.3 respectively.)

5.6 ADDITIONAL PROBLEMS

1. For each of the following compounds, the δ values for the ^{13}C NMR signals are listed. Assign the signals to each carbon in the molecule.

Methyl ethyl ketone $CH_3COCH_2CH_3$: 8, 29, 37, 208
Butanal $CH_3CH_2CH_2CHO$: 14, 16, 46, 202
Crotonaldehyde $CH_3CH=CHCHO$: 18, 135, 154, 193
Isobutyronitrile $Me_2CHC\equiv N$: 22, 20, 124
Anisole $C_6H_5OCH_3$: 55, 114, 121, 130, 160
Benzyl acetate $CH_3COOCH_2C_6H_5$: 21, 66, 128, 128.5, 136, 171
m-cresol m-$CH_3C_6H_4OH$: 21, 113, 116, 122, 129, 140, 155
Ethyl trifluoroacetate $CF_3COOCH_2CH_3$: 14, 65, 115 (quartet, J = 285 Hz) 158 (quartet, J = 42 Hz)

2. Figure 5.12 is the undecoupled ^{13}C NMR spectrum of a 60 : 40 mixture of deuteriobenzene and 1,4-dioxane, (This is the ASTM test for spectrometer ^{13}C sensitivity: see section 14.3.4.) Explain its appearance, in particular the reasons for a 1:1:1 triplet at δ 128 but a 1:2:1 triplet at δ 67. Measure and assign the coupling constants; the spectrum was recorded on a 300 MHz instrument, from which you can calculate the carbon-13 frequency.

3. Figure 5.13 shows two spectra for trifluoroethanol. The upper trace is the carbon-13 spectrum, undecoupled. The lower trace is a triple resonance experiment (see section 4.10.3); the carbon-13 resonances are simultaneously decoupled from both proton and fluorine. State the frequencies of the two decoupling fields, B_2 and B_3. (The fluorine decoupler power was held at 50 W during acquisition of the FID, but reduced to 2 W during the delay period, to obviate overheating of the sample.) Analyse the spectrum multiplicity in terms of the coupling to proton and fluorine. The spectrum was

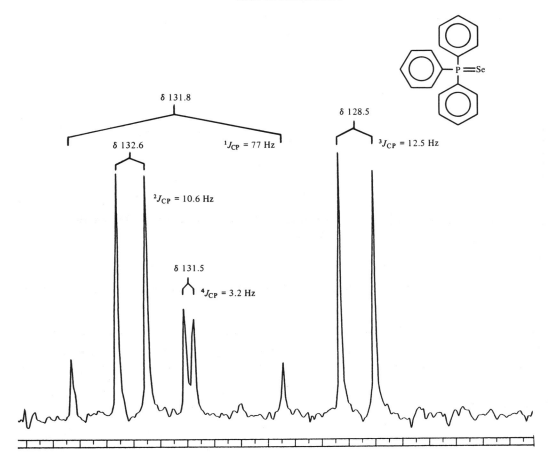

Figure 5.11 ^{13}C NMR spectrum of triphenylphosphine selenide, $Ph_3P=Se$ (20 MHz, in $CDCl_3$)

recorded at 20 MHz, and the two chemical shift positions are given; from this calculate the frequency scale of the spectrum and thence all of the coupling constants. For comparison, the proton NMR spectrum of this compound is shown in figure 4.4.

4. Figure 5.14 shows (above) the broad band proton decoupled ^{13}C NMR spectrum of codeine (the mono methyl ether of morphine) $C_{18}H_{21}NO_3$. Note: in the computer print-out (not shown) two close signals arise at δ 42.724 and 42.767: the scale expansion on the left shows them resolved, and thus all 18 lines can be identified. In the off resonance proton decoupled spectrum (below) scale expansions of the regions 35–50 and 110–150 ppm are given. Assign as many of the resonances as possible, using the following sequential approach.

(a) The aromatic ring: draw the structure of benzene, bearing the substituents MeO, RO, R and R in the same positions as in codeine, and predict the chemical shifts of the ring carbons using table 15.13.

(b) Predict the chemical shift positions of the cyclohexene ring: use as a base the δ values shown in table 15.9 for cyclohexene itself. For the alkane carbons, use table 15.12 to compute the influence of the substituents OH, OR, R and (R + Ar). Do likewise for the alkene carbons, using table 15.13.

Note that the aromatic and alkene carbons must appear in the off resonance decoupled spectrum either as doublets or singlets: compare these with the broad band decoupled spectrum. Note in particular that the signal at δ 127 remains a singlet, and the line at δ 128 is a doublet – which partly overlaps the δ 127 signal in the lower spectrum. Although distorted, the signals at δ 113 and 120 are doublets.

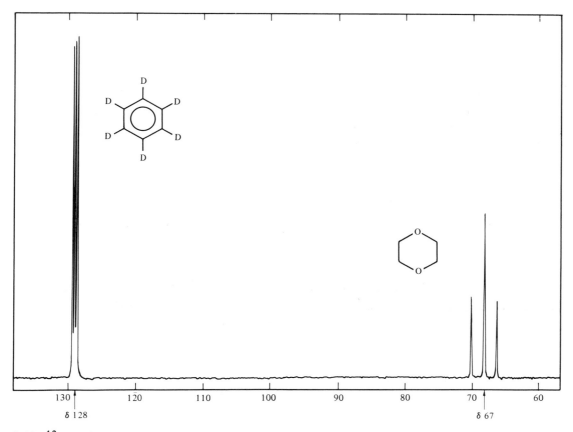

Figure 5.12 ^{13}C NMR spectrum (coupling retained) of a 60:40 mixture of deuteriobenzene and dioxane (75 MHz, neat)

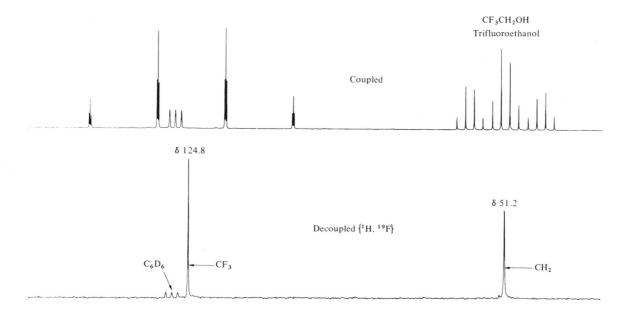

Figure 5.13 ^{13}C NMR spectra of trifluoroethanol, showing (below) the effect of triple resonance in decoupling both proton and fluorine (20 MHz, in C_6D_6)

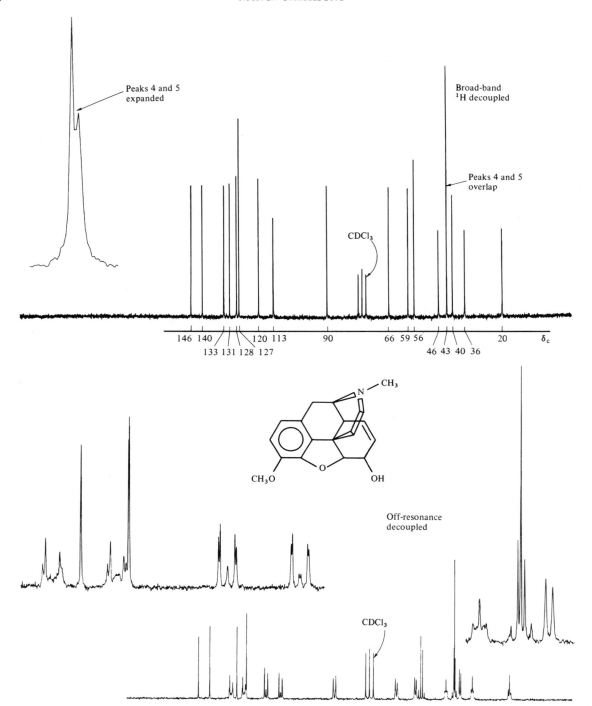

Figure 5.14 ^{13}C NMR spectra of codeine, both proton decoupled (above) and off resonance decoupled (below) (20 MHz, in CDCl$_3$)

(c) The six membered heterocyclic ring can be analysed using the chemical shifts of piperidine as base (table 15.11). Thereafter compute the influence on the alkane carbons (table 15.12) of the substituents (Ar, CH_2=CH–, $PhCH_2$– (taken as R), and $-\overset{\vert}{C}H-O-$ (taken as R)).

(d) For the remaining ring, use tetralin as the model (table 15.11).

(e) Use table 15.1 to predict the positions of the two methyl resonances.

Note that the alkane carbons will appear as singlets, doublets, triplets and quartets in the lower spectrum. A clear quartet is seen at δ 56 and a clear doublet is seen at δ 40 (scale expanded above). Although distorted, the signals at δ 20, 36 and 46 (expanded above) are all triplets. Peaks 4 and 5 are also shown in the scale expansion: close examination shows this to be an overlapped singlet and quartet.

6 More Advanced Theories of NMR

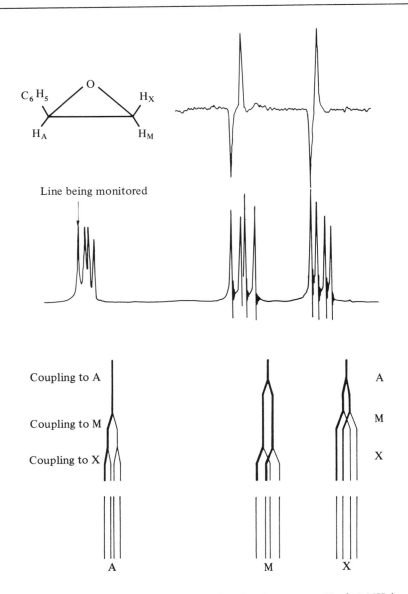

The INDOR experiment on the molecule of styrene oxide (90 MHz)

The two quite separate theoretical models of NMR, first set out in section 1.8 and elaborated in chapter 2, must be further extended to permit the description and explanation of several more complex NMR experiments.

The energy levels of quantum theory and their populations can be used to give a more quantitative approach to the coupling constant, J, and lead to an understanding of the sign of J and its measurement. The energy levels of more complex spin systems will also be rationalised by these arguments.

The mathematics and physics of precession are complex, but by examining pulse irradiation and relaxation processes with respect to a rotating frame of reference, many useful NMR techniques can be satisfactorily modelled without mathematical elaboration.

6.1 THEORY OF SPIN–SPIN COUPLING – II

Whereas the multiplicity of NMR signals can be deduced in the simplest cases from considerations of the $(n + 1)$ rule discussed in section 4.6, the manner in which nuclear spins interact depends on the physical state of the sample. In solids, there exists a powerful direct interaction among the nuclear dipoles which requires special techniques to study, and this is delayed until chapter 7.

Routine NMR spectra are recorded in the liquid state and, if the sample is a solid, it must be dissolved in a suitable solvent. In non-viscous liquids and solutions (and in gases) random molecular tumbling is sufficiently rapid to average the direct dipolar interaction effectively to zero, but there remains a very much weaker spin–spin coupling which gives rise to the splittings observed in the spectra seen up to now: J is a measure of the magnitude of this interaction.

6.1.1 Electron-coupled Spin–Spin Interactions Between Directly-bonded Nuclei

The weaker internuclear coupling transmits its effects *via* the electrons of intervening bonds, and is about one thousand times weaker than the direct dipolar coupling. Some impression of its characteristics can most easily be understood with reference to figure 6.1 (which applies only to nuclei with $I = \frac{1}{2}$). Typical atoms in the figure would be ^{13}C and ^{1}H.

Two electrons sharing an orbital must have anti-parallel spins (Pauli exclusion principle); the electron spin and the nuclear spin also combine either parallel or antiparallel, and we need consider only the case where the antiparallel pairing is the more stable. The nuclear magnetic dipole of A in figure 6.1(a) is aligned with $\mathbf{B_0}$,

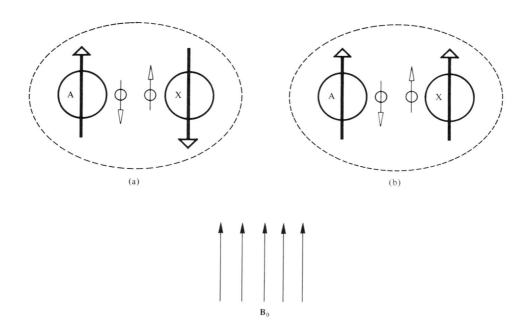

(a)   (b)

$\mathbf{B_0}$

Figure 6.1 Through-bond spin coupling for two directly bonded atoms A and X. The electrons in the bond must remain antiparallel, but the nuclear spins may be antiparallel (a) or parallel (b). Usually, (a) is the more stable arrangement

and the electron nearest to A (loosely, the electron associated with A) has its spin antiparallel to A. The other electron in the A–X bond (loosely, the electron associated with X) is antiparallel to the first electron, and nucleus X is in turn antiparallel to that.

Thus the most stable arrangement of nuclear and electronic spins in two directly-bonded atoms leads to the spins of nuclei A and X being antiparallel. The orientation shown in figure 6.1(b), with the spins of A and X parallel, is of higher energy.

> Coupling between the nuclei of directly-bonded atoms arises through pairing of nuclear and electronic spins. Usually, the more stable system has the two nuclear spins antiparallel.

This is based on a very simplistic model; exceptions exist, but the principles remain useful. The magnetogyric ratios of A and X must have the same sign for the situation in figure 1.6 to arise, so that a ^{15}N–^1H bond would be a converse relationship.

It is worth pausing to recall the calculations of energy relationships in chapter 1 (see for example worked example 1.4); the energy of these interactions is measured in a few hertz, and since, from $\Delta E = h\nu$, 15 Hz corres-

ponds to about 10^{-32} J, we are dealing with exceedingly small energy differences. Correspondingly, from Boltzmann theory (see section 2.16) in a given ensemble of nuclei, because ΔE is so small, the nuclei will be divided almost exactly equally between the two energy levels.

6.1.2 Electron-coupled Spin–Spin Interactions Between Protons in CH_2 Groups

More complicated is the case of two magnetic nuclei bonded commonly to a non-magnetic nucleus, and we can regard the methylene group as representative (see figure 6.2(a).)

If we let proton A have its spin parallel to $\mathbf{B_0}$, the 'nearby' electron adopts antiparallel spin and thus the electron near carbon is again parallel to $\mathbf{B_0}$. The next electron in the chain leading to X is in a carbon orbital degenerate with the first, and Hund's rule (maximum multiplicity) stipulates that it too must be parallel as shown. Thereafter the last electron is antiparallel and proton X is parallel.

> Coupling between nuclei bonded to a common non-magnetic nucleus usually stabilises the arrangement with the nuclear spins parallel.

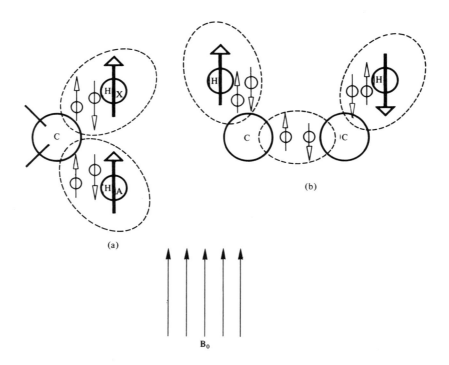

(a)

(b)

$\mathbf{B_0}$

Figure 6.2 Through-bond spin coupling for two protons joined geminally (a) and vicinally (b) through carbon. Usually, two-bond coupling systems are more stable with the nuclear spins parallel to each other, and for three-bond couplings the system usually is more stable when the two coupling spins are antiparallel

The principles can be extended to show that whether parallel or antiparallel arrangements are stabilised depends very much on the number of intervening bonds. Thus in H−C−C−H coupling it is again the antiparallel arrangement of nuclear spins which is usually stabilised, as in figure 6.2(b).

We are now in a position to see how these interactions lead to the splitting of NMR absorption lines.

6.2 ENERGY LEVELS FOR AN AX COUPLING SYSTEM

Two isolated nuclei A and X give rise to NMR absorptions whenever they undergo transition from one spin state to another; the simplest case is for $I = \frac{1}{2}$ nuclei such as protons, and the transitions are between aligned and opposed orientations, that is, between (A↑) and (A↓) and between (X↑) and (X↓).

The ways in which these spins can be combined are four in number

(A↑) (X↑) lowest in energy, with both spins aligned with B_0

(A↓) (X↓) highest in energy, with both spins opposed to B_0

(A↑) (X↓) and (A↓) (X↑) of intermediate energy

We can conveniently use the labels introduced in figure 1.10 and describe the four spin combinations as $\alpha\alpha$, $\alpha\beta$, $\beta\alpha$ and $\beta\beta$. These represent four different energy levels, whose values alter if the interaction between nucleus A and X is weak or strong, that is, if the coupling constant is zero or large.

The relative energy levels are set out (but not to scale) in figure 6.3. Transitions (that is, NMR absorptions) are only allowed if *one* spin at a time changes its orientation; thus the four allowed transitions are A_1 and A_2 which interchange (A↑) and (A↓), and X_1 and X_2, which interchange (X↑) and (X↓). (For nuclei with negative magnetogyric ratios such as nitrogen-15 (see chapter 2) the energies of the α and β states are reversed.) If the spin–spin interaction between A and X is zero, then A_1 and A_2 are of equal energy and only one absorption line is observed in the spectrum for A. Similarly X_1 and X_2 are equal and give rise to only one line. The spectrum consists of two singlet signals, corresponding to the transitions at (a) in figure 6.3.

> This system represents a coupling constant $J = 0$.

If antiparallel spins are stabilised by spin–spin coupling (and parallel spins destabilised) then the four transitions

are all unequal and four absorption lines arise in the spectrum corresponding to two doublets, A_1, A_2, and X_1, X_2, as shown at (b) in figure 6.3.

> This system represents a coupling constant J, defined as positive.

If parallel pairing is stabilised by electron-coupled interaction (and antiparallel destabilised) again four lines appear, as a pair of doublets, arising from the transitions shown at (c) in figure 6.3.

> This system represents a coupling constant J, defined as negative.

The energy increases or decreases (ΔE) brought about by the coupling interaction lead to shifts in the frequencies of the lines. Thus when $J = 0$, the A transitions correspond to the energy gap between levels 1 and 3 and between 2 and 4 (both transitions being of equal frequency). When the coupling stabilises the antiparallel arrangement of nuclear spins (J positive) the A transition (1 to 3) is decreased by an amount corresponding to $2\Delta E$, and thus its frequency is *lowered*, whereas the A transition (2 to 4) is increased by an amount $2\Delta E$, and its frequency is *increased*. Thus line A_1 corresponds to transition (2 to 4) and line A_2 corresponds to transition (1 to 3): this is the doublet shown at (b) in figure 6.3.

Conversely, if coupling stabilises the parallel spin arrangement (J therefore negative), then as seen at (c) in figure 6.3, the A_1 and A_2 lines correspond respectively to transitions (1 to 3) and (2 to 4).

Similar arguments explain the labelling of the X transitions: the two different X transitions, (1 to 2) and (3 to 4) give rise to different lines in the spectrum depending on whether J is positive or negative.

The separation between the lines in the doublets is equal to $4\Delta E$, and this is the coupling constant J. In terms of magnitude, note that the chemical shifts of A and X are much more nearly equal than is implied in figure 6.3, and that ΔE is very small.

It will bring perspective to these interactions if we put some real values on the energy changes, based on the simple AX system in cytosine, shown in figure 4.6. The chemical shifts for the two protons both involve transitions corresponding to about 60 000 000 Hz, the chemical shift difference between them being only 1.8 ppm, or 108 Hz. The coupling constant, J, is 8 Hz so the energy change involved for each energy level in the coupling interaction is a mere 2 Hz. Clearly the diagram is out of scale by a factor of tens of millions.

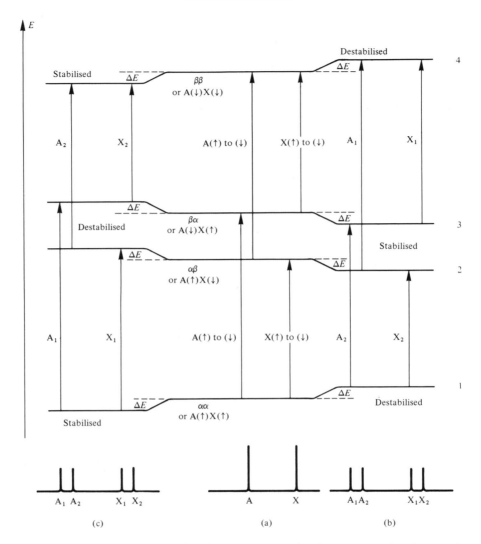

Figure 6.3 The coupling interaction among nuclei alters the energy levels and transition frequencies: the coupling constant, J, is a measure of this energy of interaction

An alternative representation for the energy levels in the AX system is shown in figure 6.4. This helps to emphasise the commonality of the energy levels and will be useful when we come to consider how changes in the populations of the levels of one nucleus can cause changes in the populations of the levels in the other nucleus to which it is coupled.

6.2.1 The Sign of the Coupling Constant, J

In sections 6.1.1 and 6.1.2 two different circumstances were considered in nuclear spin combinations, and these are defined arbitrarily as either positive J (if antiparallel spins are more stable) and negative J (if parallel spins are more stable). A careful comparison of figure 6.3(b) and 6.3(c) will reveal that for a simple AX spectrum of four lines, the appearance of the spectrum will be identical whether J is positive as at (b), or J is negative as at (c): figure 6.4 shows the essential points. It follows that simple examination of an AX spectrum such as figure 4.6 does not reveal whether J is positive or negative. This is a general conclusion for all first order spectra.

The appearance of non-first order spectra is dependent on the sign of J, hence it is important to appreciate its origin.

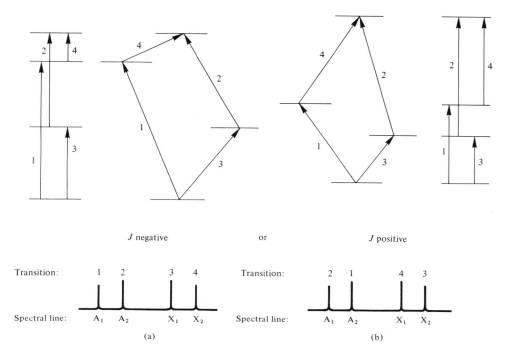

Figure 6.4 The relative energies in an AX coupling system, represented in different ways. Each nucleus has two energy levels and, when these interact, four new (shared) levels are generated

Special double irradiation methods can reveal the relative signs of coupling constants in for example AMX spectra, and these are discussed in section 6.4.

It can be stated fairly that most interpretive NMR applications to structure determination are unaffected by a knowledge or ignorance of the sign of J, and for this reason, the values of J_{HH} selected in table 15.7 are given without sign. It is however of paramount importance in theoretical work, and Further Reading lists appropriate references to more theoretical texts.

6.2.2 Factors Influencing the Coupling Constant, J

Considering the number of magnetic nuclides in the periodic table, it is impossible within reasonable compass to summarise the factors which influence all of the possible homonuclear cases far less than the heteronuclear possibilities. Since empirical information is so abundant in available reviews, our purpose is best served by listing these in Further Reading, while table 6.1 shows the enormously wide variation in J values that are typical. More values are included in the separate chapters on NMR in specific nuclei: see for example sections 4.6–4.8 for proton coupling and 5.5 for carbon-13 coupling.

Table 6.1 Examples to indicate the wide range in the value of the coupling constant, J

	System	J/Hz
J_{HH}	H–H (in the hydrogen molecule)	240
	H–C–H	12
	H–C–C–H	8
	H–C–C=C–H	1
	H–C–F, H–C–C–F, etc.	1–50
	^{13}C–H	120
	^{13}C–Hg	2500
	^{31}P–^{31}P	600
	^{31}P–^{19}F	1400
	^{31}P–Pt	3000

Generally, the two factors which most influence coupling constants are (a) the product of the two magnetogyric ratios and (b) the number of intervening bonds. The electron distribution in these bonds is also vitally involved, so that electronegative substituents and conformational effects come into play in various subtle ways.

6.2.3 Non-first Order AB Spectra

In proton NMR, non-first order spectra are the rule rather than the exception, and we saw in section 4.9 that in the simplest AB case there are two differences from the AX case that arise: (a) the line intensities change and (b) the line positions change, so that the origin chemical shift positions are no longer the mid-points of the doublets (see figure 4.22). A proper analysis of AB spin systems is outside the scope of this present non-mathematical approach, but qualitatively the effect involves further changes in the energy levels indicated in figure 6.3. Further interactions, and mixing of the levels, depend very much on the ratio $\Delta\nu{:}J$. The calculation of δ values shown in figure 4.22 can be adopted if exact data are demanded.

6.3 ENERGY LEVELS FOR AN AMX COUPLING SYSTEM

For three protons with widely separated chemical shift, the twelve-line AMX spectrum arises, and assignments of coupling constants (J_{AM}, J_{AX}, J_{MX}) were considered in section 4.7.5.

An extension of the arguments of section 6.2 shows that, since each of the three protons has two spin states (α and β) then there are eight ways in which they can be considered, as shown in figure 6.5. (The levels $\alpha\alpha\beta$ and $\alpha\beta\beta$ are shown without any attempt to indicate relative energies.)

The arrows indicate the twelve allowed transitions, in each of which only one spin is inverted at a time.

Note again, as an extension of the system in figure 6.4, that each energy level is shared by three spin states (one from each of the orientations of A, M and X).

It will be profitable to focus on a few of the transitions. Those transitions which involve the A spin changing from α to β are the transitions for the four lines in the A part of the spectrum (transitions 1, 5, 7 and 12). For the four M lines (in which M changes from α to β) the four transitions 2, 4, 9 and 11 are involved. In the remaining transitions lie the corresponding four X lines.

The actual appearance of the spectrum will depend on the relative sizes and signs of the coupling constants, but the general appearance of figure 4.18 is typical.

Although the energy diagram in figure 6.5 allocates the correct relationship among the A, M and X lines, it cannot directly say which are the lines A_1, A_2, A_3 or A_4 and so on, unless the relative signs of the coupling constants J_{AM}, J_{AX} and J_{MX} are known.

6.4 DETERMINATION OF THE RELATIVE SIGNS OF J

The sign of J is primarily of theoretical interest but it would be remiss not to look briefly at two techniques which allow the sign to be determined. Each uses double irradiation, and each can be understood in terms of figures 6.3, 6.4 and 6.5.

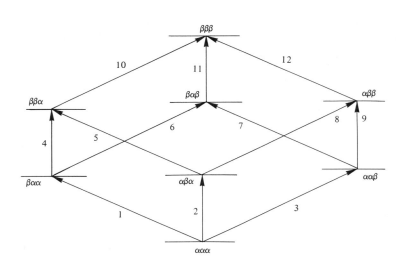

Figure 6.5 Shared energy levels for an AMX coupling system. The spin of each nucleus can be α or β, and the eight different combinations are shown (with the A spin followed by the M and X spins)

6.4.1 Spin Tickling

If a weak RF signal is used to double irradiate one line of a multiplet, then the perturbation brought about leads to splitting of lines in the multiplet(s) with which the irradiated nucleus is coupling. The effect is illustrated in figure 6.6 for the simplest AX case. Note also the general (experimentally observed) feature that while one line is split sharply, the other is split more broadly: the sharp splitting is associated with transitions which share a *regressive* relationship (1 and 3, 2 and 4 in figure 6.4) while transitions which form *progressive* pairs (1 and 4, 3 and 2 in figure 6.4) give the broader splitting.

In this case the A_1 line is shown to be involved with the transition 1 in figure 6.4, left, since irradiation at A_1 splits X_1 (transition 3) regressively and X_2 (transition 4) progressively.

Problem Example 6.1

Describe the result of a spin tickling experiment on the same AX system when line A_2 is tickled.

The same arguments can be used in spin tickling experiments on AMX and more complex systems, allowing deductions to be made about the relative signs of coupling constants. The absolute values of J cannot be derived from these experiments.

6.4.2 INDOR – Internuclear Double Resonance

Heteronuclear decoupling methods are commonplace, and broad band proton decoupling is the normal practice for routine carbon-13 NMR spectra recording: it is unfortunate that the name INDOR is applied to a quite different variety of double irradiation, since its uniqueness sets it apart.

The simplest example of the technique can be seen in an AX coupling system, whose energy levels are shown in figure 6.4. In INDOR, the line intensity of one of the A lines is monitored, while the X lines are double irradiated.

For the example shown in figure 6.7, the first INDOR experiment is described as follows.

The line intensity of line A_1 is observed, and the recorder pen on the instrument follows changes in this intensity, moving *up* for *increase* and *down* for *decrease*: simultaneously, the pen moves across as the decoupler frequency is scanned across the two X resonances. When the decoupler is tuned to the line X_1 frequency, the line intensity of the observed A_1 line decreases, and the pen records a *negative* INDOR signal, and when the decoupler irradiates X_2, a *positive* INDOR peak is recorded.

The second INDOR experiment monitors the A_2 line intensity, again while scanning through the X frequencies.

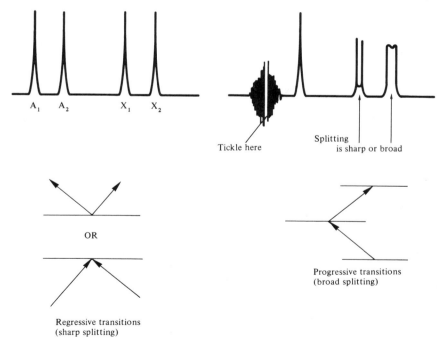

Figure 6.6 The principles of spin tickling, which perturbs those lines which are associated by coupling: the perturbed lines are either split sharply or broadly, depending on the relationship (progressive or regressive) in the shared energy level

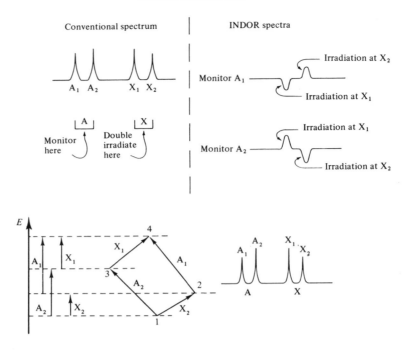

Figure 6.7 The principles of internuclear double resonance, INDOR, which monitors line intensity changes while coupling nuclei are being double irradiated

At X_1, a positive INDOR signal is now obtained and irradiation at X_2 gives a negative INDOR peak.

The explanation lies in the populations of the energy levels and in the manner in which they change during double irradiation (double resonance).

When the X_1 transition (3 to 4) is irradiated, nuclei in level 3 absorb energy and move to level 4: this depletes level 3 and augments the population of level 4. The A_1 line intensity is governed by the probability of undergoing the transition (2 to 4), but an increase in the population of level 4 renders the A_1 transition less probable, and the line intensity falls (a negative INDOR peak is recorded). When the decoupler scans through the X_2 frequency (transition 1 to 2) the population of level 1 is diminished and that of level 2 in increased, rendering more probable the transition (2 to 4); line A_1 of the spectrum therefore increases in intensity and a positive INDOR signal results. The second INDOR experiment, in which the intensity of line A_2 is continuously monitored and the X resonances irradiated, gives the converse changes shown in the figure.

Problem Example 6.2

If the coupling of the nuclear spins had generated the energy system shown in figure 6.4(a), describe the results of an INDOR experiment in which line A_2 is monitored.

INDOR can be used to examine spin relationships in much the same way as spin tickling; the decoupler power needed for INDOR is about one fifth of that for spin tickling (and about one twentieth of that for full decoupling) so the method is highly selective, causing minimum perturbance to nuclei with frequencies close to the irradiation frequency.

Note that in INDOR progressive and regressive relationships can also be identified, since a positive INDOR signal arises from progressive relationships, and a negative signal from regressive.

INDOR can be used to identify coupling systems in complex spectra: suppose that a doublet appears in a proton spectrum, with the associated multiplet (the other half of the coupling system) lost in a complex of peaks at another part of the spectrum. The line intensity of one line of the doublet is monitored, while the decoupler is scanned through the complex part of the spectrum: INDOR signals will be obtained at the precise frequency of the lines with which the doublet is associated, identifying their positions and the coupling constant exactly.

In the energy diagram for an AMX coupling system

(figure 6.5) the INDOR method can also be applied, giving information about the relative signs of the three coupling constants, J_{AM}, J_{AX} and J_{MX}.

Figure 6.5 allows the various possibilities to be rationalised; the simplest case is when all twelve lines of the spectrum are widely spaced and when all three coupling constants are positive. When this is so, then consider the four A lines first.

These involved the A nucleus changing from α to β, and thus the transitions 1, 5, 7 and 12 are involved, as discussed in section 6.3, but no decision can yet be made on associating any line with any transition; to do this we must study their relationships with the M and X nuclear spin states — whether α or β.

Thus, transition 1 is associated with M_α and X_α; 5 is associated with M_β and X_α; 7 is with M_α and X_β; finally 12 is with M_β and X_β.

The INDOR experiment now establishes the interconnections, by monitoring A lines and irradiating at M and X to establish progressive and regressive relationships. An example is shown at the chapter head, of monitoring line A_1 in the AMX system of the epoxide ring in styrene oxide. INDOR signals arise from lines M_1, M_3, X_1 and X_2, which means that M_1 and M_3 correspond to the same orientations of X, and that X_1 and X_2 correspond to the same orientations of M. Since, therefore, lines A_1 and M_1 have the same spin orientation of X in common, J_{AX} and J_{MX} have the same sign. Also, line A_1 and X_1 correspond to the same orientation of M, so J_{AM} and J_{MX} have the same sign.

Further INDOR experiments on the system confirm these assignments.

6.5 NET MAGNETISATION AND ITS VECTOR REPRESENTATION

In any NMR sample, there will be several million nuclei interacting with the static magnetic field B_0, and more of them will be in the lower energy state (aligned with the field) than in other states. At equilibrium, we can represent this as in figures 1.1 and 6.8(a) (for spin $= \frac{1}{2}$ nuclei): if all the magnetic dipoles are added algebraically, there will be a net excess aligned with B_0 (along the $+ z$-axis) and it is convenient to represent this slight excess of magnetism by a vector arrow, the *net magnetisation vector*, M_0, as shown in figure 6.8(b). Now, instead of considering an entire ensemble of nuclei made up of millions of bar magnets, we can describe many NMR phenomena as if the whole sample were represented by one resultant bar magnet, M_0. The direction of the

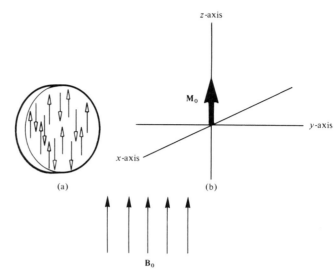

Figure 6.8 Net magnetisation along the z-axis, and its representation by a vector arrow

net magnetisation can also be specified with respect to the cartesian axes, x, y and z.

The size of M_0 will be different for different nuclei, since it depends on the relative populations of the available energy states, and this is governed (at equilibrium) by Boltzmann theory as we saw in section 2.16. For example, the net magnetisation vector for ^1H is clearly much greater than that for ^{13}C or ^{15}N.

We saw alternatively in chapter 2 that the precession model for protons in NMR pictures the nuclei as precessing around the z-axis on the surfaces of cones (of half angle $55°$) but that, strictly, the positions of the nuclei with respect to the xy plane are uncertain, and only the z-components can be measured. The reason for this relates to the direction of the applied field B_0, which we defined as acting along the z-axis (see figures 2.3 and 2.8).

What happens if a second magnetic field B_1 is applied along the x-axis? This is a crucial question.

The answer involves the physics of gyroscopes and torques, the essence of which is given in sections 14.1 and 14.2.

The second field, B_1, constitutes a torque acting upon the nuclei, and so the positions of the nuclei, previously being *random* with respect to the xy plane, are now *focused*. Because of the odd behaviour of bodies with spin angular momentum however (gyroscopes), the effect is to focus the nuclei towards the y-axis as shown in figure 6.9.

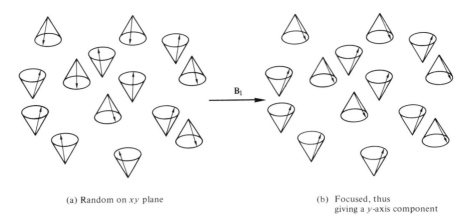

(a) Random on xy plane

(b) Focused, thus
     giving a y-axis component

Figure 6.9 Because nuclei are spinning, the effect of a polarised RF current along the x-axis has the effect of focus-sing the nuclei towards the y-axis. (A similar result would arise if the nuclear magnets were ordinary, *non-spinning* compass needles, and if a *static* magnet were acting along the y-axis.) The focussing creates a magnetisation component along the y-axis

In the NMR experiment, this problem is complicated by the fact that the second magnetic field ($\mathbf{B_1}$) is the fluctuating magnetic component of the RF signal along the x-axis, and in section 3.7.4 it was shown that this could be resolved into circularly polarised components, rotating around the z-axis.

The simplest situation arises if the incoming RF has the same frequency as all of the precessing nuclei, in which case $\mathbf{B_1}$ rotates around the z-axis 'in phase' with the nuclei. Where this is not so, an alternative viewpoint can simplify the physics involved.

6.6 FRAMES OF REFERENCE IN NMR

In the fifteenth century, Copernicus suggested that the movements of sun, stars and planets in our sky were more simply described by considering that the earth was rotating around the sun, rather than the converse. Shock-ing though his suggestion may then have been, it was a mathematical device which led to simpler equations of motion for the heavenly bodies; in physics and mathe-matics, many motions can be simplified by a suitable choice of the *frame of reference*. In NMR, there are two important frames of reference, each of which will be introduced through the observing eyes of the spectro-scopist as follows.

6.6.1 The Laboratory Frame

A proton in a 2.35 T magnet will be 'seen' precessing around a cone at 100 MHz (as in all of the theory discus-sed up until now) when the observing spectroscopist is standing beside the NMR instrument.

A carbon-13 nucleus will be 'seen' similarly precessing at 25 MHz in the same instrument. Most NMR phenom-ena can be satisfactorily described using this *laboratory frame of reference*.

6.6.2 Rotating Frames of Reference

A spectroscopist, imaginatively standing inside the NMR instrument with his feet on the xy plane, his body along the z-axis, and spinning around the z-axis at 100 MHz, will 'see' the protons lying on cones but not rotating around him. If he elects to spin at 25 MHz he will 'see' the carbon-13 nuclei static on cones, but at this same spinning rate, he will then 'see' the protons still preces-sing (since with respect to the laboratory frame their precession frequency is 100 MHz).

The precessional frequency of the protons 'seen' by the observer with respect to the 25 MHz rotating refer-ence frame will be 75 MHz (the difference between the two 'laboratory frame' frequencies). This is a general relationship.

It will be appropriate later to discuss certain phenom-ena with respect to different frequencies of rotating frames, usually designated for example as the *carbon rotating frame*, or the *proton rotating frame*, the rota-tion frequencies being 25 MHz and 100 MHz respectively when $\mathbf{B_0}$ is 2.35 T, and so on.

Worked Example 6.1

With respect to the proton rotating frame of reference

(at 100 MHz) what would be the precession frequency of carbon-13 nuclei?

Answer 6.1

75 MHz. (The magnitude is simply the difference in frequencies: the carbons would of course appear to be going 'backwards', implying negative sign).

Worked Example 6.2

In a $^{13}C-^1H$ group, the proton signals appear as a doublet, with J_{CH} = 120 Hz. With respect to the carbon rotating frame, what are the two proton frequencies, assuming the proton chemical shift to be 100 MHz exactly ($\delta = 0$)?

Answer 6.2

In the laboratory frame, for protons at 100 MHz, B_0 = 2.35 T so ν_c = 25 MHz. If we consider the uncoupled circumstances first, with δ = 100 MHz, then in the carbon rotating frame at 25 MHz the proton will be precessing at 75 MHz. Since the proton signal is split into a doublet of separation 120 Hz, one of the proton frequencies is at (75 MHz + 60 Hz) and the other at (75 MHz − 60 Hz). Note the involvement of the coupling constant, J, in determining frequencies with respect to a rotating frame of reference.

In these two examples lie the kernel of several advanced techniques discussed in chapter 7.

6.6.3 Axes of Rotating Frames, x', y' and z

By convention, we have used x-, y- and z-axes to define spatial effects in NMR, and these static axes therefore relate to the laboratory frame. We can specify a new set of axes for a rotating frame of reference, but, since this will rotate around the z-axis of the laboratory frame, the z-axis will be common to both frames of reference. The other axes in the rotating frame are labelled x' and y'. It is important to appreciate that Bloch's first major paper on magnetic induction (in 1946) described his fundamental NMR experiments using the rotating frame of reference, but it was some time before their significance in chemical applications of NMR became important.

6.7 PULSED RADIOFREQUENCY IN THE ROTATING FRAME

The rotating frame can be used to describe the continuous wave (CW) experiment in NMR, and Bloch's original equations were derived from such methods. The major merit of the rotating frame of reference is that it permits reasonably clear pictures of most of the exten-

sive range of pulse experiments which are at the growth points of NMR applications in chemistry, and the terminology will be introduced in this context.

6.7.1 Magnetisation on the y'-axis

The net magnetisation vector M_0 as shown in figure 6.8(b) was appropriate for the spins at equilibrium. The effect of B_1 in focusing the spins was illustrated in figure 6.9(b) but this can equally be represented in terms of a resultant vector (M_1) which is no longer aligned with the z-axis. In the rotating frame of reference, this vector M_1 is displaced towards the y'-axis as shown in figure 6.10(b). In the same rotating frame, the component of B_1 which is involved is static along the x'-axis; it is acting as a torque to rotate the vector M_0 to M_1.

The NMR receiver is tuned to receive signals in the y'-axis. At (a) in figure 6.10 there is no y' component of M_0 and so no signal is received. At (b), M_1 does have a component along the y'-axis and this leads to an NMR signal being received.

The pulse NMR experiment can now be succinctly described by vectors and rotating frames.

> A radiofrequency pulse acts on the equilibrium magnetisation, and rotates the vector M_0 towards the y'-axis.

6.7.2 Pulse Width and Flip Angle — 90° and 180° Pulses

The amount by which the vector M_0 is rotated depends on B_1, the power of the RF pulse. This is the product of its duration (or *pulse width*) and voltage amplitude; a hard pulse consists of a short burst at high amplitude, while a soft pulse consists of a rather longer burst of lower amplitude. Considering for the moment only the pulse width, figure 6.11 shows a series of signals received for different pulse widths (measured in μs). The explanation for the variation in signal intensity relates again to the instrumental norm that has the receiver tuned to the y'-axis. A very short pulse (5 μs) rotates M_0 by a very small amount, giving a very small y'-axis component (figure 6.10(b)), while a 15 μs pulse gives the maximum positive signal, corresponding to rotation of the magnetisation vector through 90°. This is shown in figure 6.10(c) where the y'-axis component is at a maximum. This is a special value of the pulse width, and such a pulse is called a 90° pulse. (The magnitude of the 90° pulse width varies for different nuclei, as we shall see later.)

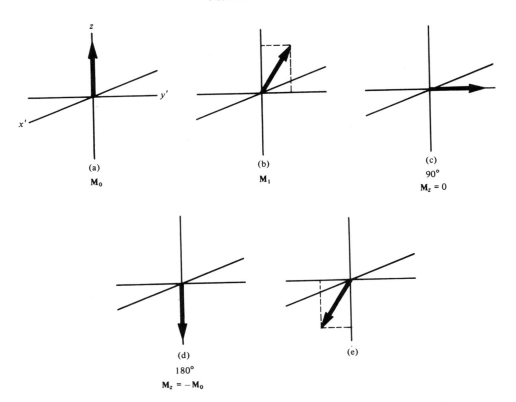

Figure 6.10 Flip angles. At (a) no signal lies on the y'-axis; at (c) the y'-axis component is maximum and at (d) it is zero; at (e) the signal is negative on the y'-axis. Particular significance attaches to the 90° ($\pi/2$) and 180° (π) pulses

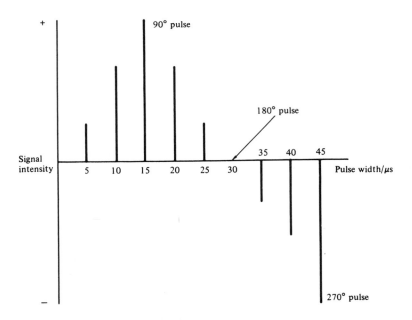

Figure 6.11 Signal intensity as a function of pulse width (and flip angle, θ), the power of the RF pulse $\mathbf{B_1}$ is also involved in determining θ, since $\theta = \gamma \mathbf{B_1}$

> After a 90° pulse, there is maximum magnetisation along the y'-axis, but zero residual magnetism on the z-axis.

Since 90° = $\pi/2$ radian, the pulse can be called a $\pi/2$ pulse.

In terms of the energy levels shown earlier in figures 1.1, 2.5 and 6.3, a 90° pulse promotes sufficient nuclei from the lower energy level to the upper, such that the populations become equal. No further absorption of radiofrequency can occur until relaxation intervenes and this is equivalent to *saturation* in CW NMR (see section 2.17).

If a much more powerful or longer pulse is applied, then the signal intensity, measured as the y'-axis component, becomes less. A 30 μs pulse produces no y'-axis component, and so zero signal is received. Such a pulse corresponds to rotating **M** through 180° (figure 6.9(d)), and this too is a very special pulse width, since not only is the y'-axis component zero, but also the z-axis component is maximum and negative.

> After a 180° pulse, the net magnetisation vector is inverted, and no signal is received.

A 180° pulse can also be called a π pulse.

Pulse widths in excess of 180° have the effect of rotating $\mathbf{M_0}$ until the component on the y'-axis is nega-tive, and a negative signal arises (as for the 35 μs and longer pulses). The vector then lies as in figure 6.10(e) and so on.

It will be useful to point out here that a sequence of pulses can be applied rather than a single pulse. For example a 90° pulse followed immediately by a 180° pulse will be equivalent to a 270° single pulse. Later, in chapter 7, several multipulse sequences that build on this concept will be described.

The total effect of an RF pulse can be expressed therefore as a function of the power applied, $\mathbf{B_1}$, and of the duration of the pulse, the pulse width: equally, it can be expressed as the angle θ through which the net magnetisation vector is flipped over toward the y'-axis, the *pulse angle* or *flip angle*. Note that θ is proportional to $\gamma \mathbf{B_1}$.

The precise value of a 90° pulse can only be measured by experiment, since several instrumental and nuclear idiosyncracies are implicated. It is often easier to determine the 180° or 360° pulse width (when the signal intensity drops to zero) and the 90° pulse width is one half or one quarter of this respectively. Although automated programs are available to perform a series of experiments from which the operator can extract the value for the 90° pulse (see figure 6.12) these are not usually time-saving.

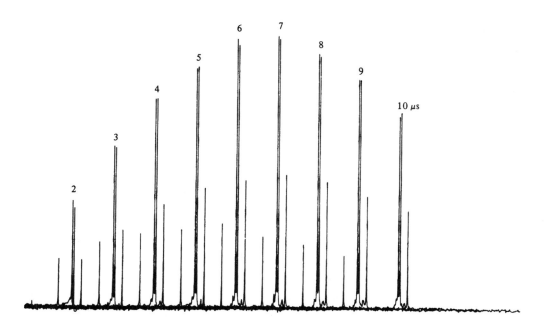

Figure 6.12 Automatic variation of flip angle to find the 90° pulse width: maximum signal is near 7μs but more exact measurement may be necessary for accurate experiments. (The sample is ethylbenzene, aromatic ^{13}C resonances only: 20 MHz, in $CDCl_3$)

Although superficially it would appear attractive to make all pulses 90°, this is not necessarily so. Since a 90° pulse reduces the z-axis component of M_0 to zero, time must elapse so that relaxation can restore the equilibrium spin populations before a further pulse is applied (the phenomenon of relaxation we will return to shortly.) A small flip angle on the other hand (figure 6.10(b)) gives a commensurately small reduction in the z-axis component but also a substantial y-axis component, and the equilibrium value, M_0, is soon recovered. In practice therefore, a compromise must be struck between a pulse width which gives a sensible y'-component while still leaving the z-component substantially undiminished. The y'-component is a function of $\sin \theta$, and the z-component of $\cos \theta$.

Problem Example 6.4

Estimate graphically, from figure 6.12, the pulse angle produced by a 2 μs pulse, and calculate the corresponding values of y' and z magnetisation as a fraction of M_0. (Hint: the signal intensities at 2 μs and 7 μs relate directly to the y' magnetisation. First estimate this as a fraction of the 90° pulse.)

6.8 RELAXATION AND THE ROTATING FRAME

It was necessary to present some qualitative ideas of relaxation earlier (section 2.17) without defining precisely the nature of the different relaxation modes. Its importance in recording spectra was also met in chapters 3, 4 and 5. Now that the excitation stage (irradiation) has been described with respect to the rotating frame of reference, we can do the same for relaxation.

Relaxation is vitally important also in recording spectra by the continuous wave method, but it is more generally useful to focus on the pulse method, which alone is used semi-routinely to measure relaxation rates.

Felix Bloch derived a set of equations in 1946 (the Bloch equations) which allowed relaxation to be correlated with the net magnetisation vector. He specified its resolution along the x', y' and z-axes, and specified also that the direction of B_0 shall be considered along the z-axis. In his original crossed coil spectrometer, B_1 (the RF input) acted in a copper coil wound around the x-axis and his detector coil was wound around the y-axis (see figure 3.3).

In particular, he distinguished between relaxation resolved along the z-axis, which he called *longitudinal relaxation*, and relaxation components on the xy plane, which he called *transverse relaxation.*

6.8.1 Longitudinal Relaxation – Spin–Lattice Relaxation – T_1

The physical meaning of longitudinal relaxation is best appreciated by recalling that M_0 represents the equilibrium populations of spin states (Boltzmann law), and thus is the lowest total energy condition for the system of nuclear spins. In this state, the total enthalpy is at a minimum and we can interpret this alternatively as having a low 'spin temperature'. All of these (equivalent) alternative statements are useful viewpoints.

Any departure from this state implies a change in total energy for the system (an increase in enthalpy, or increase in spin temperature).

Irradiation of the nuclei by, say, a 90° or 180° pulse increases the energy of the system: in vector terms this leads to a *reduction of* M_z, the component of M_0 along the z-axis, as shown in figure 6.10. In time, the equilibrium populations will be restored by transfer of the excess energy out of the spin system and into the surrounding environment, and M_z will return to M_0. This return to equilibrium is named *longitudinal relaxation*.

Where does the excess energy go? In the surrounding molecules (including solvent molecules) there are fluctuating electric and magnetic dipoles by virtue of the vibrations and rotations of bonds and atoms, and it is to these nuclear dipoles that the excess energy is transferred and dissipated. The process is thus mainly *dipolar relaxation*.

There are several other relaxation mechanisms, but dipolar relaxation is typical, and indeed predominates in $^{13}C-\{^1H\}$ spectra.

The entire surrounding framework of molecules is generically named 'the surrounding lattice', and longitudinal relaxation is also called *spin–lattice relaxation*.

> Longitudinal relaxation leads to a lowering of the enthalpy of the nuclear spin system. The excess energy is transferred out by dipolar interaction to the surrounding environment (the lattice).

The return of M_z to M_0 is usually exponential, so that it is a first order rate process with a rate constant in reciprocal time (s^{-1}). It is convenient to define a time T_1 (in seconds) which is simply the reciprocal of the rate constant: T_1 is then a measure of the relaxation rate, and is called the *longitudinal relaxation time*, or, more commonly, the *spin–lattice relaxation time*.

Methods for measuring T_1 are given in section 7.2 and typical values with their significance are discussed there.

6.8.2 Transverse Relaxation – Spin–Spin Relaxation – T_2

After a 90° pulse, **M** lies along the $+y'$-axis (figure 6.10) and this corresponds to the nuclei being 'focused' or 'in phase' as described in section 6.5 and illustrated in figure 6.9(b).

At the end of the pulse, the nuclei are free to return to their former randomness with respect to the xy plane, as in figure 6.9(a).

(A component of this randomising is the spin exchange process represented in figure 2.8, at the left of the figure, where nuclei are shown undergoing random upward and downward transitions.)

These relaxation processes reduce the $\mathbf{M}_y$ vector as shown in figure 6.13; starting from the focused condition at (a) more and more individual nuclei spread out around the xy plane, reducing $\mathbf{M}_y$ until at (e) the original xy randomness means that $\mathbf{M}_y$ has returned to zero.

These processes do not alter the component of **M** along the z-axis, and do not change the enthalpy of the system. They do however increase the entropy, and they can be regarded as entropy processes.

The term *transverse relaxation* embodies the xy nature of the process, and the randomising interactions among the nuclear spins leads to the alternative name *spin–spin relaxation*.

> Transverse relaxation (spin–spin relaxation) is the exponential decay of net magnetisation across the field direction (within the $x'y'$ plane).

The rate of $x'y'$ relaxation can be resolved into the separate x' and y' components, each being a first order process with a rate constant in reciprocal time (s^{-1}). As for T_1, it is more convenient to define a *transverse relaxation time* (*spin–spin relaxation time*), T_2, which is the reciprocal of the rate constant.

Methods for measuring T_2 are given in section 7.3, but some of the interfering parameters must be discussed first.

6.8.3 T_2 and Field Homogeneity

The focusing of spins by a 90° pulse will be limited in efficiency unless all of the nuclei concerned have *exactly* the same precession frequency: if not, then those with higher frequencies will run ahead of the rotating reference frame, and those with lower frequencies will fall behind.

This is not the quantised *randomisation* process of T_2; 'fast' nuclei and 'slow' nuclei retain their abnormal frequencies, and are consistent and predictable in this characteristic.

Since however it has the same effect as the true T_2 process (it leads to spreading out on the $x'y'$ plane, and hence transverse relaxation) it must be considered as a competing event.

One major factor which affects the exact frequencies of precession is the homogeneity of the magnetic field experienced by individual nuclei.

There are several sources of inhomogeneity. The flux density $(\mathbf{B}_0)$ may not be precisely uniform over the whole sample or there may be slight temperature gradients in the sample, affecting frequency.

A most important contribution arises in studying NMR in solids. The orientation of one molecule with respect to its neighbours will create dipolar environments which change the effective field experienced by each differently oriented molecule: thus protons in one molecule in one part of the solid sample will come to resonance at different frequencies from the corresponding protons in another molecule in a different orientation in the sample.

This *chemical shift anisotropy* is averaged out in non-viscous solutions by the rapid tumbling of the molecules.

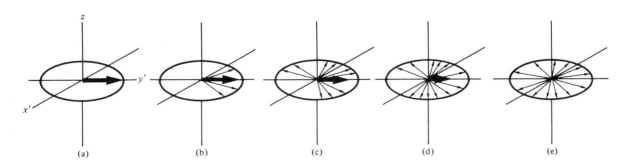

Figure 6.13 Decline of the net y'-axis magnetisation, as individual nuclei exchange spins and go out of phase with the rotating frame. Eventually, their y components are randomised (e)

Viscous solutions (for example solutions of polymers or large biological molecules) are intermediate in this respect because of slow molecular diffusion.

A corollary of this observation is that studies of T_2 values for such species can lead to valuable deductions about their molecular motions.

6.8.4 Line Width, Ringing, T_1 and T_2

In section 2.18 the importance of life-times in determining line widths was discussed in relation to the Heisenberg Uncertainty Principle: we can now see more precisely how both T_1 and T_2 are involved, since each in its own way determines spin state life-times.

A simple calculation allows us to estimate the minimum line width which T_1 and T_2 permit, since each can take the role of Δt in ΔE. $\Delta t = h/2\pi$, since each is a measure of average life-time of particular nuclear spin state. Thus, since $E = h\nu$, $\Delta E = h\Delta\nu$ and $\Delta\nu = \Delta E/h$. But $\Delta E = h/2\pi\Delta t$ so

$$\Delta\nu = 1/2\pi\Delta t \quad \text{or} \quad 1/2\pi T_1 \quad \text{or} \quad 1/2\pi T_2$$

The significance is that the uncertainty in measured frequency (the *limiting line width*) is of the order $1/T_1$ or $1/T_2$.

In a very homogeneous magnet, the measured transverse relaxation time will be at its maximum, although it is exceedingly difficult to be certain that true values of T_2 are being assessed: it is convenient to define an *effective transverse relaxation time, T_2^**, which subsumes the true value of T_2 and remaining inhomogeneities. In recording CW spectra, after resonance there remains transverse magnetisation, and the more uniform the field the longer will this persist: as the scan continues, new frequencies are generated in the sample, and form the ringing pattern of beats demonstrated at the head of chapter 1. Long ringing is a measure of slow transverse relaxation and hence of magnet homogeneity.

In non-viscous solutions, $T_1 \simeq T_2$, but inhomogeneities and diffusion processes shorten T_2 and hence give broad lines. Whereas in non-viscous solutions line widths may be as narrow as 0.1 Hz, in polymers the 'lines' can be several thousand hertz wide. It is this factor which makes line width studies important in polymer chemistry and biochemistry.

6.9 THE NUCLEAR OVERHAUSER EFFECT – NOE

One particular practical involvement of the NOE was important in carbon-13 NMR spectroscopy (chapter 5

section 5.1.3) where signal enhancement was an advantage in recording broad band decoupled spectra.

The effect is more versatile than this one use, and has important implications in any study which involves double irradiation. To accept the many diverse influences of the NOE we must accept certain theoretical statements, for which there does not always exist a visualisable model.

The two conditions which always apply to the NOE are (a) it arises only during the double irradiation of one nucleus, and affects another nucleus which must be close, but which is not necessarily coupling with the irradiated nucleus, and (b) it is associated with dipolar relaxation mechanisms.

Pulse techniques to maximise or minimise the NOE will be introduced in section 7.1.

6.9.1 The NOE in Stereochemistry

A simple example from proton NMR illustrates how the observation of the NOE is evidence that two groups of protons lie close together in the molecule.

Figure 6.14 shows the proton NMR spectrum for isovanillin, with scale expansion of the ring protons and a normal integration trace superimposed: this gives the correct integration (one hydrogen) for the doublet at δ 6.9, which corresponds to the proton H_C on the ring. If the protons on the CH_3O group are double irradiated and *simultaneously* a second integration trace recorded, this shows an increase of about 30 per cent over the normal (and correct) integration for proton H_C.

Since the NOE involves dipolar interaction between near neighbours, this experiment establishes that the CH_3O protons are nearest to that with $\delta = 6.9$: thus the δ 6.9 signal is unambiguously assigned to H_C.

Many elegant extensions of this have been used to examine the stereochemical relationships in complex molecules: a few of the simplest are shown in formulae 6.1 with the ringed protons indicating the groups that give the NOE.

The effect is a mutual one, so that if irradiation of proton A leads to NOE enhancement in proton B, then the converse will also be true. It may however be easier to irradiate one nucleus than the other, if its chemical shift is separated from others in the spectrum. Also, if irradiation of A gives, say, a 30% increase in the intensity of B, irradiation of B may not lead to the same increase in the intensity of A, since A may possess other means of dipolar relaxation than through B.

The practice of stereochemical studies based on the NOE is fraught with problems of technique, since all

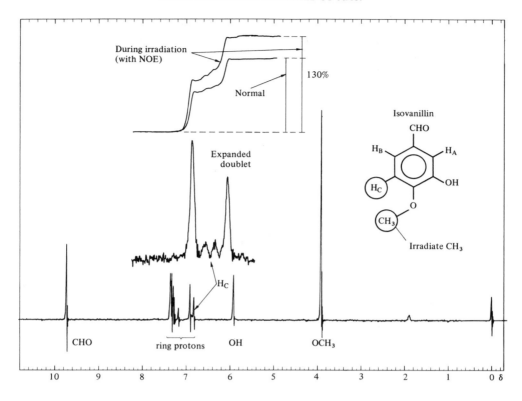

Figure 6.14 Nuclear Overhauser Effect. In isovanillin the doublet signal at δ 6.9 is assigned to H_c since double irradiation at CH_3 increases the doublet intensity by about 30 per cent (100 MHz, in $CDCl_3$)

(6.1)

other relaxation modes must be eliminated to ensure that the dipolar relaxation is dominant. It is essential for example to remove all oxygen from the sample (by degassing, nitrogen bubbling or freeze-thaw cycles) since, being paramagnetic, oxygen efficiently accelerates relaxation. Attempts to prove that two groups are not close together by establishing the absence of the NOE is clearly a much less convincing logic.

6.9.2 Theory of the NOE

Overhauser's original work correlated the polarisation of metal nuclei and double irradiation of their conduction band electrons, so that the theory needed to satisfy the present purpose is far removed from its origins: although it will be useful, it is incomplete.

In isovanillin (figure 6.14) the intensity of the H_C signal ultimately depends on the populations of its two energy levels: any influence which accelerates relaxation will lead to depopulation of the upper level and to increased absorption. This is the familiar relationship of figure 6.15(a).

If it happens that the nearby protons in the CH_3O group are the major vehicles for dipolar relaxation of H_C, then any perturbation of the CH_3O protons will also have an effect on H_C. Double irradiation of the CH_3O protons causes them to undergo more rapid transitions among their own energy levels, and we can consider that this increased activity at CH_3O leads to an increase in the rate of relaxation of H_C, and so its signal intensity (rate of absorption) increases.

This is the NOE, and this explanation is widely applicable to other (but not all) instances of NOE intensity changes.

In carbon-13 NMR, the NOE was observed in the carbon-13 signal intensities, when the proton was decoupled. Proton decoupling produces an NOE in the spectra of

any nucleus to which it is coupled, so that the NOE appears in the ^{1}H-decoupled NMR spectra of ^{15}N, ^{19}F, ^{29}Si, ^{31}P and so on. In fluorine chemistry, if broad band fluorine decoupling is used, the NOE is again present in the observed spectra, be it ^{1}H, ^{13}C or ^{31}P and so on.

For two coupled nuclei (homonuclear or heteronuclear) the energy level system shown in figure 6.15(b) applies; this is a modified form of figure 6.4.

Double irradiation of the X nucleus will stimulate transitions from levels 1 to 2 and from 3 to 4, these being 'allowed' because one spin is changing at a time. Transitions (3 to 2) and (4 to 1) are not 'allowed' in the context of the selection rules of quantum theory, since each involves a double inversion of spins ($\beta\alpha$ to $\alpha\beta$ and $\beta\beta$ to $\alpha\alpha$ respectively).

Although they cannot be used in radiative processes, they can operate *via* dipolar interactions and it is necessary to accept that the transition 4 to 1 is dominant. The resultant chain of changes in population (3 to 4, 4 to 1, 1 to 2) increases the relative populations of levels 1 and 2 and hence also the probabilities of the A transitions arising, so that the A lines increase in intensity.

The theory introduced above is an extract from very extensive studies: two other extracts are useful in applying NMR to chemical problems.

6.9.3 The Size of the NOE

Calculations show that the maximum possible effect on the line intensity of nucleus A when nucleus X is irradiated changes it, relatively, from 1.0 to $(1.0 + \gamma_X/2\gamma_A)$, where γ_X and γ_A are the respective magnetogyric ratios: these are listed in the Appendix.

For example, in ^{13}C–$\{^1$H$\}$ spectra, X is proton and A is carbon. Irradiation of proton increases unit line intensity in the carbon-13 spectrum to $(1.0 + 26.75/2 \times 6.73)$

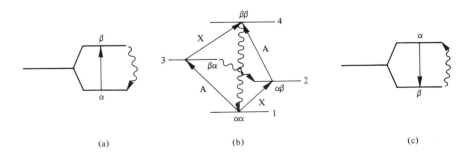

(a)   (b)   (c)

Figure 6.15 Mechanism of dipolar (radiationless) relaxation, catalysed by the nuclear Overhauser effect, NOE. Double irradiation at X, working in conjunction with transition (4 to 1), boosts the populations of both level 1 and level 2

which is approximately 3: that is, the line intensity is increased by a factor of three.

For homonuclear cases (^{1}H–{^{1}H} or ^{19}F–{^{19}F} spectra) the maximum change in line intensity is from 1.0 to 1.5, an increase in 50% (see figure 6.14).

The Nuclear Overhauser Effect is defined as the difference in intensities of the lines, before and after, and is given the symbol η (eta).

$$\eta = \frac{\gamma_X}{2\gamma_A}$$

Occasional confusion may arise in specifying the line intensities, especially as NOE is often taken to mean Nuclear Overhauser Enhancement. Recall that the value of η is *added* to the original intensity.

6.9.4 The Sign of the NOE – Nuclei with Negative γ

From the formula $\eta = \gamma_X/2\gamma_A$, there is no difficulty in reconciling the theory of section 6.9.2 with the commonest exemplars of the NOE, since most NMR nuclei have positive γ.

When γ is negative the pictorial approach breaks down. Indeed in section 2.8 we saw that the relative signs of spin angular momentum and magnetic moment vectors are the same for most nuclei (γ therefore positive), while for a few, such as the important nitrogen-15 nucleus, they are opposite, and this did not accord with the classical relationships between positive charge and direction of spin. The rift arose from the inability to predict how proton and neutron spins combine vectorially.

For nitrogen-15, the predicted NOE in proton decoupled spectra is $\eta = \gamma_H/2\gamma_N$ which from the Appendix is $26.75/2 \times (-2.7)$ which is -4.9. That is, a line intensity of $+1.0$ will, with maximum NOE, change to -3.9, and correspond to a negative signal.

This has considerable practical import in nitrogen-15 NMR, and will be returned to in chapter 11.

As for a pictorial theory, it must be noted that for all nuclei with positive γ (the majority) the lower energy state has the magnetic moment vector and the angular momentum vector aligned with the field, designated the α or $+$ state. For electrons and for nuclei with negative γ this is not so, and the lower energy state is β, as in figure 6.15(c).

The changes in populations associated with the NOE for nuclei with positive γ are represented in figure 6.15(a), but for negative γ nuclei these are reversed, and the NOE somehow stimulates emission rather than absorption, leading to negative NMR signals.

Worked Example 6.3
Given the following magnetogyric ratios, ^{19}F, 25.16; ^{1}H, 26.75; ^{13}C, 6.73, calculate the maximum NOE, η, obtainable in (a) ^{1}H–{^{19}F} and (b) ^{13}C–{^{19}F} spectra.

Answer 6.3
(a) $\eta = 25.16/2\ (26.75) = 0.47$ (b) $\eta = 25.16/2\ (6.73) = 1.87$.

Note: in ^{1}H–{^{19}F}, line intensity 1.0 rises to 1.47; in ^{13}C–{^{19}F}, line intensity 1.0 rises to 2.87. In each case, this is the maximum achievable.

Problem Example 6.5
Use the data in the Appendix to calculate the maximum NOE effect in ^{31}P–{^{1}H} spectra and in ^{29}Si–{^{1}H} spectra.

6.9.5 Time Dependence of Spin Decoupling and the NOE

Double irradiation of nucleus A gives rise to several effects in the NMR signal of nucleus X as we have seen, but spin decoupling and the NOE are perhaps the most prevalent in routine spectra: each however has different time characteristics.

Briefly we can say that decoupling is rapidly established, and is equally rapid in decay.

The NOE is more slowly established, and is likewise slower to decay. We can imagine that to establish the NOE in an AX spin system (figure 6.15(b)) the system must be irradiated for some time to permit the establishment of all of the new, non-Boltzmann, population levels, whereas decoupling takes place immediately the irradiated lines are perturbed.

For many spectra, it is an advantage to decouple fully from one nucleus (commonly proton) and to accept also the maximum NOE that this brings. It is possible, because of the different time dependencies, to maximise the NOE but still produce a fully coupled spectrum, and conversely to obtain a fully decoupled spectrum while avoiding the intensity changes of the NOE. The practical details are discussed in section 7.1.

7 Multipulse and Computational Methods in NMR

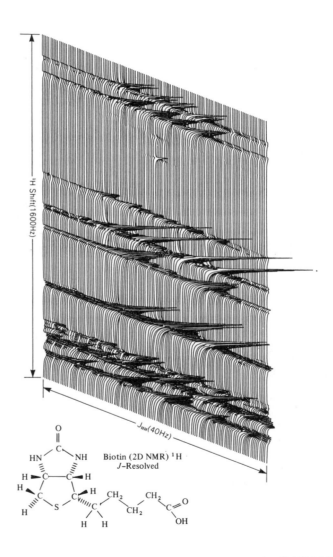

'H Shift(1600Hz)

J_{HH}(40Hz)

Biotin (2D NMR) ^{1}H
J-Resolved

2D ^{1}H NMR spectrum of biotin (homonuclear J-resolved) (400 MHz)

Computer controlled pulse programmes can derive a great deal of data from NMR experiments and the variety of these is nearly limitless. The two principal facilities which only computer linked spectrometers allow are (a) the precise timing of radiofrequency signals through several independent irradiation or detection channels and (b) accumulation, manipulation and presentation of data in many distinctive ways, both numerical and graphic.

This chapter will illustrate these in the control of the NOE, the measurement of relaxation parameters, suppression of unwanted resonances, together with techniques for increasing the sensitivity of NMR spectra from less abundant nuclides ('rare' spins), and for recording NMR spectra on solids and on living animals.

Whereas simplification of spectra by decoupling is always an aid to interpretation, the information eliminated (multiplicity and J values) is also valuable: the presentation of coupling information in two-dimensional forms leads to clearer perceptions of the bonding relationships among atoms in the molecule.

The aim of this chapter will be limited by problems of selection, but before dipping into the cornucopia it must be clear that many of these multipulse experiments are time consuming in spectrometer and operator time, and many also require persistence before unflawed spectra can be recorded. Their potential should be weighed against these cautions. A full pictorial understanding of 'how they work' is not possible from simple theory, but fortunately this need be no barrier to their use in interpretative applications.

7.1 GATED DECOUPLING AND NOE

The nuclear Overhauser effect operates whenever double irradiation is used, and it is particularly important in broad-band decoupled carbon-13 NMR spectra. It is seen to be an asset when increased signal intensity is the primary concern (see section 6.9.3), but since the line intensities are changed by a generally unpredictable amount, quantitative information by signal integration is not accurate (unlike the integrations in proton NMR spectra).

In interpretative work, the NOE is usually considered qualitatively: it should be noted here that in chemical physics the precise measurement of the NOE is of great theoretical interest, and high experimental skill is needed to isolate extraneous effects entirely from pure Overhauser effects.

There are two variants of double irradiation in pulse FT NMR that can selectively exclude or include the

NOE. To understand how they operate, it is necessary to accept the different time dependences of spin decoupling and the NOE, mentioned briefly in section 6.9.5.

7.1.1 Coupling, NOE and Time

The rate at which nuclei are decoupled during double irradiation is fast: correspondingly, the rate at which coupling is re-established (when the double irradiation is removed) is also fast.

This is intuitively reasonable if one considers spin-spin coupling as described in section 4.6.3: a nucleus A only has to 'see' nucleus B in its different magnetic orientations in order that the A line be split by the coupling, and this can be accepted as nearly instantaneous.

The rate at which the NOE builds up in a system of nuclear spins is slow, and the rate at which it dies away is also slow.

The explanation of this is that maximum NOE will only be reached after all of the involved energy levels finalise their changed populations (section 6.9.2) which involves a considerable readjustment, and takes a much longer time than coupling or decoupling. This is not fundamentally persuasive but it contains the facts that we need, and can be taken for the moment as true. The rate at which the NOE builds up is an inverse measure of relaxation rate (see section 7.2). It also therefore is concerned with changes in the z-axis component of magnetisation, while the FID is acquired along the y'-axis, so that the FID can be collected without intrusion of the NOE.

7.1.2 Gated Decoupling – NOE with Spin Splitting

A carbon-13 NMR spectrum can be recorded with all of the proton couplings still present provided that proton decoupling irradiation is absent (the decoupler is switched *off*) when the carbon frequencies are being irradiated.

If the decoupler is switched *on* for a time before the acquisition pulse is applied, the NOE will slowly build up, and the new equilibrated population changes will lead to (the desirable) signal enhancements.

The precise timing of these operations is illustrated in figure 7.1(a). At point (i), the NOE is at a maximum: when the decoupler is switched off, spin–spin coupling instantly re-establishes itself, the sample is pulsed and from point (ii) the FID is collected.

Figure 7.1 refers to the recording of a carbon-13 NMR spectrum (say at 25 MHz) while double-irradiating on proton (at 100 MHz): this yields an enhanced-intensity proton-coupled carbon-13 spectrum (sometimes called a non-decoupled spectrum).

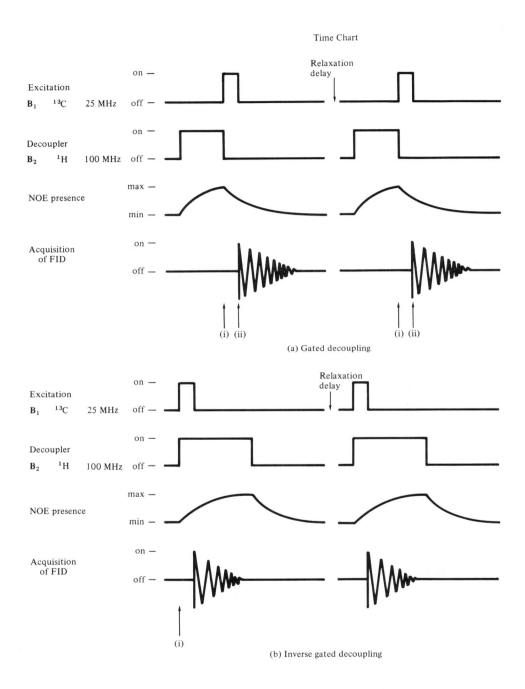

Figure 7.1 Gated and inverse gated decoupling. By 'gating' the three channels (decoupling, excitation, acquisition) the different time characteristics of decoupling and NOE can be exploited to give spectra with decoupling and no NOE, or with NOE and no decoupling

Gated decoupling can be used generally to give the increased sensitivity of the NOE in other coupled spectra, by irradiation and observation at the appropriate frequencies, such as in fluorine-19, phosphorus-31, and nitrogen-15 NMR.

Alternative means for increasing the sensitivity of NMR detection are discussed in section 7.3.

7.1.3 Inverse Gated Decoupling – Spin Decoupling without NOE

Improved quantitative information can be extracted from $^{13}C-\{^1H\}$ spectra when the NOE is minimised using the pulse sequence illustrated in figure 7.1(b). This alternative gating sequence is commonly distinguished from that of figure 7.1(a) by the name *inverse gated decoupling*: since this is not always so distinguished, it is important to be aware of the two techniques.

At point (i) the decoupling frequency is applied (say at 100 MHz) simultaneously with the excitation pulse for the carbons (at 25 MHz). At the end of the excitation pulse (which lasts only a few microseconds) there is still very little NOE built up: the decoupler is left on during acquisition of the carbon FID, but the NOE does not alter the line intensities once the FID is being collected (since the FID is collected on the y-axis). At the end of the accumulation, a delay must be incorporated before the next cycle commences, to allow the NOE to decay to zero.

7.1.4 Quantitative Analysis in Decoupled Carbon-13 NMR Spectra

Routine $^{13}C-\{^1H\}$ NMR spectra show line heights which vary considerably, as a glance through chapter 5 will reconfirm. Two factors must be addressed to produce line heights which come near to representing the correct relative intensities for the signals; these are the NOE and relaxation rates.

The influence of the NOE can be minimised as in section 7.1.3, and it is useful practice to minimise the problem of long relaxation times by adding a relaxation agent such as Cr(ACAC)₃ (see section 4.10.2).

In the spectra of simple compounds the problem of unequal line heights is not serious: indeed it can be turned to advantage in helping to identify quaternary carbons.

For the analysis of mixtures, in trying to estimate relative amounts of components, the best results come from recording spectra in the presence of Cr(ACAC)₃ (or equivalent) with inverse gated decoupling, and with a long pulse delay inserted between cycles to allow time

for full relaxation back to Boltzmann equilibrium. This pulse delay can be of several minutes' duration for complete restoration of equilibrium, but such a time penalty usually is overcome by compromise.

Typically, it is quaternary carbons and carbonyl carbons which give intensities less than unity: in a routine accumulation, the line intensities can be as low as one fifth the correct value, while with the procedures outlined above the intensities will rise to over 90% of true but not easily to 100%. It is in general not time-efficient to try to improve significantly on this.

The two spectra in figure 7.2 show the extremes of the quantitation problem in the carbon-13 NMR spectrum for acenaphthene. The quaternary carbons suffer doubly: they have long relaxation times and do not gain intensity from NOE (see table 15.18). Even with a delay time of almost 7 min, line intensities do not reach theoretical.

7.2 MEASUREMENT OF T_1 – THE SPIN–LATTICE (OR LONGITUDINAL) RELAXATION TIME

To understand the experimental requirement for measuring T_1, we need to recall that the NMR spectrometer detects magnetisation along the y'-axis, while longitudinal relaxation is (defined as being) along the z-axis (see sections 6.7 and 6.8).

The principles of all of the many methods are similar, and one method will be examined in detail. Figure 7.3 illustrates the various steps in manipulating the magnetisation vector for this *inversion recovery* technique.

7.2.1 Inversion Recovery Measurement of T_1

A 180° pulse rotates the net magnetisation vector from (a) to (b): at this point there is no signal received in the detector. A 90° pulse is immediately applied, having the effect of further rotating the magnetisation vector to (c), thus laying it along the negative y'-axis: at this point a negative signal is received in the detector, corresponding to the maximum negative z-axis value of $\mathbf{M}$. After a suitable delay, τ, when relaxation back to $\mathbf{M_0}$ is complete, the sequence can be repeated a sufficient number of times to give a strong enough spectrum by signal summation.

The whole experiment is then repeated but, after the 180° pulse, a delay (τ_1) is inserted before the measuring 90° pulse is applied. In figure 7.3 this is represented by (a) going to (b), then (after time τ_1) $\mathbf{M_z}$ decays to (d) which is detected by a 90° pulse to give (e). This second experiment is repeated to give several spectra for sum-

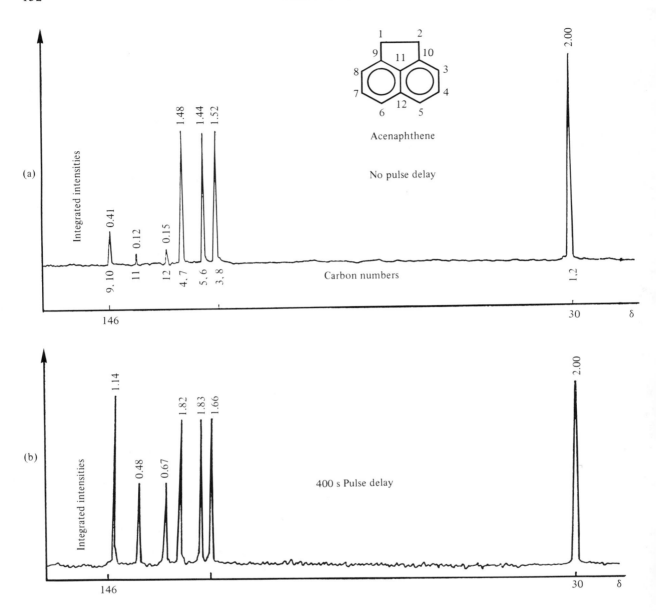

Figure 7.2 Quantitative ^{13}C NMR spectra are difficult to obtain because of the distortions of different relaxation rates and NOE (25 MHz)

mation and in each sequence a final pulse delay is inserted to restore equilibrium.

A third set of experiments consists of a 180° pulse, a longer delay τ_2 so that (a) goes to (b) goes to (f), which is measured by the 90° pulse to give (g). This sequence represents the circumstance when zero signal is detected, since M_z has declined from maximum inversion to zero. The usefulness of this in eliminating unwanted peaks is discussed in section 7.2.3.

Further series are executed with ever longer values of τ. The rate of change of signal height is usually exponential, with a first order rate constant, the reciprocal of which is T_1 (as discussed in section 6.8.1).

The title of the method as inversion recovery is now clear: the repetitive pulse sequence can be set out as

$$180° - \tau - 90° - \text{ACQUISITION} - \text{PD}$$

The whole pulse timing operation is controlled by a

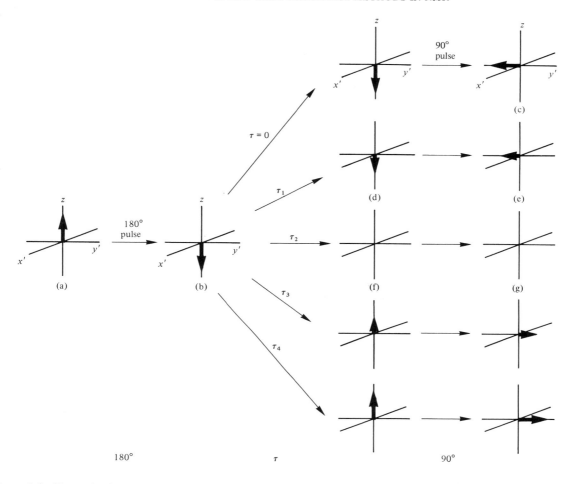

Figure 7.3 Magnetisation vectors in the measurement of T_1 by the inversion recovery pulse sequence, $180° - \tau - 90°$

mini-program, and the calculation of T_1 values (including least squares best fit of the exponential data) is then performed by a second mini-program.

There are two useful graphical methods for calculating the rate constant, k, of first order processes (in this case the exponential decline in line height). If ln (height) is plotted against time, a straight line is produced of slope k. Alternatively, the 'half-life' of the process can be found, and it is known in first order rate laws that k (half-life) = ln 2. In the case of T_1 measurements, the half-life is simply the time taken by $\mathbf{M}_z$ to relax to the point represented in figure 7.3(f) — the so-called *null point*.

Figure 7.4 shows a typical sequence of spectra acquired in this way on eugenol (the principal constituent of oil of cloves). Note in particular the short relaxation times (that is, fast relaxation) of the carbons of the CH_3 and both CH_2 groups, while the non-protonated

quaternary carbons of the ring (C-1, C-2 and C-4) have long relaxation times. This spectrum set can profitably be compared with the off resonance spectra of eugenol shown in figure 5.3.

In recording T_1 values in this way, the operator specifies appropriate values of τ (such as those shown in figure 7.4) and a pulse delay (PD) which should be about five times the value of the longest T_1 in the molecule.

Worked Example 7.1
Estimate the T_1 value for the CH_3 carbon in eugenol, using the half-life method.

Answer 7.1
From figure 7.4, the null point for the CH_3 carbon signal (corresponding to the half-life of the exponential) is near 2 s. Thus k (2 s) = ln 2 = 0.693, so k = 0.347 s^{-1}. T_1 is $1/k$ = 2.89 s (or 2890 ms).

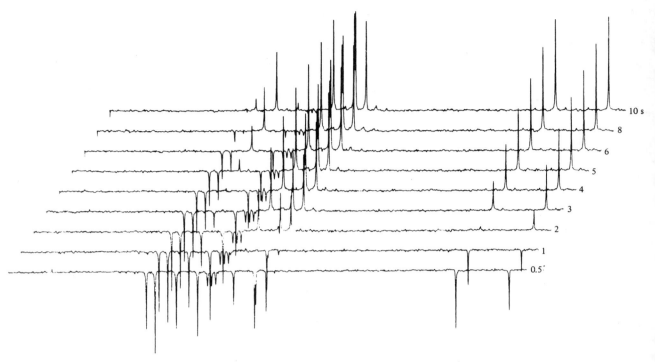

Figure 7.4 T_1 measurement in eugenol. Stack plot from successive $180° - \tau - 90°$ pulse trains, with variable delay, τ
(20 MHz, in C_6D_6)

7.2.2 Other Pulse Sequences for Measuring T_1

One drawback of the inversion recovery method is the relatively long time required to complete the entire sequence of experiments. The T_1 values obtained will only be precise if the 180° pulse is timed accurately, and more complex multipulse programs have been used to overcome this.

The need to wait until equilibrium is restored between pulse trains is also wasteful: some alternative methods accelerate the relaxation deliberately by applying a brief pulse to the magnet homogeneity coils, momentarily to spoil the homogeneity — a treatment known as *homospoil*.

Apart from inversion recovery, following a 180° pulse, other methods include *saturation recovery* (which measures rates of recovery after a 90° saturation pulse) and *progressive saturation* (in which 90° pulses are repeated at relatively short intervals so that saturation is slowly reached).

7.2.3 Significance of T_1 Values

Considering the number of different methods for measuring T_1, it is not surprising that much discussion centres on the question of which are 'correct' T_1 values.

The total process of longitudinal relaxation contains many contributing terms and several potential sources of spurious error. If any oxygen (or other paramagnetic species) is present in the sample, then this will lead to markedly faster relaxation, so that T_1 measurements must be carried out on degassed samples.

Some representative values of T_1 for several different nuclei are given in table 15.18: this is quite eclectic, but it reflects the fact that most work has been done on carbon-13. They have been used in structure elucidation work to a certain extent, as a complement to chemical shift, J values and intensity measurements — the three mainstay parameters in interpretative NMR spectroscopy.

The main interest lies in physico-chemical attempts to determine the separate components of the total T_1, since dipolar relaxation, scalar coupling effects and diffusion rates all have contributions to make. Temperature is also important, since it affects viscosities and hence molecular vibration and diffusion: these last parameters are of great interest in dealing with large molecules such as synthetic polymers or biological molecules. The field is too vast to survey, but more details can be found in the Further Reading list.

7.2.4 Peak Suppression Methods

In section 7.2.1 and figure 7.3 we recognised that at a specific time following upon a 180° pulse, the magnetisation vector of a given nucleus decays along the z-axis from $-\mathbf{M_0}$ to zero: a 90° pulse at this point therefore gives zero signal along the y'-axis and the longitudinal relaxation has reached the *null point*. Other nuclei in the same sample which have different T_1 values will produce a signal as usual; we have thus a method for eliminating the signal from a particular nucleus, by performing the inversion recovery pulse sequence with τ set at the appropriate value to use the null point of unwanted signal.

The most common circumstance where this is desirable is in recording the proton spectra of molecules which are only soluble in D_2O and which contain exchangeable protons, so that a large HOD peak arises near δ 4.7. If the HOD peak happens to obscure an interesting part of the spectrum, then it can be eliminated using the 180°-τ-90° pulse sequence with τ set at around 10.3 s. T_1 for the proton in HOD is much longer than that of most protons in organic molecules, and thus the HOD peak can easily be suppressed without eliminating protons of interest at the same time.

Figure 7.5(a) shows part of the proton NMR spectrum of a carbohydrate, maltose, dissolved in D_2O, and the massive HOD peak obscures signals which are revealed in figure 7.5(b), where the HOD peak has been suppressed.

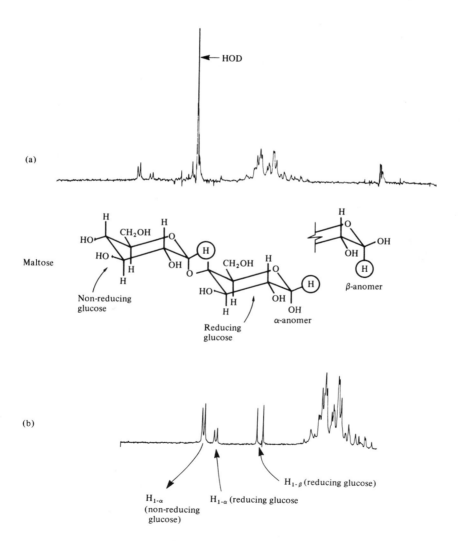

Figure 7.5 Solvent peak suppression, using $180° - \tau - 90°$ pulse train (100 MHz. Top scan CW)

Although other methods of peak suppression are used, the simplest principle is illustrated here. A much more complex method will be introduced in section 7.3.4, which involves manipulating the magnetisation vector out of phase with the detector coil. Individual transitions can also be suppressed by strong irradiation at that frequency so as to saturate the transition (*selective saturation* techniques).

7.3 MEASUREMENT OF T_2 – THE SPIN–SPIN (OR TRANSVERSE) RELAXATION TIME)

Apart from theoretical interest, the measurement of T_2 values is valuable in studying the diffusion processes of molecules, and like T_1 it is of value to polymer chemists and those interested in biological molecules.

The basic pulse method for measuring T_2 is also important in that it leads on to more complex pulse sequences to be discussed in later sections of this chapter.

7.3.1 Spin Echoes – the Simple Homonuclear Case

A signal echo arises in the receiver coil of the NMR spectrometer as a result of a refocusing or rephasing of the nuclear spins in a way which is illustrated in the sequence of events shown in figure 7.6. The necessary theory for understanding this is in chapter 6, and figures 6.9 and 6.13 should be used in conjunction with this discussion.

A 90° pulse rotates the net magnetisation vector onto the $x'y'$ plane as at (b). We must recall here that if all of the nuclei had exactly the same resonance frequency (say 100 MHz) and the rotating frame were spinning around the z-axis at exactly this frequency, then $\mathbf{M}$ would rest along the y'-axis until it decayed exponentially via (c) to zero, with time constant T_2, as pictured in figure 6.13, by spin randomisation.

This does not occur in isolation. There exist inevitable field inhomogeneities throughout a macroscopic ensemble of nuclei, so that nuclei in different parts of the sample experience different fields and come to resonance at different frequencies – some faster, some slower than the mean. (This is the main reason for NMR signals being absorption bands rather than absorption lines.)

With respect to the rotating frame then, after a time τ the important situation of figure 7.6(d) is reached. Here are shown a few individual fast nuclei (ahead of the pack) and some slow. Because of this spreading-out, the value of $\mathbf{M}$ along the y'-axis is reduced.

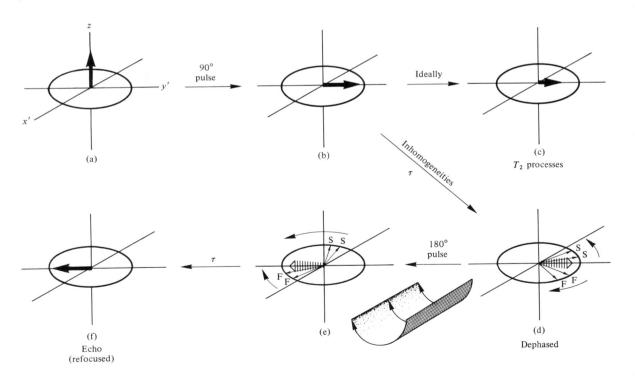

Figure 7.6 Magnetisation vectors in the measurement of T_2: the basic spin echo pulse sequence

This is distinguished from the pure T_2 process by its non-randomness, since we can label the 'fast' nuclei 'F' and the 'slow' nuclei 'S', and predict their subsequent behaviour with surety.

The inhomogeneity in frequency contributes considerably to the total transverse relaxation, and thus contributes to line broadening.

(Note that we may say the nuclei 'spread out' or 'fan out' or 'dephase' or 'lose phase coherence'.)

We will return to this *inhomogeneity broadening* shortly, but since it is a major influence in line broadening, it must be overcome in order to measure T_2. This is the purpose of the echo technique.

A $180°$ pulse on the system at (d) inverts all of the spins to (e) through a mirror plane on the $x'z$-axes. This geometry is also important, since we now note that the fast nuclei are *behind* the pack (with respect to the rotating frame) and the slow nuclei *ahead*.

After a further time τ has elapsed (total time from (b) therefore 2τ) the fast nuclei catch up on the pack again and the slow nuclei likewise fall back into line with the mean. At (f), all of the nuclei are in phase again and an 'echo' signal is received in the detector.

(Analogy: athletes of different ability spread out in a 100 metre race, but after 5 s, if they all turned about, they would arrive back together at the starting line.)

The strength of the echo signal will be less than that corresponding to the original value of **M** (at (b)): the decay in the signal is a measure of T_2, the random process of transverse relaxation.

Unfortunately, the total rate of transverse relaxation is very susceptible to diffusion effects, which slowly place the nuclei in different orientations and positions with respect to $\mathbf{B_0}$. To overcome all of the extraneous relaxation routes, much more complex multiple pulse programmes are used, still retaining this basic spin echo phenomenon.

7.3.2 Carr–Purcell–Meiboom–Gill (CPMG) Measurement of T_2

The Carr–Purcell modification of the basic spin echo method is

$$90° - \tau - 180° - \tau - (\text{echo}) - \tau - 180° - \tau - (\text{echo}) - \tau - 180°$$

Here, a sequence of $180°$ pulses continually inverts the dephased nuclei giving rise therefore to a series of echoes at times 2τ, 4τ, 6τ and until the echo dies away. The exponential decay in the echo intensity is then a better measurement of T_2.

A remaining problem is one of phase (see section 7.3.4), particularly if a long series of $180°$ pulses is applied. If the pulse angle (that is the $180°$ pulse duration) is slightly inaccurate, then the effect is to refocus the spins inaccurately, with a more rapid decline in magnetisation than that due purely to T_2. The way around this is to alter the phase of the $180°$ pulses: instead of executing them along the (normal) x'-axis, they are 'phase shifted' by $90°$ electronically and executed along the y'-axis, so that the dephased spins are inverted this time in a mirror plane on the $y'z$-axes as shown in figure 7.7. After the $90°$ pulse leading to (a), the spins dephase to (b) after time τ; a $180°$ pulse then inverts them to (c) and after a further time τ they refocus as at (d).

This is the basis of the Carr–Purcell–Meiboom–Gill pulse train. Apart from the advantage that phase errors now also cancel at each alternate echo, the echo is always along the positive y' axis and gives a positive NMR signal.

Exponential decay of the echo intensity (giving a very good measure of the absolute value of T_2) is indicated in figure 7.8.

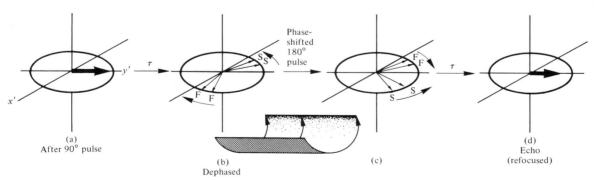

(a) After $90°$ pulse

(b) Dephased

Phase-shifted $180°$ pulse

(c)

(d) Echo (refocused)

Figure 7.7 Magnetisation vectors in the measurement of T_2: The Carr–Purcell–Meiboom–Gill (CPMG) pulse sequence, which minimises the loss of phase coherence caused by inhomogeneities

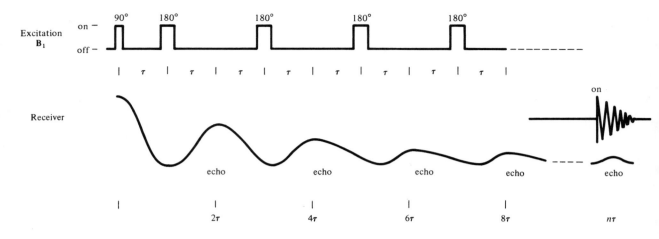

Figure 7.8 CPMG pulse sequence, showing decay of echo intensity in succession along the echo train

7.3.3 Significance of T_2 Values

Because of the difficulty in measuring T_2 values, they have found little application in structure elucidation and the main interest in them lies in studying the relaxation process and the various contributary influences, such as molecular diffusion processes.

Also of theoretical interest is the limit placed on line width (see section 2.18.1) by T_2. The line width at half height cannot be less than $1/T_2$. As an example, the T_2 value for the carbon-13 nucleus in CS_2 at 25 MHz and room temperature is 44 s, so the line width for the resonance cannot be less than 0.022 Hz, from the Heisenberg Uncertainty Principle. This high resolution (narrow line width) is of course degraded by all inhomogeneities in the field: it is sometimes convenient to calculate a total transverse relaxation constant from the observed line widths, with symbol $T_2{}^*$, taking into account both pure T_2 and the inhomogeneity broadening mentioned in section 7.3.1. This is again mainly of physical interest. For completeness, it is worth recording that T_2 can never be greater than T_1, and that in non-viscous liquids, and in small molecules in solution, T_1 and T_2 are approximately equal.

Although we will not use T_2 values to any extent in our discussions, a clear understanding of the spin echo phenomenon is essential to an understanding of many of the pulse sequences to be introduced later.

7.3.4 Coupling Constants and Phase Modulation in Spin Echoes

There are two principles in the study of spin echo methods that are difficult to conceptualise — the phenomenon of phasing (and phase angles), and the effect that out-of-phase signals have on the appearance of spectra. In order to progress to heteronuclear examples, it will be instructive to look first at some effects which arise because of phasing in a homonuclear spin echo experiment on a simple compound where spin coupling exists between adjacent protons. ($CHCl_2 - CH_2Cl$. See figure 4.7.)

> The relative phases of the signals in a spin echo experiment depend on the value of the coupling constant, J, and on the time delay, τ.

Figure 7.9(a) shows a spin echo set of proton spectra for 1,1,2-trichloroethane, with the expected doublet and triplet having near perfect first order appearance: the spectra were recorded at 200 MHz. The spacing of the 180° pulses was set at 1.0 ms (millisecond), so that the echoes likewise arose at 1.0 ms intervals. (Note that a spacing of 1.0 ms corresponds to an echo frequency of 1000 Hz.) The lowest trace in the stack plot (a normal spectrum) was recorded after the 90° initial pulse: the next was recorded after a 90° pulse and the elapse of 4 s (and hence 4000 echoes) and the last spectrum after 32 s (32 000 echoes). Recall that every echo is associated with a refocusing 180° pulse, and that for this last trace the pulse generator was switched on and off every millisecond for a total of 32 000 times.

Note the exponential decay in the echo (measuring T_2) and that no phase errors appear.

Figure 7.9(b) shows a comparable stack plot where the sampling interval (echo spacing and 180° pulse spacing) was set at 200 ms, corresponding to a frequency of 5 Hz. The lowest trace again was recorded after zero

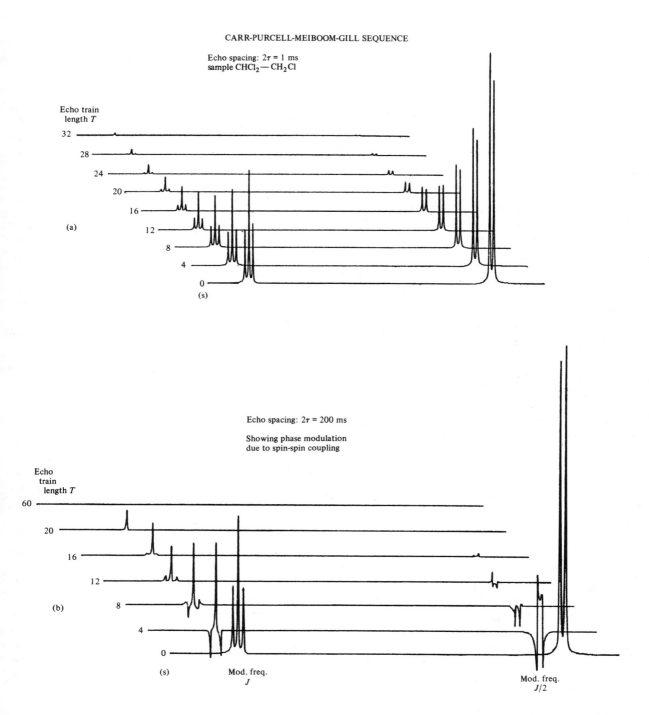

Figure 7.9 (a) T_2 stack plot for CPMG experiment. (b) Phase distortions in spin echo experiments caused by spin coupling when echo spacing is long

echoes; the next was recorded after 4 s (thus 20 echoes), and the last after 60 s (thus 300 echoes).

The phase distortions can be described qualitatively as follows.

(a) The centre line of the triplet is unaffected.
(b) After 4 s the outer lines of the triplet are approximately 180° out of phase with the centre line.
(c) After 8 s both lines of the doublet are out of phase by approximately 180°

This is a general picture which we can usefully build upon later. The points which need to be taken away are that

> Spin echo signals are modulated by coupling: the nature of the phase shifts thus arising depends on pulse repetition rates, the multiplicity and the coupling constant, J.

In figure 7.7 we saw that dephasing of the spins arises from the spread of frequencies present. For an ensemble of different protons, with different chemical shift values, there is again a spread of frequencies and (as with the inhomogeneity spread) these will be refocused at each echo without any phase mismatch.

When a proton signal is split by coupling, again different resonance positions (frequencies) are present and dephase after the 90° pulse. These coupled signals however behave differently after the 180° pulse than do chemical shift differences in frequency. As a simple example, consider an AX doublet signal with line A_1 at higher frequency than line A_2 and assume that line A_1 arises from association with the α state of X (X_α) and line A_2 with X_β. After the 180° pulse on X, its α and β states are reversed: the A_1 line (higher frequency) is then reversed and becomes the *lower* frequency line, while A_2 then becomes the *higher* frequency line. The effect of the 180° pulse therefore is a sort of double reversal, which still leaves the faster line *ahead* of the pack (not behind) so that it does not refocus at the echo, and remains out of phase with its partner, which is slower and is still left *behind* the pack.

Obviously, in a typical more complex molecule than trichloroethane, there may be different values of J present: this means that the modulation of different multiplets will produce phase shifts which are non-uniform. These principles also apply with modifications to heteronuclear coupling, and in particular to the important C–H couplings. See worked example 6.2.

From an organic chemistry point of view, this will allow distinctions among the carbon atoms of CH_3, CH_2,

CH and C groups: the pulse sequences which are used for this are discussed in section 7.6.

One last piece of geometrical arithmetic is needed to envisage the role of the coupling constant, J, in spin echoes, since this models the important differences in phase behaviour of doublets, triplets and quartets.

If we consider first a ^{13}C–^1H group, then both carbon-13 and proton signals will appear as doublets of separation J: to lend clarity to the argument, suppose that J = 120 Hz. Now consider the proton resonances, in a proton rotating frame of reference, and their magnetisation starts as in figure 7.10(a). A 90° pulse (that is, a $\pi/2$ pulse) tips the magnetisation as in (b).

The two proton resonances H_A and H_B, have frequencies which differ by 120 Hz (J H_z), therefore they will diverge on the $x'y'$ plane as shown at (c), since B has a lower frequency than A.

If we set the rotating reference frame frequency to that of (say) H_A, then H_A will 'see' H_B still rotating at 120 Hz (J Hz). H_A and H_B will therefore be in phase with each other (that is, H_B will rotate around the full 360°) 120 times per second (which is J Hz).

This can be expressed as they are first in phase again after a delay of 1/120 s or (1/J) s, as at (f).

They will be 180° out of phase, as at (e), in half this time, namely 1/240 s, or (1/2J) s.

They will be 90° out of phase, as at (d) after 1/480 s, or (1/4J) s.

Figure 7.10(g) shows the situation for a carbon-13 resonance of a CH_2 group, which consists therefore of three lines (three frequencies) separated by J Hz. The differences in frequency between C_A and C_B is J Hz, so that they have a different phase relationship from C_A and C_C whose frequencies differ by 2J Hz. Extension of these ideas to quartets (carbon-13 resonances of CH_3 groups) is the basis of distinguishing such groupings in carbon-13 NMR spectra by working upon their different phase relationships.

The important influence of coupling on phase applies to any coupling system: for the rare isotopomers containing two adjacent carbon-13 atoms, each carbon resonance is split into a doublet, which may appear as satellites as discussed in section 5.5. The unique phase behaviour of these doublets allows them to be picked out by suitable multipulse experiments, as will be elaborated in section 7.6.1.

In later discussions it will be necessary to look at how these in-phase signals (spin echoes) are detected, since they must be manipulated into the y'-axis of the receiver. Further phase shifts are needed, and the relationship

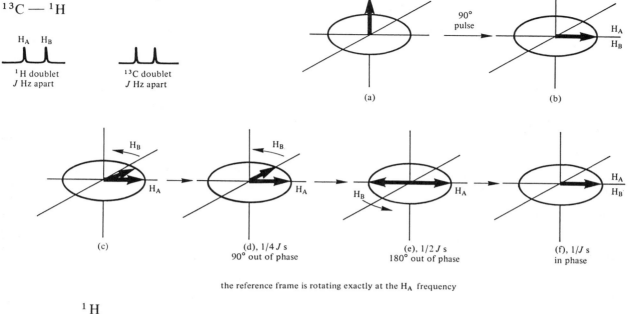

the reference frame is rotating exactly at the H_A frequency

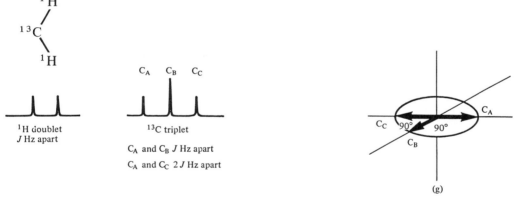

the reference frame is rotating at the C_A frequency: lines C_B and C_C have different phase relationships with respect to the rotating frame (90° and 180° out of phase)

Figure 7.10 Magnetisation vectors in phase modulation of spin echo experiments: CH_3, CH_2, CH and quaternary carbons produce different characteristic phase distortions

between carbon-13 and proton rotating frames is involved, so that only the simplest interpretation of events will prove feasible.

7.4 POLARISATION TRANSFER AND CROSS POLARISATION

Sensitivity is a constant problem in NMR studies of most nuclei, since low natural abundance and small magnetic moment (magnetogyric ratios) combine perversely as we saw in section 3.6. Fortunately, the proton not only has a strong magnetic moment and a high natural abundance (nearly 100%) but it appears frequently in coupled combination with the low sensitivity nuclei, such as carbon-13, and nitrogen-15.

> Polarisation transfer is a double irradiation technique for increasing the sensitivity of difficult nuclei by transferring magnetisation to them from the strongly magnetic proton.

Historically, the experiments of greatest interest in the present section grew out of work done in the study of solids by NMR (see section 7.6). In these studies a different technique is used to transfer the proton polarisation, and it is usually there named *cross polarisation*: polarisation transfer is also a form of cross polarisation. The differences lie both in the pulse methods used and in the nature of the coupling interaction involved: in solids it is the strong dipolar coupling which is involved, while in liquids and solutions it is the weaker scalar couplings which are involved.

This discussion will be limited to polarisation transfer from protons, since this is by far the most important case. Theory allows any nucleus likewise so to behave.

7.4.1 Selective Population Inversion

The use of 180° pulses applied at specific transitions (rather than over the whole range of shifts for any nucleus) gives rise to changes in the populations of other coupled nuclei.

As before, it is easiest to discuss this in relation to the simple AX coupling system, whose interconnecting energy levels are shown again in figure 7.11(a). The arguments assembled to explain the NOE (section 6.9) and the INDOR experiment (section 6.4.2) are all relevant here, but the effect is more dramatic because of the high RF amplitude used.

A 180° pulse exactly on the frequency of the X_2 transition markedly increases the population of level 2 while markedly decreasing that of level 1. In consequence the intensity of the A_1 line increases and that of the A_2 decreases.

The theory for the heteronuclear case (such as a ^{13}C–^1H or ^{15}N–^1H system) comes from the same physical calculations that quantify the NOE: in these examples we need only accept that the maximum possible changes in line intensity follow simply on the ratio of the magnetogyric ratios, γ. For carbon and hydrogen this ratio (the same as their NMR frequency ratio) is approximately 4; the new intensity of the A_1 line is

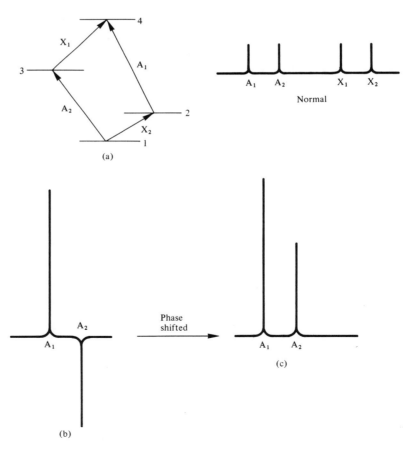

(a)

Normal

(b)

Phase shifted

(c)

Figure 7.11 Polarisation transfer, and its influence on the phase of signals

(1 + 4) and that of the A_2 line is $(1 - 4)$, giving a negative signal, so that the two A lines will be 180° out of phase as shown in figure 7.10(b).

Before passing on to correct the phase mismatch, we note that the effect of irradiating one line in (say) a proton doublet coupled to a carbon-13 nucleus has been to increase the line intensities of the carbon signals (albeit out of phase).

This is the basis of polarisation transfer experiments.

Two further details need now be addressed: having irradiated the ^{1}H resonance selectively (180° pulse, at say 100 MHz) the carbon resonances now must be sampled (at 25 MHz) by a normal (non-selective) 90° pulse. The problem of the two carbon lines being out of phase by 180° is solved by 'phase-shifting' the carbon pulse by 90° along the y'-axis (see section 7.3.2) in which case the two signals are then seen in phase, as in figure 7.11(c).

Although it was simpler to discuss the theory of polarisation transfer in relation to the selective irradiation used in SPI, the use of non-selective proton irradiation is more widely applicable: a combination of *Spin Echo plus Polarisation Transfer* (SEPT) gives rise to the bulk of multipulse NMR experiments.

Polarisation transfer (cross polarisation) in which the magnetisation comes from proton — and this is by far the most important circumstance — has also been called *proton enhanced* spectroscopy. This produces a common etymology in acronyms containing the letters PT, CP and PE: see the Compendium of Acronyms.

7.5 SUMMARISED PRINCIPLES OF SPIN ECHOES AND POLARISATION TRANSFER

1. Improved signal-to-noise in polarisation transfer spectra of difficult nuclei comes from irradiation of protons to which they are coupled.
2. Chemical shifts and coupling constants can be manipulated separately, since they have different phase characteristics in spin echoes.
3. Choice of suitable echo frequencies and delays permits this manipulation to give either coupled spectra, or decoupled spectra, or spectra which characterise different multiplicities such as doublets, triplets, quartets.
4. In all cases, manipulation of the phase (of pulses and detection) can be interposed to produce a spectrum of normal appearance (all signals positive), or to display selected resonances negatively (such as quaternary carbons) or to eliminate unwanted peaks (such as solvent peaks or peaks from abundant isotopomers).

7.6 INEPT, DEPT, AND SPECTRUM EDITING BY ADEPT

The pulse sequence of INEPT (Insensitive Nuclei Enhanced by Polarisation Transfer) has a special place in the history of multipulse NMR since it established the principles and practice of several whole generations of descendants. Refinements and modifications of the basic spin echo and polarisation transfer involvement led in due time to Distortionless Enhancement by Polarisation Transfer (DEPT).

Both of these pulse sequences improve the signal-to-noise ratio, giving increases in carbon-13 sensitivity of a factor of about 4, and in nitrogen-15 spectra of about 10. In DEPT, the elimination of phase errors (the spectra are *nearly* distortionless) arises from a less critical need to estimate the J values involved, or to set the pulse angles precisely.

Since all manufacturers of NMR instruments supply software to allow numerous variants (and much phase cycling to minimise artefacts) it will not be profitable to look at the instrumental details.

The actual spectra obtained by DEPT methods have the same characteristics as normal spectra (but at higher sensitivities) except in their ability to separate those signals associated with various multiplets.

7.6.1 Spectrum Editing — Carbon Sub-spectra

In figure 7.10 we saw that it was possible by choice of delay time to alter the phase relationships of CH_3, CH_2 and CH carbon-13 signals. Different sets of spectra can be recorded at different delay times, and these will contain multiplicity information.

Figure 7.12 shows such a set of sub-spectra for the carbons of menthol (whose ^{13}C–$\{^1$H$\}$ NMR spectrum appears also in figure 5.2). The sub-spectrum (a) shows the resonances only from those carbons in CH_3 groups: at (b) is the CH_2 sub-spectrum and the signals at (c) are from the CH carbons. These can all then be correlated with the whole spectrum shown at (d).

The value of such information in structure determination needs no advocacy.

This spectrum set was acquired using an automatic analysis (software controlled) of the various DEPT experiments, and has been named ADEPT.

One variant of the INEPT pulse sequence is shown in figure 7.13(a), and consists of a series of 90° and 180° pulses, phase-shifted along the x'-axis or y'-axis in two channels, for example in proton and carbon-13. The pulse sequence is set at an interval of $\frac{1}{4}J$ (which may have to be estimated) and a variable delay before

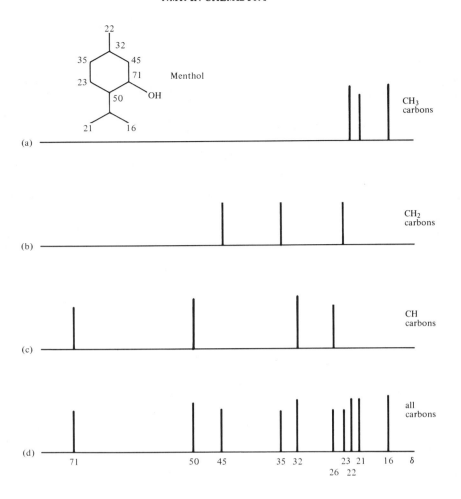

Figure 7.12 Identification of CH₃, CH₂, CH and C groups in spectrum editing of menthol (75 MHz in CDCl₃)

acquisition allows the selection of different parts of the signal, whose intensity varies depending on multiplicity and coupling constant as shown on the graph. Additional pulses may be added to introduce decoupling and to invert negative peaks (to produce normal spectrum appearance).

The DEPT procedure differs from INEPT in altering, not the delay times, but the pulse angle of the final proton pulse before acquiring the FID from the carbon-13 resonance. The basic pulse sequence is shown in figure 7.13(b).

The complex relationships of phase and signal intensity are incapable of simple rationalising. The end result is the set of sub-spectra with characteristics shown in figure 7.13.

When the θ_y pulse is 90° ($\theta 90°$) then CH₂ and CH₃ carbons cancel and only CH remains. For $\theta 45°$ and $\theta 135°$, the contributions from different carbons varie with phase such that addition and subtraction of sub spectra (called *editing*) can separate all three types a shown in figure 7.13.

To illustrate the power of the spectrum editing pro cedure, figure 7.14 shows the three sub-spectra for th carbons in cholesteryl acetate, with the proton coupling still present: in contrast, the total spectrum (δ 10–4C scale expanded) is shown in the bottom trace. Note th greater clarity with which, in particular, methyl quartet and CH doublets can be identified in the edited spectra

Quaternary carbons can be easily identified by simple procedures, as discussed in sections 5.1.3 and 5.2.

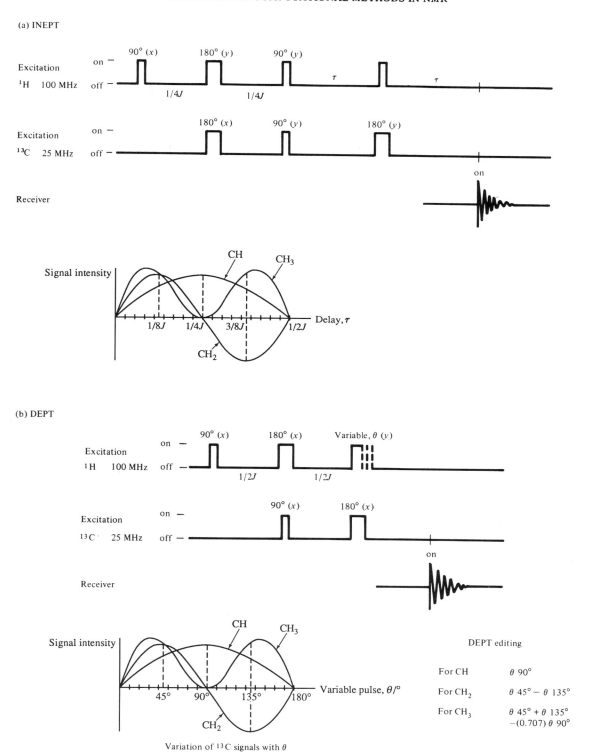

Figure 7.13 (a) Pulse sequence for polarisation transfer by INEPT (b) varying the duration of the final pulse, the DEPT sequence, produces characteristic changes in the line intensities of CH_3, CH_2, CH and C groups

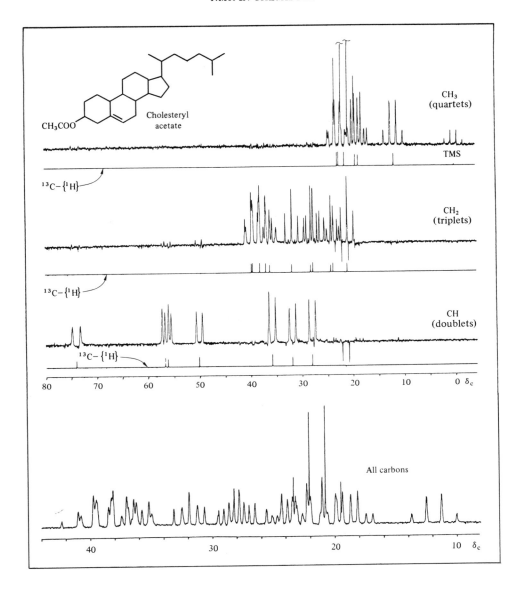

Figure 7.14 Spectrum editing of carbon NMR spectrum of cholesteryl acetate (100.6 MHz, that is, 11.7 T : in CDCl₃)

7.7 Two-dimensional NMR – 2D NMR

The presentation of data in two dimensions (pseudo-3D) allows much more information to be assembled and correlated than would be conceivable in a normal 'one-dimensional' plot. In the whole of chapter 5, in discussing carbon-13 NMR spectra, the emphasis was on simplifying the spectra, usually by broad band proton decoupling: information on multiplicity was lost, and off resonance methods restored only part of this.

The spectra in figures 7.15 and 7.16 show how different information can be plotted in two dimensions. In figure 7.15 the multiplicity is separated from the chemical shift, while in figure 7.16 the presentation correlates chemical shift positions: these represent the two main branches of 2D NMR.

The spectra will be discussed, firstly in relation to the information they convey and secondly to indicate how they are obtained.

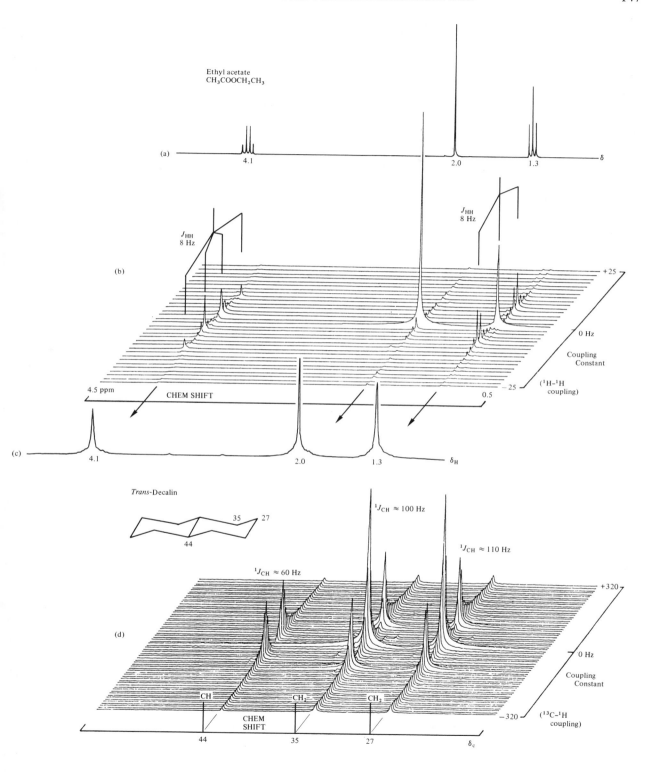

Figure 7.15   2D NMR. (a), (b) and (c) ethyl acetate proton NMR spectrum, HOMO-J resolved. (d) *Trans*-decalin 2D NMR, HETERO-J resolved (4.7 T) (200 MHz for proton, 50 MHz for carbon-13)

Some general features are profitably noted before detailed spectral information is extracted.

2D NMR spectra can be perceived in the same way as an orienteer perceives a mountain range. A model of the mountain range is properly three-dimensional, while photographs are two-dimensional substitutes, such as in figure 7.15. A contour map requires a certain interpretive skill, but contains much detail: figure 7.16 is such a contour map. The 2D NMR plot at the chapter head is of biotin (first recognised by Pasteur as an essential growth factor for yeasts). See also the cover of this book.

Various graphics tricks are available to present the same NMR data in a number of different 2D forms. As an exercise, it would be useful to imagine the ethyl acetate stack-plot redrawn in the form of a contour plot with two axes at (a) 45° and (b) 90°.

7.7.1 *J*-resolved 2D NMR Spectra

The separate presentation of chemical shift and coupling information is the basis of the spectra shown in figure 7.15.

The normal ^{1}H NMR spectrum for ethyl acetate is at (a), and its simplicity does not require 2D treatment

although it is a representative model. At (b), the chemical shift is plotted on one axis and the multiplicity on the other, but note that the mid-points of the multiplets lie on the middle row of the stack in this variation, with the coupling constant, *J*, measurable around the zero datum. (In other computer software programs *J* is measured from the edge of the axes.)

The additional information which this presentation reveals is the *projection spectrum* shown at (c): this is, in effect, a completely proton-decoupled proton spectrum. It contains the same information in one trace as would be contained in a long series of homonuclear decoupling experiments in which double irradiation was carried out at every single point, in turn, of the spectrum.

For more complex molecules, the advantages of (a) the separation of overlapping multiplets and (b) the decoupled projection spectrum can be much more rewarding. This kind of 2D NMR is named *homonuclear J-resolved*.

In figure 7.15(d) the multiplicity information for the carbon–proton couplings is shown plotted against the carbon-13 chemical shift positions for the molecule of *trans*-decalin. The projection spectrum in this case would of course be the broad band ^{13}C–{^{1}H} NMR spectrum,

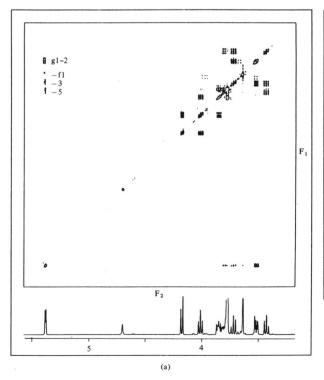

(a)

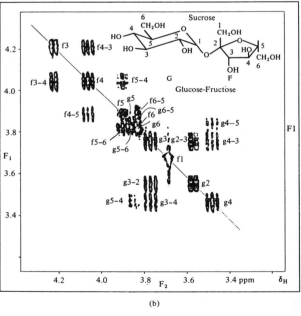

(b)

Figure 7.16 Sucrose, proton 2D NMR, HOMO-shift correlated (400 MHz, in D_2O)

which is in any event easily recorded by simpler means: the resolution of the two triplets and doublet is particularly clear. The three chemical shift positions are shown in the formula.

This kind of presentation is a *heteronuclear J-resolved* 2D NMR spectrum.

7.7.2 Shift-correlated 2D NMR Spectra

While the *J*-resolved spectra allow the identification of chemical shift positions, multiplicities and coupling constants in complex molecules, they do not necessarily establish which protons couple with which protons (and/or carbons).

Figure 7.16 shows one variant of contour plots for a spectrum recorded on sucrose; the presentation contains information which completely unambiguously establishes the coupling relationships among all of the protons (not the OH protons).

The presentation correlates the homonuclear chemical shifts (^{1}H with ^{1}H) and it is therefore a *homonuclear shift-correlated* 2D NMR *spectrum*. (The pulse sequence for this example of *correlation spectroscopy* is named COSY.)

At the bottom of figure 7.16 is the normal ^{1}H NMR spectrum for sucrose (OH protons removed): this is envisaged again projected up onto the diagonal of the matrix above.

The whole map is to be regarded as reflected about this diagonal: this is a device to ensure that all spurious peaks can be eliminated, since part of the program compares each side of the diagonal and discards as an artefact any signal which does not appear symmetrically about the diagonal.

The signals located off the diagonal correlate those protons which are coupling to each other.

For example, proton number 1 in the glucose part of the molecule, g-1, is at δ 5.7. Both vertically up from it and, as a check, horizontally along from it are signals marking those protons with which g-1 couples, that is, g-2, g-3, g-5 and f-1.

Proton f-3 at δ 4.23 can be seen to have signals above and to the right of it which confirm that f-3 couples with f-4. For f-4, the coupling to f-5 is indicated by signals up and along from it and so on.

A further modification of the technique can correlate in the same way the relationship between carbons and protons in a *heteronuclear shift-correlated* 2D NMR *spectrum*.

7.7.3 Recording 2D FT NMR Spectra — τ and the Second Time Domain Axis

The rate at which new presentations are being developed is quite staggering, and computational expertise is as much involved as chemistry. (The invention of novel acronyms is just as active a field.)

The concept of 2D FT is most easily exemplified by reopening the discussions of section 7.3.4 and looking again at figure 7.10. After a 90° pulse and a *delay period* (or *evolution period*) τ, the vectors fan out according to their different frequencies. Sampling pulses applied at different times τ will detect different frequencies, depending on their alignment with the axis of the sampling pulse. If we recall that *chemical shift* differences in frequency behave differently in the spin echo from *coupling constant* differences in frequency, then various pulse combinations allow either the chemical shift information or the coupling information to be extracted as a function of a series of different τ values. That is, the *different τ values are frequency selective*.

> The variation of signal intensity with τ is in the time domain, and its Fourier transform is in the frequency domain. This frequency domain plot is the second axis in 2D NMR spectra.

By convention, 2D NMR spectra are plotted with the evolution period variants (time or frequency respectively) labelled τ_1 and f_1, while the FID detected in successive scans is labelled in its time domain as τ_2, and in its (reciprocal) frequency domain as f_2.

While chemists are largely interested in structural and interpretive features in NMR spectra, a more physical approach focuses often on rate parameters such as T_2 or dipolar relaxation (and NOE). Thus there are for these purposes other multipulse derived variants, one of these is named NOE difference Spectroscopy (NOESY). In NOESY difference spectra, two series are accumulated — one using techniques to *minimise* NOE and the other to *maximise* it — and the two series of spectra subtracted: those nuclei which are most subject to NOE stand out above those which experience minimal NOE (see section 7.1).

7.7.4 ^{13}C Satellite Spectroscopy — Carbon–Carbon Connectivity Plots — CCCP

By examining the ^{13}C–^{13}C satellites in 2D NMR, an organic chemist attains what is an ultimate goal — the ability to identify in sequence the entire carbon skeleton of a molecule.

The discussion on satellites in section 5.5 is necessary background to the technique.

The pulse sequences which permit this construct are sophisticated (although one variant is named *INADEQUATE*). They involve several phase shifts in order to suppress the much stronger ^{13}C signals coming from isotopomers with only one carbon-13 atom per molecule. They are designed to overcome the problems of isotope shifts (see sections 5.5 and 5.5.1) and the distortions in line positions inherent in AB systems (see section 4.9).

Part of the multipulse sequence establishes a relationship between the $\alpha\alpha$ and $\beta\beta$ levels of the carbon AB doublet systems, and this test of association (coherence) leads to the name *double quantum coherence*. (Single quantum NMR absorptions interchange one spin at a time, such as $\alpha\alpha$ to $\alpha\beta$: a rare occurrence can arise where two quanta are absorbed, and such features have been observed. This present experiment does not involve such double quantum absorption.)

The key to the separation of the $^{13}C–^{13}C$ doublets from the single ^{13}C signals lies in their different phase behaviour in which phenomenon figure 7.10 is illustrative. The execution of a 90° pulse for single ^{13}C leads to a 270° flip for the doublet signals: this is the same as a −90° flip, with the impression therefore that the vector for the doublets is moving backwards.

The emphasis here is not so much on how connectivity plots are derived but on how they are used. Figure 7.17 is illustrative.

The interpretation is somewhat similar to that used in

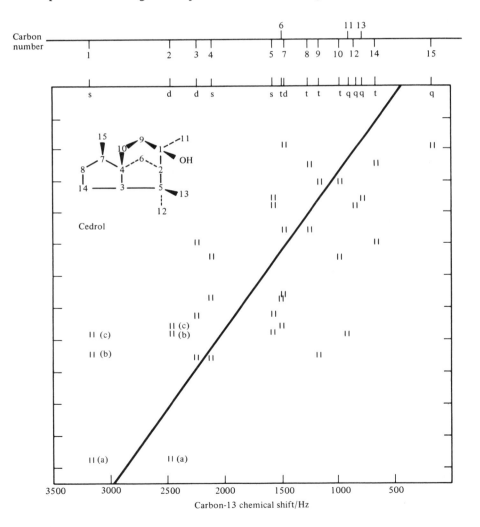

Figure 7.17 Carbon–carbon connectivity plot (CCCP) in analysis of the structure of cedrol (from cedarwood oil) (75 MHz in CDCl₃)

the shift-correlated spectrum of figure 7.16: correlated carbon atoms give rise to linking signals along the vertical and horizontal directions, the symmetry axis in this case serving the same purpose as before (identification and elimination of artefacts) but aligned differently in this particular program.

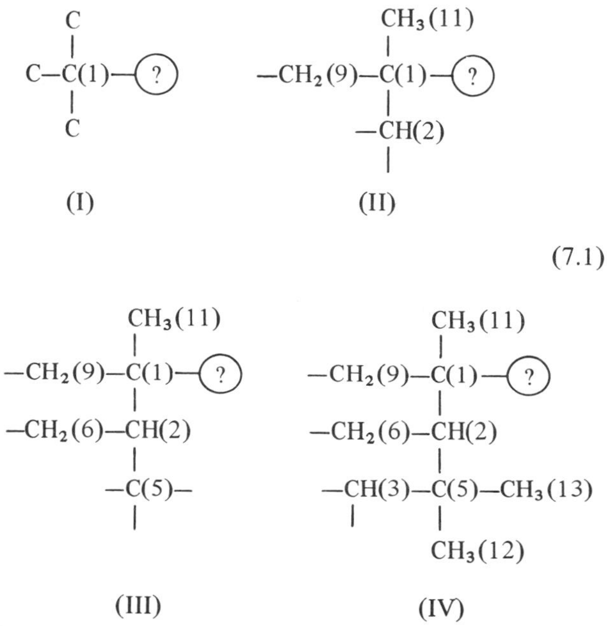

$$(7.1)$$

We can start with the carbon of highest δ value C-1 and note that it is a singlet, that is, it does not have an attached proton. Vertically down from its chemical shift position are three signals: this shows that it is attached to three other carbons, so we can write this as in formulae 7.1 (I). At this point we must leave one valency unassigned: in the end this is found to be attached to the OH group.

From each of the C-1 signals, we move horizontally to the corresponding signal symmetrically distant from the diagonal. Thus starting at the bottom from signal C-1(a), horizontally, we identify a signal which correlates C-1 with C-2. From C-1(b), moving up the chart, we correlate with a signal from C-9 and from C-1(c) we correlate with a signal from C-11. From the multiplicity given on the top spectrum, C-2 is a doublet (CH), C-9 is a triplet (CH$_2$) and C-11 is a quartet (CH$_3$).

This allows the construction of the part structure shown in formulae 7.1 (II).

We now proceed to C-2, noting from the signals vertically downwards that it is bonded to three other carbons. Starting again from the bottom, signal C-2 (a), simply correlates again with C-1. Signal C-2 (b) establishes a horizontal correlation with C-5, which is a singlet and thus non-proton bearing. Signal C-2 (c) correlates with the triplet C-6, which is thus CH$_2$. Formulae 7.1 (III) shows the growing molecular skeleton.

Proceeding now to C-5, four signals appear on the vertical, identifying the connections with C-3, C-12, C-13 and C-2 (already established). From their noted multiplicities we can now write as in formulae 7.1 (IV).

The remainder of the *carbon–carbon connectivity plot* (CCCP) can be followed as an intellectual join-the-dots exercise.

Only one signal needs comment: note that C-4 is joined to both C-6 and C-7. The middle C-4 signal might be construed as a single signal, but the symmetry test shows otherwise: since there exist two signals on one side of the symmetry diagonal (those from C-6 and C-7) then there must be two signals, albeit overlapped, for C-4.

7.8 SOLID STATE NMR SPECTRA

When molecules lie side by side in a solid sample, whether crystalline or powder, the orientation of their dipoles and magnetic nuclei are fixed and to a large extent random. The two principal effects of this in NMR are on the chemical shifts and couplings.

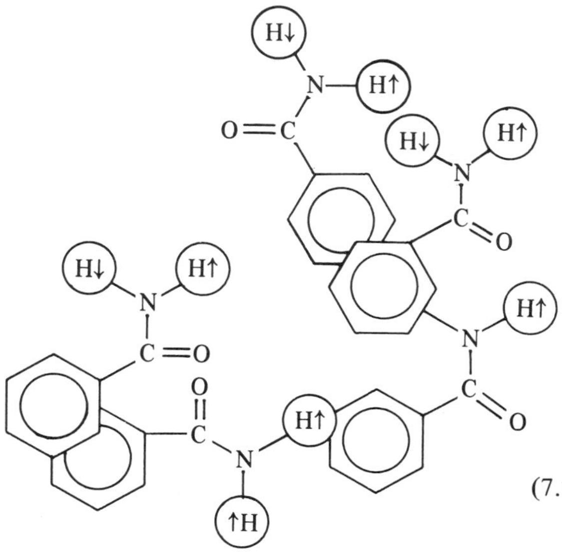

$$(7.2)$$

Chemical shift anisotropy (electrical) and *dipolar coupling* (magnetic) in a solid sample of benzamide

A simple molecule like benzamide, in the solid state, will have its protons and carbons in non-uniform dipolar environments. The chemical shifts depend on the molecular orientation with respect to the field, B_0, and are therefore much less uniform and spread very substantially, so that broad absorption bands only are observed.

Just as the benzene ring current produces anisotropic shielding zones *intramolecularly*, as discussed in section 4.2, clustering of the molecules in the solid produces even stronger *intermolecular* anisotropic shielding effects: this is named *chemical shift anisotropy*, and in the rapid tumbling of molecules in solution it is averaged to near zero.

Also, in the solid state, the magnetic dipoles of proton and carbon are held close together and couple with one another through space. This direct coupling, named *dipolar coupling*, is several orders of magnitude stronger than the couplings we have encountered up to now. (This latter *J*-coupling, or scalar coupling, is transmitted through bonds as discussed in section 6.1 so that it is much more attenuated than the dipolar coupling in solids.) The dipolar coupling is also a function of molecular orientation, so that many different values combine to spread the NMR resonances over a wide band of frequencies. A single carbon resonance can be broadened to the extent of hundreds of ppm.

In non-viscous liquids both of these problems disappear because of the rapid molecular tumbling which averages all anisotropies to zero, and decouples the magnetic nuclei by the rapid changing of their mutual orientations.

The sensitivity penalty for rare spins (carbon-13, nitrogen-15) is of course also present in solid state NMR, as is the problem of relaxation times: for some carbons in a solid environment the relaxation time, T_1, can be measured in hours.

A combination of techniques can overcome all of these difficulties.

7.8.1 Magic Angle Spinning — MAS

This technique overcomes chemical shift anisotropy. In the mathematical analysis of shielding in an applied field, the term $(3 \cos^2 \theta - 1)$ arises, where the angle θ determines the orientation of the molecule with respect to B_0. Theory shows that any shielding anisotropy (chemical shift anisotropy) falls to zero when $(3 \cos^2 \theta - 1)$ falls to zero, and this occurs when $\theta = 54.7°$ — the so-called *magic angle*.

Figure 7.18 shows the operation of magical angle spinning (or rotation) — MAS (or MAR). The sample is

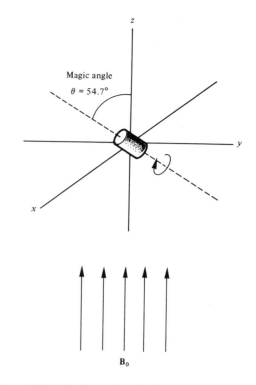

Figure 7.18   Magic angle spinning

either machined into the shape of a rotor or contained in a plastic or ceramic rotor, and the rotor is spun by an air turbine around the axis oriented exactly at the magic angle. The spinning rate must be comparable to the chemical shift anisotropy, measured in hertz: for carbon at 1.4 T this is about 3 kHz (that is 200 ppm). For MAS, high magnetic field is a disadvantage, since the same anisotropy at say 7.0 T (a 300 MHz instrument) would require spinning rates of around 15 kHz: the problem then becomes one of engineering.

7.8.2 Dipolar Decoupling and Cross Polarisation

The remaining problems of solid state NMR — dipolar coupling, low sensitivity and long T_1 values — are all tackled by a set of interrelated techniques.

Double irradiation at the proton frequency decouples the protons from carbon-13, analogously to the scalar decoupling met in chapter 5, but requiring much more power (say 100 W) than previously required. Again, there are engineering problems in coping with the heat generation.

The proton decoupling can be carried out with a multipulse technique which transfers magnetisation

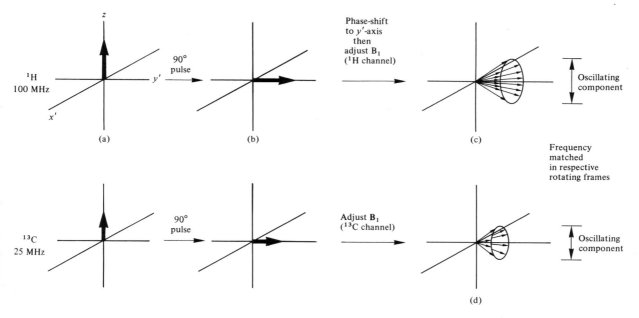

Figure 7.19 Cross polarisation — establishing the relationship between the separate proton and carbon rotating frames (the Hartmann–Hahn condition)

(polarisation) to the less abundant carbon-13 spins (section 7.4) and which also circumvents the long T_1 problem ingeniously.

The vector representation is shown in figure 7.19. A $90°$ proton pulse along the x-axis (as usual) tips the magnetisation vector for protons onto the y'-axis. This is immediately followed by a second proton RF signal but this time along the y' axis (that is, the second RF signal is phase shifted $90°$ with respect to the first) (see figure 7.19(c)). Since now the proton magnetisation vector is aligned on the y'-axis with the incoming RF, it is said to be **spin locked** in its rotating frame: we can envisage therefore the individual protons precessing as at (c) in the figure. Let us say the proton frequency is 100 MHz.

A $90°$ pulse is now applied at the carbon-13 frequency (at 25 MHz), and the carbon magnetisation then also is aligned along the y'-axis of its own rotating frame: this is rotating at one quarter the frequency of the proton rotating frame.

There must be executed at this stage the critical conditions for setting up the polarisation transfer. The amplitudes of the two RF transmitters ($B_{1,H}$ at 100 MHz for proton and $B_{1,C}$ at 25 MHz for carbon) must be adjusted so that the precession frequency for protons and carbons, ν_H and ν_C each in their respective rotating reference frames, is the same. We saw in chapter 2 that

$$\nu = \gamma B_0$$

The matching that is required here is

$$\nu_C = \nu_H \quad \text{when} \quad \gamma_H B_{1,H} = \gamma_C B_{1,C}$$

This is named the **Hartmann–Hahn matching** condition. In figure 7.19(c) and (d) we can see that each system generates oscillating components which allow transfer of magnetisation: since proton is more abundant and has a stronger magnetic moment than carbon, the polarisation transfer is from the proton set to the carbon set.

(With the protons spin locked along the y'-axis, their net magnetisation is at a maximum. Indeed, it will decline (relax) exponentially from this maximum by a first order process with a time constant which measures a different relaxation mode from T_1 or T_2. This third relaxation time is the **relaxation time in the rotating frame, $T_{1\rho}$** (spoken tee one rho). We will not be much concerned with this except in dynamic NMR (section 8.1).)

A thermodynamic viewpoint of the spin locked cross polarisation effect is often adduced. From Boltzmann theory (section 2.16) the population difference in energy levels contains a temperature term: we can define the fact that for protons the population difference is greater than that for carbons by saying that the **spin temperature** for protons is lower than that for carbons. (The principle involved here is clear from a solution of problem example 2.6.)

Cross polarisation involving the Hartmann–Hahn match can therefore be described as *transfer of spin temperature*. When the carbon spins are irradiated and the population of the energy levels nearly equalised, the carbon spins are 'hot'. The connected proton set constitutes a 'cold' reservoir, considerably more effective (higher heat capacity) than the carbon set in absorbing spin temperature. The carbon set can therefore give up its heat to the proton reservoir several times before the proton reservoir itself becomes heated.

This leads to the useful picture in figure 7.20. With protons spin locked, the carbons are irradiated, but rapidly relax, since they give up their heat to protons. The carbons can therefore be excited again much more rapidly than would be possible from their normal T_1 relaxation mode. Several carbon *contact times* with proton can be executed before it is necessary to allow the protons themselves to relax: this is fairly rapid, since T_1 for protons is short, so the cycle can begin again after a minimum of delay.

7.8.3 Applications of Solid State NMR

Many interesting species cannot be examined in the liquid phase: coal and other minerals, polymers, biological samples and many inorganic salts are a few examples. In many cases it is possible, using the combined battery of techniques discussed, to obtain NMR spectra comparable

with liquid state spectra. The practical difficulties are substantial, and the spectrometer must have a wide enough bore to accommodate the spinning apparatus.

Decoupling and cross polarisation cannot help in recording proton NMR spectra on solids; magic angle spinning must also be at faster rates than for carbon. An alternative in solid state proton NMR is to supply a very rapid series of pulses which, essentially, move the magnetisation vector around the axes so rapidly that it is tantamount to MAS. Several variants are known, but the original is best known from its picturesque acronym WAHUHA (from Waugh, Huber and Haeberlen).

7.9 BIOLOGICAL NMR

7.9.1 NMR Imaging – Zeugmatography, Tomography

Figure 7.21 shows reconstructed NMR images of a human brain. The techniques of three-dimensional image reconstruction have been used before with X-rays and with heat sensors (thermography) but these NMR images derive from the proton-bearing species present, principally water and fats (the long alkane chain protons of the fatty acid moieties).

In essence, the pictures are joined together by computer, after the brain has been scanned in several modes along different slices of its solid shape, rather in the

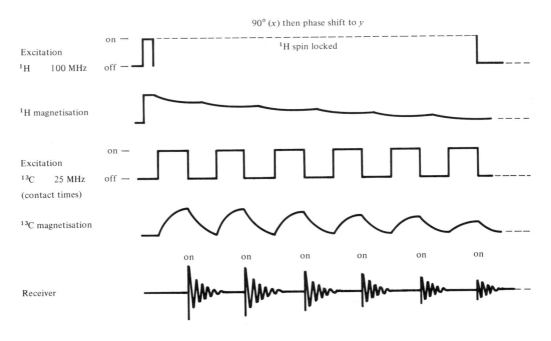

Figure 7.20   Pulse sequence for multiple contact cross polarisation

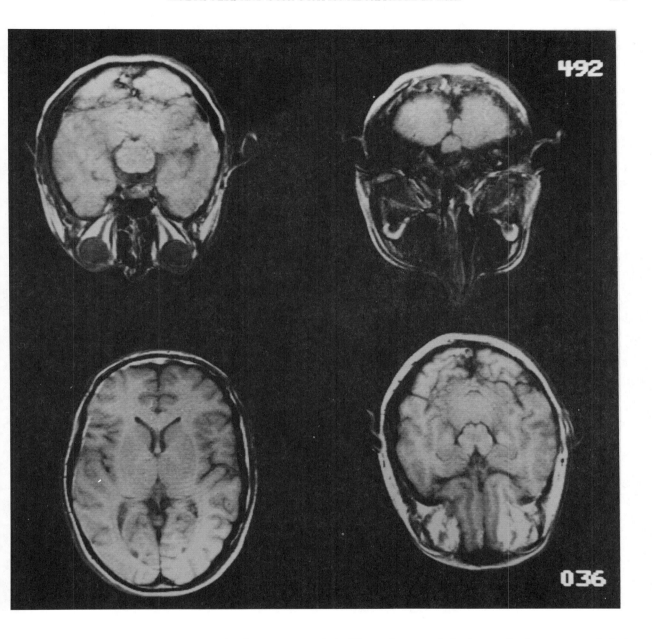

Figure 7.21 NMR imaging by tomography (zeugmatography). These pictures of the human brain were recorded at 64 MHz, each slice being 4 mm thick.

manner that contour maps indicate slices of terrain which are at the same altitude.

Two Greek words, zeugma and tomos, respectively refer to joining things and slicing things (as in the figure of speech zeugma and in atoms and microtomes): two alternative names for *NMR imaging* are *zeugmatography* (coined by the first demonstrator of the method, Paul Lauterbur) and *NMR tomography*.

The medical and biological potential of the method is enormous, both in research and pathology.

It has already been established *in vitro* that normal tissue and malignant tissue differ in the values of proton T_1 and T_2 for the water present. The ability to detect this *in vivo* is an exciting possibility. While X-ray tomography reveals certain dense features of the object, NMR tomography reveals others: the NMR method can probe the soft tissues more effectively than X-rays, and is not the source of any known hazard to living systems.

Several different approaches to NMR imaging are used, but the principles are embodied in considering the detection of the water protons in a head. They will all come to resonance at the same frequency (that is, give a coherent signal) if the field strength is uniform across the head. If, instead of applying a uniform field, a field of known and variable gradient is applied, then a correlation can be established between the proton frequency and its distance along the gradient.

It is then a matter of scanning various locations in the head with the field gradient, recording signals at each successive location, and reconstructing these signals by computer to give a form of density map of the object. Locations with large amounts of water (soft tissues) give images which are distinctive from, say, bone.

Although a horizontal superconducting magnet system at 200 MHz (for proton) is available commercially, the field strengths used in NMR imaging are often not very high (proton frequencies of 4–20 MHz) since performance at higher frequencies is affected by tissue conductivity. In biomedical work, the horizontal geometry is preferred for easy limb or body access, and superconducting magnets are used because of their high stability.

Most NMR imaging uses the proton resonance in water, but both carbon-13 and phosphorus-31 imaging have been demonstrated, in spite of the fact that their lower sensitivity makes them orders of magnitude more difficult. It is also possible separately to image the proton resonances from water and fats, thus permitting specific studies of fatty deposits.

7.9.2 Surface Detection and Topical Magnetic Resonance, TMR

NMR studies on living systems can be carried out without the imaging process outlined above. It is possible to detect high resolution signals from within a body by the use of specially designed magnets and/or RF coils.

Instead of constructing the NMR magnet to produce a homogeneous field over the entire magnet core, carefully contoured field gradients can be introduced to create a small spatial volume of homogeneous field inside the body being examined: nuclei within this volume will give rise to sharp NMR signals, while nuclei in adjacent space will experience non-uniform fields and give broad-line signals (which add to the base-line and can subsequently be subtracted from the sharp resonances by computational techniques). Because of the

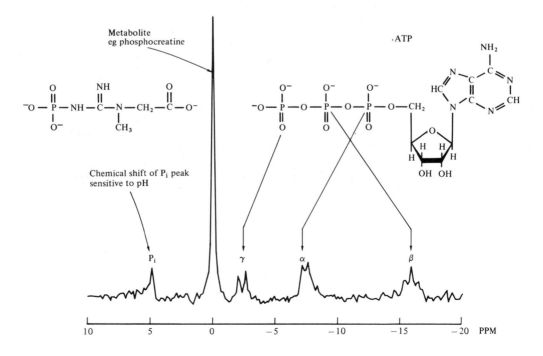

Figure 7.22 ^{31}P NMR spectrum recorded live on a human forearm: the chemical shift of the inorganic phosphate signal varies with tissue pH (64.8 MHz, *in vivo*)

ability to examine tissues at specific internal locations (or places) the technique has been named *topical magnetic resonance*, TMR (from the Greek, topos, a place).

Using such profiled magnetic fields, the subject can be placed inside close-fitting RF coils, or alternatively, the RF coil can be placed on the body surface and, dependent on coil diameter and RF power, different depths of tissue can be sampled.

Figure 7.22 shows the ^{31}P NMR spectrum taken from a human forearm; the resolution enables the separate resonances from inorganic phosphates, phosphorus metabolites (such as phosphocreatine) and the three signals from ATP to be identified. (The ^{31}P NMR spectrum of ATP is also shown in figure 10.2.) This high degree of resolution permits *in vivo* biomedical studies on metabolic processes; the method is usually distinguished from biological *NMR imaging* (where NMR resolution need not be so high, and where proton resonances are the main interest) by the title biological *NMR spectroscopy*. The potential of the method is in process of being fully exploited, and studies on proton, carbon-13 and phosphorus-31 NMR are well established, with other elements offering unique additional information (such as fluorine-19 studies on anaesthetic action).

Whole-body NMR spectra can be obtained with large bore superconducting magnets such as that shown at the head of chapter 10; the design permits a choice between NMR imaging, or spatially selective high resolution spectroscopic experiments (TMR). Extensive coverage of the various methods and their applications in living systems are given in the book by David Gadian, listed in Further Reading.

8

Dynamic NMR

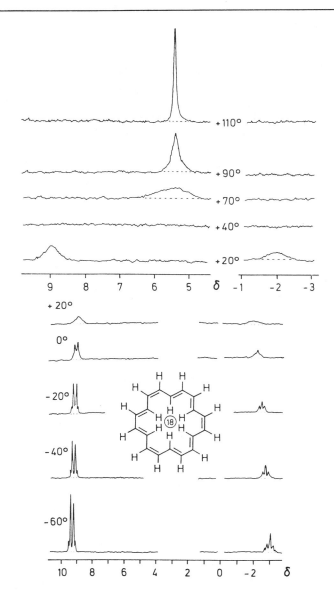

Effect of temperature on the proton NMR spectrum of [18]annulene (100 MHz)

Molecules are in constant motion, and the different conformations which are interconverted by bond rotations and other molecular gymnastics often have different NMR spectra. Figure 8.1 shows a number of compounds which exist in rotationally related forms: NMR can be used to study the kinetics of these exchanges. Also shown in figure 8.1 are examples of reactions (prototropy or tautomerism) in which the exchange involves bond breaking and making: the rates of these reactions can also be studied by NMR. The inversion of atoms such as nitrogen is also shown, and is amenable to NMR study.

The use of NMR to measure rate parameters is generi-

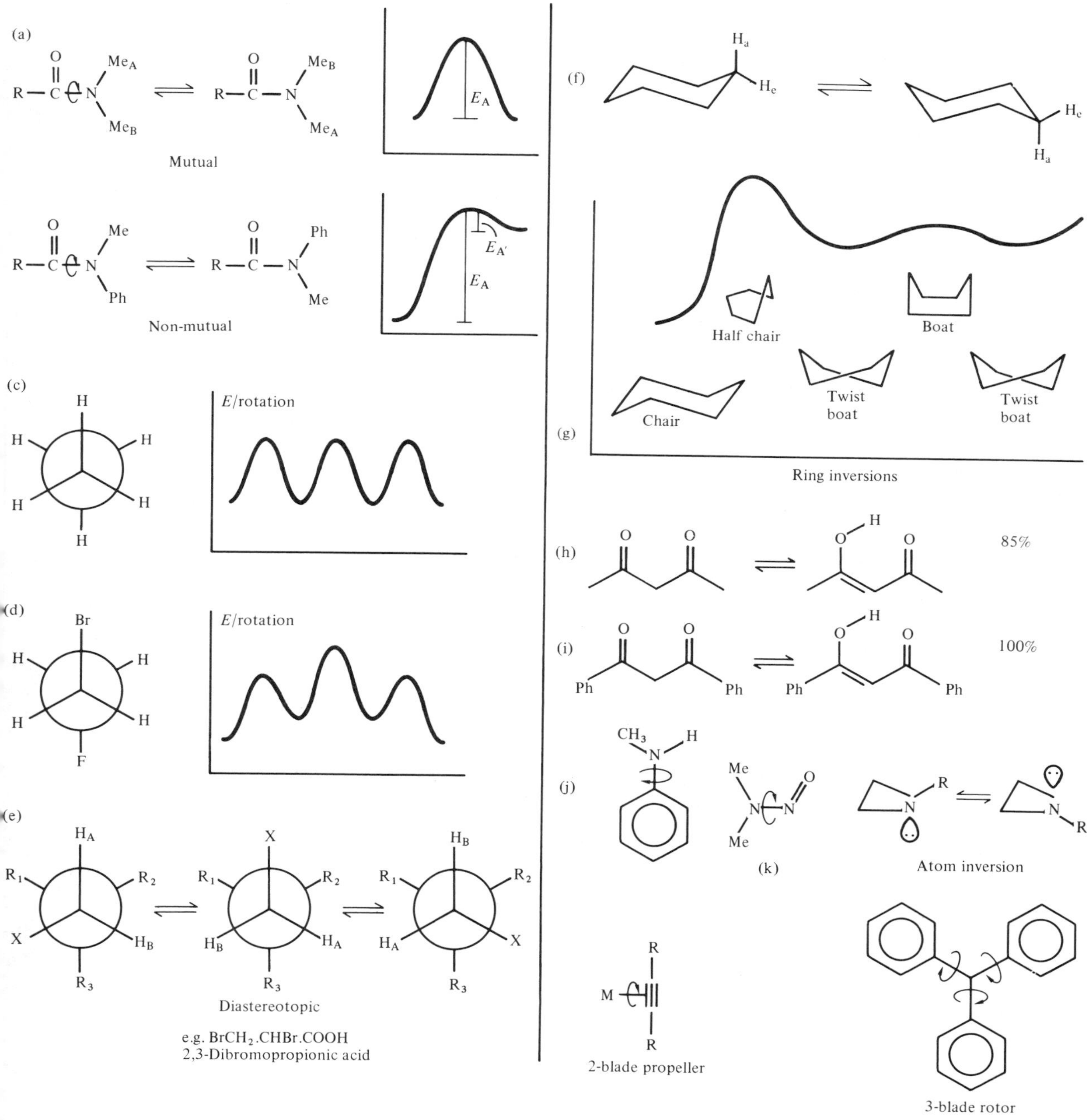

Figure 8.1 Exchange processes amenable to study by NMR

cally named *dynamic NMR*, sometimes simply DNMR.

Several instances have already been met of processes whose time scale determines the nature of the NMR spectrum obtained: see for example sections 4.2.3, 4.2.5 and 4.3.2. This chapter looks at the subject more systematically, and indicates the experimental methods used to measure rate constants and activation parameters: the unique contribution of NMR to these studies, and the approximate range of rates amenable to the method, will be outlined; intimate details of the treatment of these kinetic data will be omitted.

The ability to vary accurately the temperature of the sample under examination is an inseparable adjunct to dynamic NMR: aspects of the variable temperature probe were outlined in sections 3.9 and 4.5.1.

8.1 RATE PROCESSES AND THE HEISENBERG UNCERTAINTY PRINCIPLE

The Heisenberg Uncertainty Principle tells us that in order to resolve NMR signals (that is, to record them separately) a 'sufficient' time is necessary, this time, Δt, being the life-time of any particular state which we wish to detect. Several instances have already been encountered of the involvement of Δt in NMR phenomena: see for example sections 2.18 and 4.7.4.

The Uncertainty Principle can be expressed either in terms of the uncertainty in energy (ΔE) or in frequency ($\Delta \nu$) by substituting $E = h\nu$ appropriately: thus

$$\Delta E \cdot \Delta t \simeq h/2\pi$$

or $$\Delta \nu \cdot \Delta t \simeq 1/2\pi$$

The processes set out in figure 8.1 all occur at rates (measured in s^{-1}) which can be deduced from the life-times of each separate state (Δt, measured in s).

Thus slow rates (long life-times) lead to separate NMR signals, while fast rates (short life-times) lead to overlapped or coalesced signals.

> The Uncertainty Principle correlates life-times, rates and resolution. The minimum life-time for resolving signals is given approximately by
>
> $$\Delta t \approx \frac{1}{2\pi \Delta \nu}$$

Since line width is also defined in Uncertainty Principle terms (as discussed in section 6.8.4), rates can also be calculated from detailed line shape analysis.

8.1.1 Chemical Shift and Exchange Rates

In many of the examples shown in figure 8.1, the chemical shift values of certain of the nuclei in the molecule alter during the exchange. The simple example of the methyl groups in N,N-dimethylacetamide however illustrates the special case in which the exchange produces indistinguishable molecules: this type (see figure 8.2) is termed *mutual exchange* or *mutual site exchange*. At lower temperatures, restricted rotation around the C—N bond produces different shielding zones for the methyl groups, so two methyl resonances arise in the spectrum. As the sample temperature is raised, rotation becomes more rapid, and in consequence the life-time of each methyl group in each separate shielding zone is reduced: the signals broaden (Heisenberg Uncertainty Principle). Ultimately the life-times become so short (rotation so rapid) that only one resonance is detected mid-way between the separate signals.

The energy barrier to rotation in this case (see table 8.1) is measured by the energy of activation, E_A, which is about 80 kJ mol^{-1}: it is possible to calculate E_A from the measured temperature dependence of the appearance of the spectrum, and in this the *temperature of coalescence* of the signals (around 72°C) is of central importance. More precise details are given in section 8.2.

For other unsymmetrical amides the C—N rotation will produce different forms, each of different energy: the energy profile for such a *non-mutual site exchange* is shown in figure 8.1(b). At any one temperature, both rotational isomers will be present, and the amount of each at equilibrium can be calculated in favourable cases from the separate signal intensities (by the usual process of integration). The calculation of E_A in such cases is somewhat more difficult than in the simpler mutual exchange processes.

More complicated still are the rotations of hindered ethanes: figure 8.1(c) shows ethane itself (with the energy profile for rotation) and figure 8.1(d) shows the increasing complexity of the energy barriers to rotation when substituents are present. (The inclusion of fluorine is of more than passing interest: fluorine-19 chemical shifts are much more widely spread than those of the proton, and ^{19}F NMR is often therefore a more convenient and sensitive probe for energy studies than proton NMR.)

The molecule in figure 8.1(e) has a pair of protons (H_A and H_B) adjacent to a chiral centre, in this case an asymmetric carbon atom. The three Newman projections show that these protons are always in non-equivalent environments, no matter the rotation, and this situation

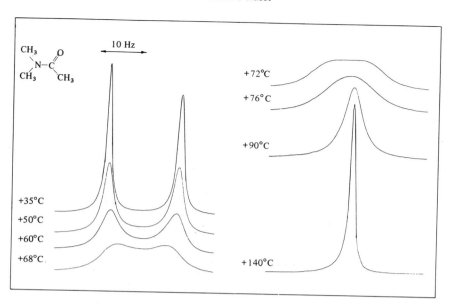

Figure 8.2 Effect of temperature on the proton NMR spectrum of N,N-dimethylacetamide, a simple mutual exchange system (90 MHz)

obtains generally for other chiral centres. These protons are called *diastereotopic*, have different chemical shifts, and therefore show coupling to each other. (They also couple differently to any other neighbouring magnetic nuclei, and are thus magnetically non-equivalent (see figure 8.3.)

The axial and equatorial protons of cyclohexane (figures 8.1(f) and 8.4) have chemical shift values of

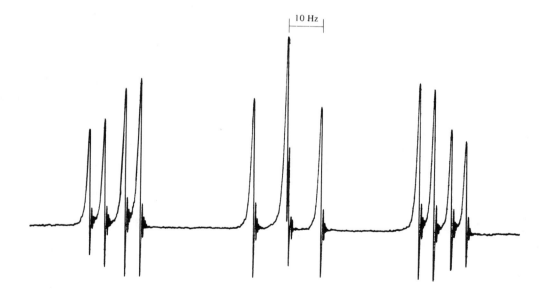

Figure 8.3 Proton NMR spectrum (at 35°C) of 2,3-dibromopropionic acid, $BrCH_2 . CHBr . COOH$. The CH_2 protons are diastereotopic, and together with the CH proton make up an AMX coupling system (100 MHz in $CDCl_3$)

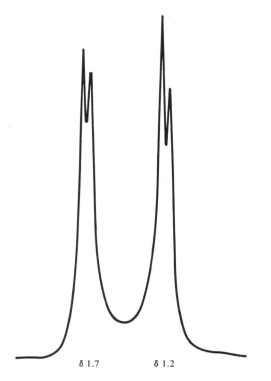

δ 1.7   δ 1.2

Figure 8.4 Proton NMR spectrum of cyclohexane at −100°C, showing the separate signals from equatorial (at δ 1.7) and axial (at δ 1.2) protons (100 MHz)

δ 1.2 and 1.7 respectively, but the two signals are only observed if the sample is cooled to about −60°C: at higher temperatures the exchange is rapid and only a time-averaged signal at δ 1.45 is seen. The ring inversions of substituted cyclohexane derivatives is a rich field of study in conformational exchange rates, as calculations of E_A for inversions must take into account the possibility of various energy maxima and minima corresponding to chair, boat and twist forms: see figure 8.1(g). The biggest energy barrier is associated with converting the stable chair conformation, *via* the half chair, to one of the twist boat forms. For cyclohexane itself, this E_A is variously reported around 43 kJ mol^{-1}; substituted derivatives vary with the size (and polarity) of the substituents and their relative positions in the molecule. At low temperatures, when the inversions are 'frozen', the axial and equatorial protons not only have different chemical shifts but different coupling constants; this leads to a more complex proton spectrum. The carbon-13 NMR shifts of cyclohexanes also reflect conformational effects, but these have been less studied than those for proton.

In all cases where rotation and/or conformation effects give rise to different chemical shifts for the components present, the ability of the NMR method to resolve separate isomers depends on the chemical shift difference (in hertz) between the signals. This, of course, varies with field strength: how this complicates the experimental measurement of E_A values is discussed in section 8.2.

Worked Example 8.1
At 25°C, the proton NMR spectrum of N,N-dimethylnitrosoamine (see figure 8.1(k)) consists of two singlets, separated by 0.65 ppm. For this molecule, use the Heisenberg Uncertainty Principle to calculate approximately the minimum life-time, Δt, necessary to resolve these two signals at 1.4 T.

Answer 8.1
At 1.4 T, proton frequency is 60 MHz and 0.65 ppm corresponds to a difference in frequency, $\Delta \nu$, of 0.65(60) = 39 Hz. The minimum life-time needed to resolve signals 39 Hz apart is $1/(2\pi\Delta\nu) \simeq 1/(6 \times 39$ Hz) or approximately $1/(240$ s$^{-1})$ or 0.004 s. Another way of picturing this is to note that the signals can be resolved so long as the rate of rotation (the reciprocal of the life-time) is no faster than 240 times per second.

Problem Example 8.1
What is the (approximate) maximum rate of rotation which would still enable the signals in the above example to be resolved at 25°C in a 2.35 T instrument (operating at 100 MHz)?

For keto-enol tautomerism (figure 8.1(h)), the ratio of isomers is easily measured in proton NMR spectra by simple integration of the separate signals: the alkene proton of the enol and the CH$_2$ group of the keto form can, in all of the shown examples, serve as the quantitative marker for each respective mole fraction. From NMR, we know now that acetylacetone (2,4-pentanedione) exists to the extent of 85% in the enolic form. The compound sold under the name of dibenzoylmethane does not have this structure, but exists totally in the enol form (3-hydroxy-1,3-diphenylprop-2-en-1-one) (figure 8.1(i)).

The carbon-13 NMR spectrum of N-methylaniline (figure 8.1(j)). (PhNHCH$_3$), at temperatures down to −120°C shows the effect of free rotation of the Ph−N bond: only four signals appear for the ring carbons. Near −135°C, the rotation 'freezes' and the resulting anisotropy produces six separate resonance positions for the ring carbons.

The remainder of the formulae in figure 8.1 merely serve to indicate the diversity of molecular motions which have been quantified by the use of NMR spectroscopy. The dramatic effect of temperature on the proton NMR spectrum of [18]annulene is shown at the chapter head: ring inversion ultimately equilibrates all protons.

8.1.2 Spin Coupling and Exchange Rates

Life-times and residence times must be considered in explaining the spin–spin splitting which OH protons generate in the NMR spectra of alcohols and in other proton exchange processes.

Figure 4.17 shows the simple case of ethanol, in which acid catalysis has accelerated proton exchange to the extent that resolution of the splitting to OH is impossible (when the residence time is too short). The same effect could have been produced by raising the temperature of the sample to speed up the exchange.

It is important to contrast the involvement of the coupling constant, J, in dynamic NMR with that of the chemical shift differences discussed in section 8.1.1.

Whereas changes in the magnitude of $\mathbf{B_0}$ alter chemical shift differences (when measured in Hz) the coupling constant, J, is unaffected.

Worked Example 8.2
From figure 4.17, the OH coupling constant is 6 Hz. What is the maximum rate of proton exchange which will still permit resolution of the splitting between OH and CH?

Answer 8.2
The minimum life-time for resolution of the coupling is given approximately by $\Delta t \simeq 1/(2\pi\Delta\nu)$ which in this case relates to the separation between the lines, that is, to the coupling constant, J. Thus $\Delta t \simeq 1/(2\pi J)$ or $1/(6 \times 6$ Hz) or $1/(36$ s$^{-1})$. If the protons interchange faster than about 36 times per second, no coupling will be detected.

Problem Example 8.2
Figure 4.17 was recorded at 100 MHz. In a 7.0 T instrument, what minimum life-time is necessary (from the Uncertainty Principle) in the proton exchange in ethanol to ensure detection of the OH splitting?

In alkane chains, adjacent CH_2 groups rotate so rapidly with respect to each other that no chemical shift differences (nor coupling differences) are detected, so that these CH_2 protons are effectively magnetically equivalent.

Restricted rotation in substituted ethanes, such as 1,2-dibromoethane, not only leads to chemical shift differences but also to more complex coupling inter-

actions. The rather special example shown in figure 8.3 is the proton NMR spectrum for 2,3-dibromopropanoic acid at room temperature. The protons of the CH_2Br group are diastereotopic: all three protons are magnetically non-equivalent, and an AMX system results. The spectrum is still AMX at high temperature. Note that (accidentally) $J_{AM} = J_{MX}$ so the middle lines of H_M overlap.

8.1.3 Line Shape (Band Shape) and Exchange Rates

The nature and width of NMR absorption bands has been discussed in section 2.18 and again in section 6.8.4. In dynamic NMR the analysis of line shape leads to considerable insight into several rate processes: the exchanges shown in figure 8.1 all affect line shape but relaxation parameters are also implicated (T_1, $T_{1\rho}$, T_2 or T_2^*). Much of the detailed analysis of line shape derives from Bloch's original equations, and it has to be assumed that each NMR signal, in the absorption mode, is Lorentzian. The mathematics of depicting theoretical curves is formidable, and can only successfully be approached by computerised simulation of the expected line shapes. More details are to be found in more physical texts, listed in Further Reading.

The extraction of kinetic data from line shape analysis has several advantages over variable temperature experiments on δ and J effects. There are several systems in which the E_A is either too small or too large, and the system either cannot be cooled sufficiently (to 'freeze' it) or heated sufficiently (for the signals to coalesce). In other cases, the compound may be thermally labile and decompose if heated towards coalescence temperature.

Polymers and viscous systems which give broad line spectra can be treated kinetically by line shape analysis and, although the method is capable of yielding E_A values without the need for variable temperature, the techniques are specialised and do not warrant the necessary comprehensive discussion here.

Simulated spectra are shown in figure 8.5 for two simple cases: the simulation program can accommodate many factors including the number of exchange sites, the chemical shift differences, the population differences and different E_A values operating between different parts of the molecule. Although an infinity of possibilities exists, the principles are indicated by these simple examples.

8.1.4 Relaxation Times and Exchange Rates

Several differently defined relaxation times were discussed in chapters 6 and 7, (T_1, $T_{1\rho}$, T_2 and T_2^*) and

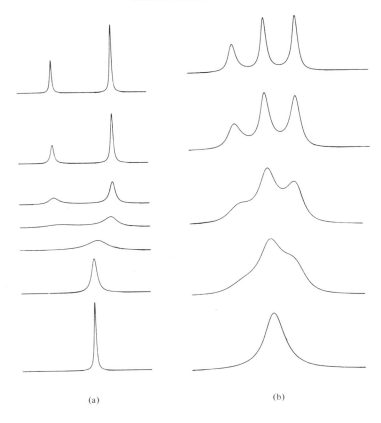

(a)   (b)

Figure 8.5 Temperature dependence of the line shapes for two possible non-mutual exchange systems (simulated)

methods for measuring them were outlined. Each of these parameters can make specific contributions to the study of exchange, since each may have different time characteristics for a given system. Thus, in general, T_1 can be longer than T_2, and this implies the ability of T_1 measurements to relate to slower processes than can be matched with T_2. The effective T_2 ($T_2{}^*$) is more easily measured than T_2 (although the spin echo method has been applied for the latter) and line shape analysis gives information on $T_2{}^*$ changes. Conversely, $T_{1\rho}$ can be used to study very fast exchanges, even up to rates approaching 10^6 per second.

The details of these experiments also involve the use of band width analysis and computerised simulation.

8.2 ENERGY OF ACTIVATION

A full discussion of equilibria and chemical kinetics is inappropriate here, and too extensive in scope. It has been convenient up to now to refer to the exchange

energy barrier (rotation, inversion, ring-flip) as E_A, the energy of activation; this is implied also in the reaction profiles in figure 8.1. E_A is part of the Arrhenius equation (see section 8.2.1) but this approach does not always give accurate predictions since it wrongly assumes E_A to be independent of temperature. Strictly, the free energy of activation ($\Delta G\ddagger$, spoken delta G double dagger), the enthalpy of activation ($\Delta H\ddagger$) and the entropy of activation ($\Delta S\ddagger$) are interconnected by $\Delta G = \Delta H - T\Delta S$, and different experimental procedures are required to measure each separate parameter.

Some published data do not record exactly whether E_A, $\Delta G\ddagger$, or $\Delta H\ddagger$ is being specified, although for most interpretive purposes it makes only differences in detail: the most sophisticated treatments measure $\Delta G\ddagger$, while most casual users merely use the general term E_A, which derives from the Arrhenius equation.

8.2.1 The Arrhenius Equation and the Eyring Equation

Henry Eyring (see chapter 14) made major contributions to rate theory and some brief note of how his work can be applied to measuring exchange rates in NMR is relevant.

The energy of activation, E_A, for a simple reaction such as the rotation of amides, can be assessed from the Arrhenius equation for the reaction rate, k.

$$k = A \exp(-E_A/RT)$$

In this, R is the gas constant, T the absolute temperature and A roughly corresponds to the fraction of species that reach the transition state and successfully pass over to the product side of the reaction: A is called a 'constant', in spite of the fact that it does vary a little with T.

The value of E_A is found by plotting $\ln k$ against $1/T$: for the many reactions which give a straight line plot, the slope is $-E_A/R$ and the intercept is $\ln A$. Not all reactions give a straight line, since for some processes E_A is not temperature independent (which an Arrhenius type reaction must be).

A different approach gives the Eyring equation (which can be expressed in various ways). It can be written

$$k = K \frac{k_B T}{h} \exp(-\Delta G\ddagger/RT)$$

In this, k is the rate constant, k_B is the Boltzmann constant, h is the Planck constant and $\Delta G\ddagger$ is the free energy of activation; as stated above, $\Delta G\ddagger = \Delta H\ddagger - T\Delta S\ddagger$, so that $\Delta G\ddagger$ includes both enthalpy and an entropy content.

The 'constant' K is analogous to the 'constant' A in the Arrhenius equation, and is likewise subject to variation in non-simple reactions: much argument surrounds the significance of K, but it relates, like A, to 'reaction success rate'. Provided the transition state can easily transfer energy to the surroundings (and this is commonly true in large molecules) then K is near unity.

We need only consider the simplest circumstances of a mutual exchange such as represented in figure 8.2 for the rotation of dimethylacetamide or of dimethylnitrosoamine. For such first order cases, H. S. Gutowsky showed that the rate of rotation, k_c, at the temperature of coalescence, T_c is given by

$$k_c = \frac{\pi(\Delta\nu)}{\sqrt{2}}$$

The life-time, t_c, of the separate isomers at the point of coalescence is the reciprocal of the rate, $1/k_c$, so

$$t_c = \frac{\sqrt{2}}{\pi(\Delta\nu)}$$

Note that this is different (by a factor of $\sqrt{2}/2$) from the approximate values predicted from the Uncertainty Principle in section 8.1.

The Gutowsky equation is probably the most widely used equation for measurement of exchange kinetics by the coalescence method, but there are known to be systematic errors in the calculations. In particular, as we saw above, as coalescence is approached the signals move closer together ($\Delta\nu$ becomes smaller) and refined calculations must take account of this. Other expressions for t_c have been used, including $t_c = (\sqrt{2} \ \pi\Delta\nu)^{-1}$: some measure of the lack of agreement among chemists is found in comparing three methods which give estimates of t_c which differ by a factor of three.

If we substitute the value of k_c, however calculated, into the Eyring equation, convert natural log to $\log_{10}$, and substitute the values for k_B, h, and R, then the Eyring equation evolves usefully to

$$\Delta G\ddagger = 19.12 \ T_c (10.32 + \log T_c - \log k_c)$$

Despite the problems of calculating k_c, and the difficulty in identifying exactly the coalescence point corresponding to T_c, many approximate measurements of energy barriers have been made by this method.

> The free energy of activation for many exchange processes can be evaluated approximately from T_c using the Eyring equation in this form.

8.2.2 Typical Values of Activation Energies

Having noted the obscuring problems of whether $\Delta H\ddagger$, $\Delta G\ddagger$ or E_A is being measured, and making suitable approximations, the energy barriers for some representative exchanges, determined by NMR methods, are listed in table 8.1.

8.3 THEORY OF COALESCENCE

A reasonable interpretation of the coalescence of NMR signals at high temperatures in exchange processes pictures the nuclei as experiencing an 'average environment' as the exchange rate becomes very fast.

We saw that in the simplest case (two site, non-coupling, mutual exchange) the 'averaged' chemical shift position is exactly mid-way between the two separate values. We also can note from figure 8.4 that, as coalescence approaches, the two separate signals begin to move towards the mean. A moment's contemplation will convince us that there is no certainty that chemical shifts measured at room temperature for an exchange system, even though separately resolved,

Table 8.1 Energy barriers (in kJ mol^{-1}) for representative exchange processes, as measured by NMR: different values are derived from different methods

Molecule	Process	Energy barrier/kJ mol^{-1}
HCONMe$_2$	rotation of C−N	82–88
CH$_3$CONMe$_2$	rotation of C−N	80
tert-butyl-CONMe$_2$	rotation of C−N	47
CF$_2$Br.CFBr$_2$	rotation of C−C	41
CFBr$_2$.CHBr$_2$	rotation of C−C	42
CH$_3$CBr$_2$.CBr$_2$CH$_3$	rotation of C−C	67
	rotation of C−C	50–70
cyclohexane	chair → twist flip	43–45
Me$_2$NNO	rotation of N−N	88–97
Me$_2$NH	inversion of nitrogen atom	18
ClNH$_2$	inversion of nitrogen atom	43
DMSO	inversion of sulphur atom	166
	rotation of Rh-ethylene bonds	63

represent the maximum separation that would be observed were the sample temperature to be lowered.

There is also a more realistic explanation of the 'averaged' chemical shift position: this signal arises in the spectrum at a precession frequency which is different from that of any frequency actually present in the molecule.

Consider the frequencies of (say) H$_A$ and H$_B$ in such an exchange, with values ν_A and ν_B: at coalescence the new frequency is the mean, ν_M, $\frac{1}{2}(\nu_A + \nu_B)$. Suppose that ν_A is higher than ν_B, and let us construct the process in a rotating frame of reference, revolving around the z-axis at the mean frequency of ν_M.

For conditions of *slow exchange*, H$_A$ and H$_B$ spend 'long' times in each exchange site (long enough for several precessions to be recorded at their separate frequencies).

For *fast exchange*, a nucleus may spend a short time in site H$_A$, in which case it will be precessing in the rotating frame *faster* than ν_M. But it will then move to site H$_B$, and will precess at ν_B, which is *slower* than ν_M. Continually jumping from the two sites alternately moves each nucleus ahead of ν_M and behind ν_M, the net result being that each nucleus appears to be precessing at frequency ν_M, the frequency of this rotating frame. Figure 7.10 will help to visualise this.

For conditions of moderately fast exchange, the Heisenberg Uncertainty Principle explains the line broadening observed.

8.4 THE NMR TIME SCALE – WHAT IS IT?

The ability of NMR to study time dependent phenomena is related to all of the factors discussed throughout this chapter: these include the separate temperature dependencies of chemical shifts, coupling constants and relaxation times.

The NMR time scale is enormously wide, and should not be thought of as having quite narrow limits. A few examples will illustrate that the life-times involved may vary from a few microseconds to a few tenths of a second, corresponding to exchange rates of the order $10-10^6$ per second.

The coalescence of coupled signals is easier to deal with, since it is field independent. But in table 6.1 were listed some representative J values which ranged from J_{HH}, approximately 10 Hz, through J_{HF}, approximately 50 Hz, to J_{CHg}, approximately 2500 Hz. The minimum coupling life-times, predicted approximately from the Gutowsky equation, range from 10^{-2} to 10^{-4} s (4.5×10^{-2} s to 1.8×10^{-4} s).

The NMR time scale for non-coupling chemical shift environments is field dependent. Two proton signals may be 10 ppm apart, but this can correspond to 600 Hz (at 1.4 T) or 5000 Hz in a 500 MHz instrument. The 'time scale' which relates to a coalescence condition in these two cases runs approximately from 0.8 ms to 0.09 ms: that is, the higher field experiment (500 MHz, 11.75 T) is able to examine exchanges in which the life-times are nearly one tenth of those at 60 MHz.

Worked Example 8.3

Use the Gutowsky equation to calculate the life-time of each rotamer of N,N-dimethylnitrosoamine, when the signals just coalesce in a 60 MHz experiment. Compare this life-time with that calculated in worked example 8.1, where the signal positions are stated to be 39 Hz apart.

Answer 8.3

At coalescence the life-time is given by

$$t_c = \frac{\sqrt{2}}{\pi(\Delta\nu)} = \frac{1.41}{3.14 \times 39 \text{ Hz}} = 0.012 \text{ s}$$

Problem Example 8.3

Use the Gutowsky equation to calculate k_c for N,N-dimethylacetamide, whose 90 MHz proton spectrum is shown in figure 8.2. (Estimate $\Delta\nu$ at T_c and *not* at room temperature.)

8.5 CHEMICALLY INDUCED DYNAMIC NUCLEAR POLARISATION – CIDNP

Figure 8.6 shows two proton NMR spectra for the ethyl group in thiophenetole, PhSEt. (Phenetole is PhOEt.)

The spectrum at (b) is the expected set of signals for an ethyl group, and is in all respects normal.

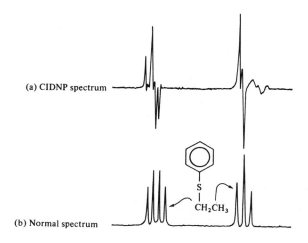

Figure 8.6 Appearance of a CIDNP spectrum in the radical reaction leading to thiophenetole, ethyl phenyl thioether, $PhSCH_2CH_3$

Thiophenetole can be synthesised in a number of ways, but if it is prepared by the reaction of thiophenol with ethyl radicals (formed by thermolysis of dipropionyl peroxide), the equations are as in formulae 8.1.

This reaction can easily be carried out within an NMR sample tube, and if the spectrum is recorded during the reaction, then figure 8.6(a) is the result.

Some of the lines in the spectrum show enhanced absorption (designated A lines) while others show emission characteristics (E lines).

This phenomenon, first observed in 1967, was originally thought to be similar in origin to nuclear Overhauser effects, with dynamic polarisation of the population levels, hence it was named *chemically induced dynamic nuclear polarisation*, or CIDNP. This name has become established in spite of the fact that the origin of the phenomenon is now known to be quite different from the NOE.

8.5.1 Applications of CIDNP

CIDNP effects are observed only in radical reactions.

Many synthetic and decomposition mechanisms have been assessed by the presence or absence of CIDNP during reaction progress. If CIDNP is absent, then, assuming the experimental parameters have been set up correctly, a radical process is eliminated. On the other hand, if CIDNP is observed, it certainly proves that radical processes are involved; but since reaction mechanisms are never simple (and radical processes in particular may follow alternative routes) the presence of CIDNP is not a proof that the main reaction route follows a radical mechanism.

$$CH_3CH_2CO-O-O-COCH_2CH_3 \xrightarrow{\Delta} 2CH_3CH_2CO-O^{\cdot} \xrightarrow{\Delta} 2CH_3CH_2{}^{\cdot} + 2CO_2$$
dipropionyl peroxide

(8.1)

$$PhSH + CH_3CH_2{}^{\cdot} \rightarrow \rightarrow \rightarrow PhSCH_2CH_3$$
thiophenol   thiophenetole

The thermal and photochemical decomposition of peroxides have been widely studied for CIDNP effects, not only as a vehicle for mechanistic evaluations but in studying the phenomenon *per se.*

The qualitative applications are typified by the example given in figure 8.6. Another example is the decomposition of dibenzoyl peroxide, $(PhCOO)_2$, in the presence of a source of hydrogen atoms; the benzene signal gradually moves to emission, with an intensity that may reach 100 times the 'normal' absorption intensity.

8.5.2 The Nature of CIDNP

It is not possible to give a satisfactory explanation of the theory associated with CIDNP, without recourse to chemical physics. The nature of the CIDNP effects, and whether E or A influences each line, have been comprehensively studied and categorised by Kaptein.

The essence of the theory treats a radical pair in terms of several alternative fates: either the pair will recombine or disproportionate, or they will diffuse apart and recombine with other radicals or reactants. The effects will also depend on whether the radical pair is formed from singlet or triplet precursors. Finally the electron spins and the nuclear spins will interact, causing changes in spin orientations. The extent of this is influenced not only by the g-factor for the electrons but also by the J value (and sign) of any internuclear coupling. This in effect alters the populations of the nuclear spin states in the product, with concomitant changes in the absorption and emission intensities.

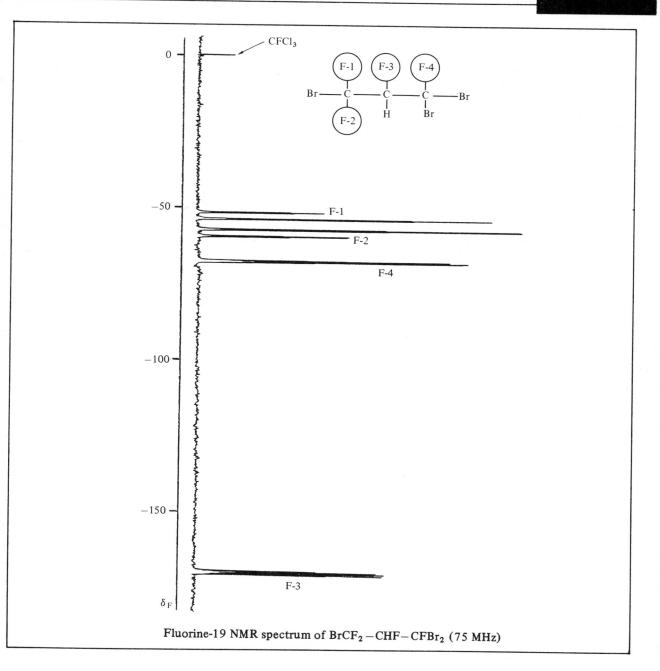

Fluorine-19 NMR spectrum of $BrCF_2-CHF-CFBr_2$ (75 MHz)

With 100% natural abundance and a large magnetic moment, fluorine-19 NMR creates no problems in sensitivity. The range in chemical shifts is very wide over all, around 800 ppm, although most resonances of carbon–fluorine environments occur within a 300 ppm scan. Strong coupling to other nuclei results in long range effects and these (like all coupling effects) influence both the fluorine-19 spectrum and that of the other nucleus. Since $I = \frac{1}{2}$ the coupling patterns are easily deduced.

Because of the wide range of δ values, fluorine-19 spectra are usually first order in their multiplicities, and this allows very detailed structural analyses to be made from the observed splitting patterns.

9.1 FLUORINE-19 CHEMICAL SHIFTS

At 2.35 T, fluorine-19 resonances are at 94 MHz: the range of δ values in common environments is around 300 ppm, so the spread of frequencies is approximately 30 000 Hz. This enormous range, greater than that for any other commonly studied NMR nucleus, does create some instrumental problems in recording and in digitising fluorine-NMR spectra, but these need not concern us here.

Figure 9.1 shows a representative selection of δ values, referenced to CFCl$_3$, with the usual convention that positive δ means higher frequency than CFCl$_3$, and conversely for negative δ. As for other nuclei, theory alone is inadequate in rationalising the observed structural influences on shifts, and empirical data are all we need rely on: fortunately these are comprehensively available in specialist texts. See the list in Further Reading.

In practice, where it is necessary to interpret spectra in terms of one or more feasible molecular structures, the number of fluorine chemical shift environments is often all that is necessary to make the distinction. As a simple example, the ^{19}F NMR spectrum of SF$_4$ at low temperature consists of only two resonances, each of which is a triplet. This establishes that there are two magnetically equivalent environments, each with two fluorine atoms.

The structure therefore cannot be tetrahedral (I) (formulae 9.1) nor can the trigonal bipyramid arrangement (II) hold: SF$_4$ has the structure (III), with the non-bonding electrons of sulphur occupying one of the equatorial positions.

At higher temperatures, rapid intramolecular exchange takes place and the spectrum evolves to a time-averaged singlet. Similar dynamic NMR studies show that in PF$_5$

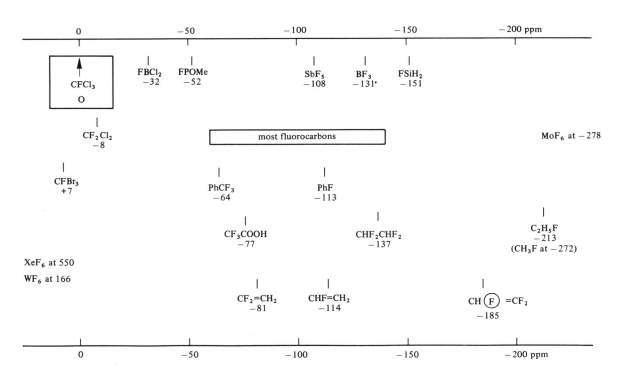

Figure 9.1 Fluorine-19 chemical shifts

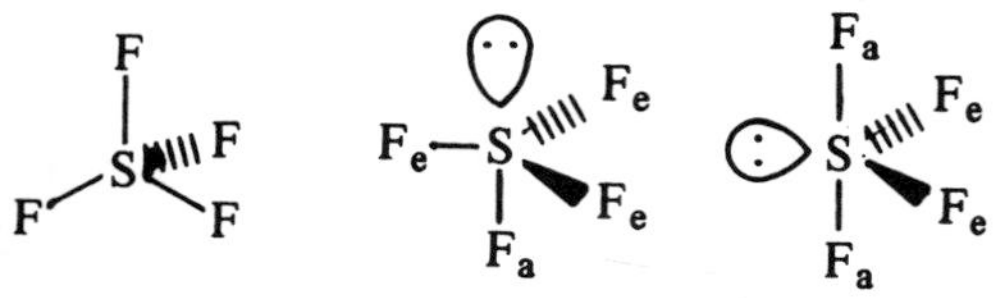

singlet resonance (I)

doublet for F_e quartet for F_a (II)

two triplets (III)

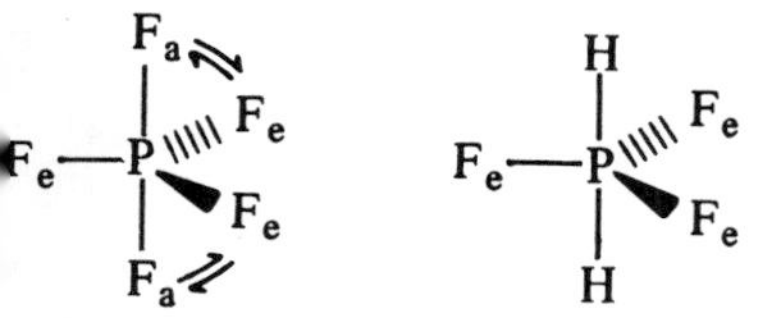

$$(9.1)$$

Table 9.1 Representative fluorine-19 coupling constants

System	Type	Typical J value/Hz
$>C<^F_F$	$^2J_{FF}$	150–270
(F-benzene)	$^nJ_{FF}$	5–20
CF_3 CF_3 (cis)	$^5J_{FF}$	14
CF_3 ... CF_3	$^5J_{FF}$	2
HF	$^1J_{HF}$	530
$>C<^F_H$	$^2J_{HF}$	45–65
(vinyl ^F_H)	$^2J_{HF}$	70–90
$F-C-C-H$	$^3J_{HF}$	0–45 (highest values *trans*)
(vinyl F, H)	$^3J_{HF}$	5–20 (10–50 for *trans*)
$-^{13}C-F$	$^1J_{CF}$	160–370
$^{13}C-C-F$	$^2J_{CF}$	30–45
$^{13}C-C-C-F$	$^3J_{CF}$	5–25
$^{13}C-C-C-C-F$	$^4J_{CF}$	1–5
$-^{31}P----F$	$^nJ_{PF}$	800–1500

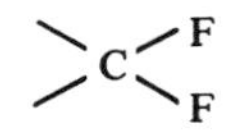

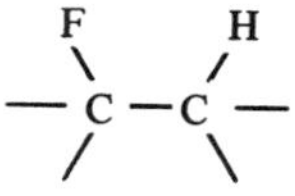

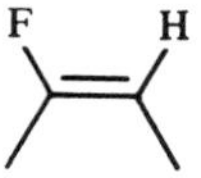

the exchange is different, since even at low temperatures one equatorial F atom is fixed while the remaining pairs of axial and equatorial fluorines undergo rapid exchange, and this is borne out by the multiplicity observed.

9.2 FLUORINE-19 COUPLING CONSTANTS

Fluorine coupling is influenced by spatial proximity as well as by the number of intervening bonds. Long range fluorine coupling over four or five bonds leads to quite extensive splittings: the effects observed can be divided into different categories, depending on whether we are dealing with coupling of fluorine to abundant nuclei (such as with other fluorines, protons or phosphorus) or coupling to rare nuclei (such as carbon-13) or coupling to nuclei with spin greater than one half (such as nitrogen-14).

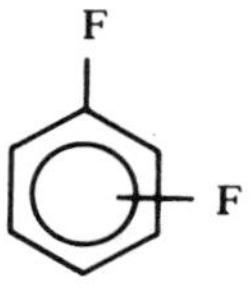

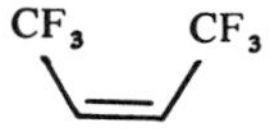

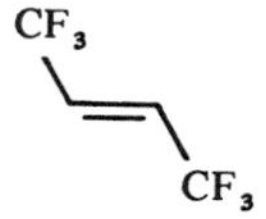

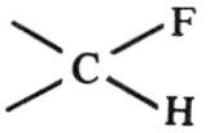

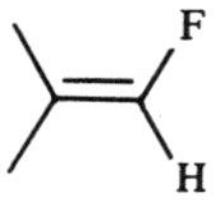

Table 9.1 lists a very small selection of J values, which are extensively listed in the specialist texts recommended for Further Reading.

9.2.1 Coupling of Fluorine-19 with Fluorine-19

The fluorine-19 NMR spectrum of perfluoropyrimidine is shown in figure 9.2, and at high temperature the signals are broadened by coupling to nitrogen-14 — a feature we shall return to in section 9.2.4.

At −40°C the clear multiplicities can be interpreted in terms of the number of non-equivalent fluorine sites, namely F-2, F-4,6 and F-5. Thus F-2 shows a doublet of triplets generated by the larger $^5J_{2,5}$ splitting superimposed on the smaller ^4J coupling to F-4,6 (triplet splitting). The two fluorines F-4,6 appear as a double

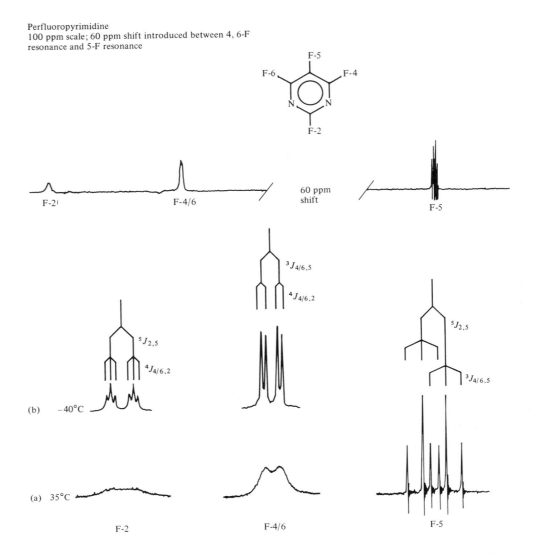

Perfluoropyrimidine
100 ppm scale; 60 ppm shift introduced between 4, 6-F
resonance and 5-F resonance

Figure 9.2 Fluorine–fluorine coupling in perfluoropyrimidine (84.6 MHz)

doublet, showing ^3J to F-5 and ^4J to F-2. Lastly, F-5 is an overlapping doublet of triplets, with the large doublet splitting to F-2 combining with the smaller triplet splitting to F-4,6. (The spectrum was recorded at 56.4 MHz, 1.4 T. The smallest coupling constant is 5.1 Hz, which allows the scale to be deduced.)

The complete fluorine-19 NMR spectrum of a tetra-fluoropropane derivative is shown at the chapter head. The molecule is $CF_2Br.CHF.CFBr_2$; the two fluorines on C-1 are diastereotopic, non-magnetically equivalent, and therefore give rise to separate signals at $\delta - 53$ and $- 59$, with different coupling constants.

The slightly distorted AB system which they produce is shown in expanded scale in figure 9.3(a), still showing the couplings to fluorine on C-2 and on C-3, and to proton on C-2. In figure 9.3(b), the proton is decoupled, and the simplified multiplicity can then be assigned more easily.

The coupling constants are found from the measured line frequencies on the print-out: the large AB splitting is 174 Hz. Thereafter the A lines are split by the two remaining fluorines C and D, with $J = 18$ Hz and 13 Hz respectively. The B lines are split correspondingly by 17 Hz and 13 Hz. Drawing these on graph paper confirms

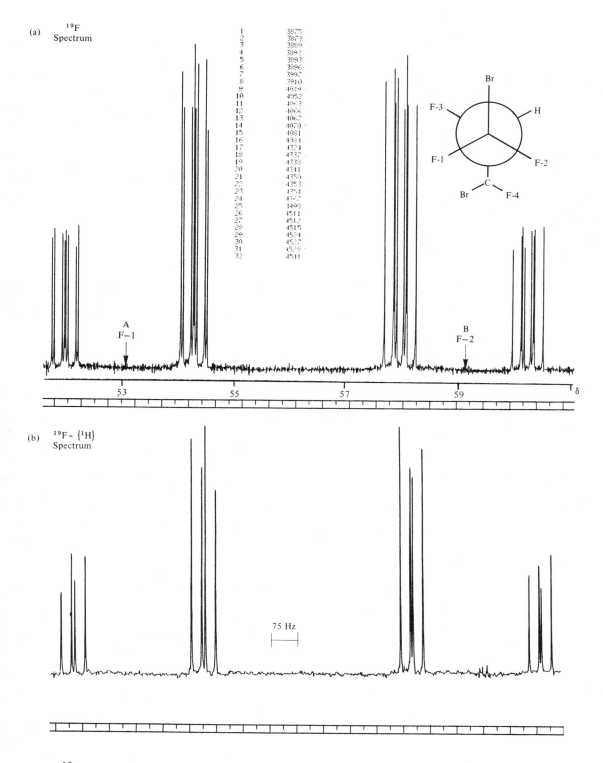

1	3875
2	3878
3	3889
4	3892
5	3893
6	3896
7	3907
8	3910
9	4049
10	4052
11	4063
12	4066
13	4067
14	4070
15	4081
16	4084
17	4324
18	4337
19	4338
20	4341
21	4350
22	4353
23	4354
24	4357
25	4498
26	4511
27	4512
28	4515
29	4524
30	4527
31	4528
32	4541

(a) ¹⁹F Spectrum

A F—1

B F—2

(b) ¹⁹F – {¹H} Spectrum

75 Hz

Figure 9.3 ¹⁹F NMR spectrum of $CF_2Br.CHF.CFBr_2$ F-1 and F-2 only (75 MHz in $CDCl_3$)

the multiplicity appearance of figure 9.3(b). Finally, the measured coupling between the A fluorine and proton ($^3J_{HF}$) is 3 Hz, and for the B fluorine the corresponding coupling is 12 Hz. A scale drawing of these splittings reconstructs completely the appearance of figure 9.3(a). (Strictly, interpretation should take account of AB distortions, see section 4.9.)

9.2.2 Coupling of Fluorine-19 with Proton and Phosphorus-31

All of the nuclei ^1H, ^{19}F and ^{31}P occur at natural abundances of 100% (or nearly so), and the multiplicities of signals in each separate resonance are predictable from the simplest $(n + 1)$ splitting rules. Thus in a very simple compound such as H_2PF_3 (assuming the three fluorines to be equatorial and equivalent, and the two hydrogens to be axial and equivalent) the ^{19}F NMR spectrum will show one chemical shift position, with the resonance split into a doublet ($^1J_{PF}$) then triplets ($^1J_{HF}$). Correspondingly the ^1H and ^{31}P NMR spectra will reveal quartet splittings ($^1J_{PF}$ and $^1J_{HF}$ again). The proton signal will be further split by phosphorus (giving a doublet of separation $^1J_{PH}$) and this coupling will be repeated in the ^{31}P NMR spectrum, whose signal will show the triplet splitting from the two protons ($^1J_{PH}$ again).

Figure 4.14 shows the proton and fluorine-19 NMR spectra for trifluoroethanol: the multiplicities can be correlated with the familiar $(n + 1)$ approach.

9.2.3 Coupling of Fluorine-19 with Carbon-13

The natural abundances of ^{19}F and ^{13}C are 100% and 1.1% respectively. This means that in every compound containing carbon and fluorine, all of the isotopomers contain ^{19}F, but only 1.1% contain ^{13}C. When we record the ^{13}C NMR spectrum, every isotopomer which contains ^{13}C also contains ^{19}F; but when we record the ^{19}F spectrum most of the signal strength comes from isotopomers containing only ^{12}C, and thus the ^{19}F NMR spectrum shows no splitting by ^{13}C. (The 1.1% of ^{13}C produces only weak satellite signals, whose distribution was discussed in section 5.5.3.)

The ^{13}C spectrum for trifluoroacetic acid (CF_3COOH) was the subject of worked example 5.8 in section 5.5.3, and the problem was approached from the carbon-13 viewpoint. That section helps to emphasise the mutuality of nuclear coupling.

Worked Example 9.1

Predict the detailed appearance of the ^{19}F NMR spectrum of natural abundance trifluoroacetic acid, CF_3COOH.

Answer 9.1

Only one main singlet resonance will appear, since all three fluorines are equivalent. There will be two satellite pairs present at extremely low intensity. The first pair will be astride the main ^{19}F resonance, with a total separation of 44 Hz. Outside these will be another pair, separated from each other by 284 Hz. Each of the satellite line intensities will be about 0.5% of that of the main ^{19}F signal.

Problem Example 9.1

The $^{13}C-\{^1H\}$ NMR spectrum for trifluorotoluene, $C_6H_5CF_3$, is shown in figure 9.4 with scale expansion above. Given the listed J values, identify the four separate quartets. (The *para* carbon is the singlet at δ 129: this accidentally overlaps one line of the quartet with $J = 32$ Hz.)

Note that in the $^{19}F-\{^1H\}$ NMR spectrum of this compound it would be unlikely that analysis of the several weak carbon-13 satellites could be realised without extreme amplification (see however section 10.2.3).

9.2.4 Coupling of Fluorine-19 with Nitrogen-14

Some arguments will be presented here for a specific example, and used to illustrate a general problem and the means of circumventing it. We saw some of the effects of quadrupolar relaxation in sections 4.5 and 4.8, and they can be seen again in the ^{19}F NMR spectrum in figure 9.2.

Quadrupolar nuclei such as ^{14}N interact with electric field gradients in their surroundings, and transitions among the available energy levels will occur rapidly if the dimensions and orientations of these gradients are matched to the dimensions of the relaxation processes. If the surrounding gradients are tumbling too rapidly, then the quadrupolar nucleus will not be able to transfer energy efficiently to them and its relaxation rate will be slow.

At high temperatures (or if the electric field gradients are symmetrical as in NH_4^+) the ^{14}N nucleus will spend sufficient time in its three possible energy states to produce 1:1:1 triplet splitting with nearby magnetic nuclei, such as ^{19}F. At intermediate temperatures, this may be poorly resolved and simply give rise to broadening of the ^{19}F resonances (see figure 9.2).

At lower temperatures, quadrupolar relaxation is efficiently matched to the slowly tumbling molecules (with their slowly tumbling electric field gradients), so that the ^{14}N life-times become very short: there is then insufficient time for ^{14}N to exhibit splitting of the ^{19}F

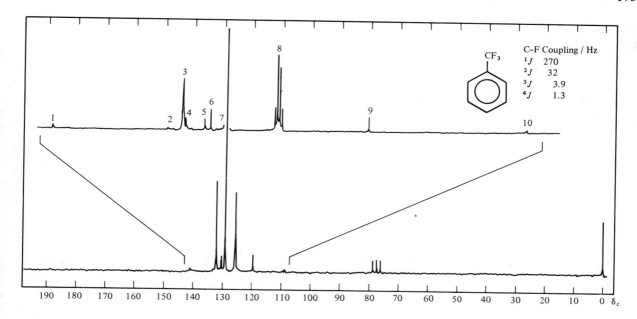

Figure 9.4 ^{13}C NMR spectrum of trifluorotoluene, PhCF$_3$ (25 MHz)

resonances (Uncertainty Principle) and the ^{19}F reson-ances are sharper.

This simple expedient can be used to good effect in other circumstances where quadrupolar broadening arises. Although the same effect can be achieved by agitating the ^{14}N nuclei with double irradiation at the ^{14}N resonance frequency, this requires an instrument to be suitably equipped with the necessary RF circuitry, and is more expensive than low temperature work.

10

Phosphorus–31 NMR Spectra

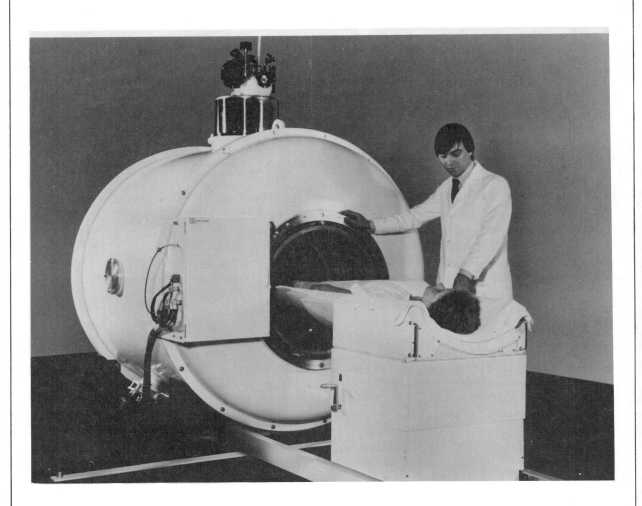

Magnet for whole-body NMR. With a field strength of 1.6 T and bore of 760 mm, *in vivo* studies of phosphorus metabolism are possible

With 100% natural abundance, a spin of $\frac{1}{2}$, and moderately large magnetic moment, phosphorus-31 falls into the class of 'easy' NMR elements. Its importance in biological processes is crucial, and *in vivo* measurements of ^{31}P NMR spectra were introduced in section 7.9. It is also part of a rich vein of interesting structural organic chemistry, and the use of NMR in determining the stereochemistry of organometallic compounds is ubiquitous. At the chapter head is a 'whole body' NMR magnet used in the examination of biological processes in animals.

present survey the chemical shifts in figure 10.1 are illustrative rather than comprehensive.

Apart from the extreme fringe, electronegative substituents in phosphorus(III) compounds give signals in a moderately narrow range (about δ 100–250) while the corresponding phosphorus(V) analogues have less widely spread shifts. The effect of alkyl substitution (proceeding from methyl through to *tert*-butyl) produces a consistent shift to higher frequencies.

Unfortunately theory does not fully rationalise the empirical facts.

10.1 PHOSPHORUS-31 CHEMICAL SHIFTS

The precession frequency for ^{31}P at 2.3 T is 40.5 MHz. The most widely used reference for ^{31}P NMR chemical shifts is an external sample of 85% aqueous phosphoric acid (H_3PO_4): this is far from ideal. There is always a problem in correlating shifts to an external sample, but H_3PO_4 does not even produce a sharp resonance signal, and with more recent instruments the shifts can be related *via* the deuterium lock signal to TMS. For accurate data there is an abundant literature, and for the

10.2 PHOSPHORUS-31 COUPLING CONSTANTS

As is found in the δ values for ^{31}P, J values depend on the oxidation state of the phosphorus: the values vary over an enormous range, as indicated by the selection shown in table 10.1.

Because the spin of ^{31}P is $\frac{1}{2}$, the multiplicities generated (mutually) with other nuclei are usually easily interpreted: in the ^{31}P NMR spectra, first order splittings are the norm because of the wide range of chemical shifts.

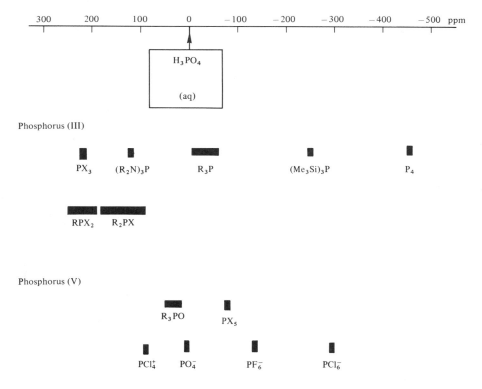

Figure 10.1   Phosphorus-31 chemical shifts

Table 10.1 Representative phosphorus-31 coupling constants. Wide variations arise: these figures are not limiting

System	Type	Typical J value/Hz
>P-P<	$^1J_{PP}$	180–230
>P=P<	$^1J_{PP}$	270
$-O-\overset{\overset{O}{\|\|}}{\underset{\underset{O^-}{\|}}{P}}-O-\overset{\overset{O}{\|\|}}{\underset{\underset{O^-}{\|}}{P}}-$	$^2J_{POP}$	20
>P-Rh-P<	$^2\overline{J_{PMP}}$	20–30
>P-H	$^1J_{PH}$	200
$-\overset{\overset{O}{\|\|}}{\underset{\|}{P}}-H$	$^1J_{PH}$	400–850
$-\underset{\|}{P}-C-H$	$^2J_{PH}$	0–50
$-\underset{\|}{P}-F$ P(III) and P(V)	$^1J_{PF}$	80–1500
$-\underset{\|}{P}-^{13}C$ P(III)	$^1J_{PC}$	0–25
$\overset{\|}{\underset{\|\|}{>}}P-^{13}C$ P(V)	$^1J_{PC}$	50–300
$-\underset{\|}{P}-Rh$	$^1J_{PRh}$	30–150
$-\underset{\|}{P}-Pt$	$^1J_{PPt}$	2000–4000

10.2.1 Coupling of Phosphorus-31 with Phosphorus-31

Figure 10.2 shows the ^{31}P NMR spectrum of adenosine triphosphate, ATP; this was reproduced under another context in figure 7.2, but is here shown at greater resolution, with broad band proton decoupling.

The ability of phosphorus to form chains of polyphosphate linkages is well known: the triphosphate group in ATP is representative, but longer chains are found in the alkali metal polyphosphates used in detergents to bind to soil particles and hence render them hydrophilic. Note that the two $^2J_{PP}$ coupling constants

are slightly different (19.3 Hz and 19.6 Hz) so that the middle phosphorus atom, P_β, is split into a double doublet: this is only seen at high resolution, since at lower resolution the peaks appear to overlap into a triplet signal.

10.2.2 Coupling of Phosphorus-31 with Proton and Fluorine-19

With all of these nuclei having spin of $\frac{1}{2}$, the principles of mutual coupling should by now be familiar, and the ^{31}P NMR spectrum in figure 10.3 is interesting only in the sense that trimethyl phosphite, $(CH_3O)_3P$, is often used as here in the test of resolution for ^{31}P NMR. First order rules apply, and $(n + 1)$ predicts ten lines in the phosphorus signal: since the outer two lines are at very low intensity — with a ratio of 1:126 between outer and middle lines expected from Pascal's triangle — the spectrum appears to be an octet. The ^1H NMR spectrum for $(MeO)_3P$ is a doublet.

The ^{31}P NMR spectrum for PF_3 is a quartet, and its ^{19}F NMR spectrum is a doublet, and so on.

10.2.3 Coupling of Phosphorus-31 with Carbon-13

We can now pick up several threads and work through an interpretation of the ^{31}P NMR spectrum for triphenylphosphine selenide, Ph_3PSe, shown in figure 10.4.

The ^{13}C NMR spectrum of this molecule was seen in figure 5.11 and the coupling to ^{31}P explained the carbon signal multiplicities. The discussions on carbon-13 satellites (sections 5.5 and 9.2.3) are also apposite to this exercise. The Appendix shows that the natural abundance of ^{77}Se is only 7.6%: it has spin $= \frac{1}{2}$.

The main ^{31}P NMR signal arises from isotopomers containing no carbon-13 or selenium-77, and therefore it appears as a singlet. The selenium-77 manifests itself in the most widely separated pair of satellites, separated by 730 Hz ($^1J_{PSe}$). Thereafter, there arise ^{31}P resonances from the four different kinds of ^{13}C isotopomers: each has ^{13}C in different positions in the ring, at C-1, C-2,6 (*ortho*), C-3,5 (*meta*), and C-4 (*para*). The satellite pairs therefore are separated, respectively, by 77 Hz ($^1J_{CP}$), 10.6 Hz ($^2J_{CP}$), 125 Hz ($^3J_{CP}$) and 3 Hz ($^4J_{CP}$).

Problem Example 10.1

Predict the influence of carbon-13 and phosphorus-31 couplings on the ^{77}Se NMR spectrum for Ph_3PSe, and confirm these by examining the spectrum in figure 13.3.

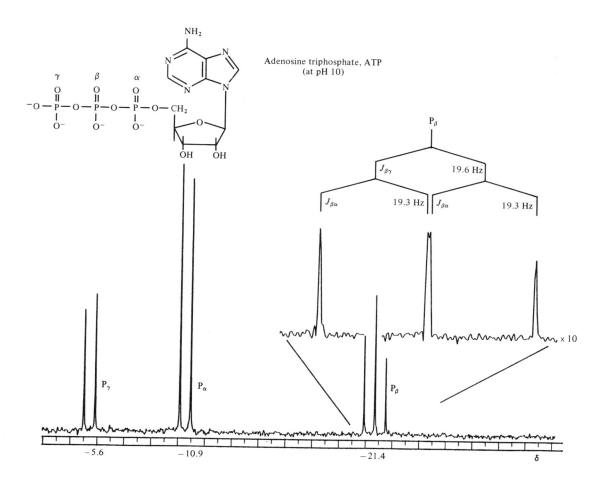

Figure 10.2 ^{31}P NMR spectrum of adenosine triphosphate, ATP (32 MHz in D$_2$O)

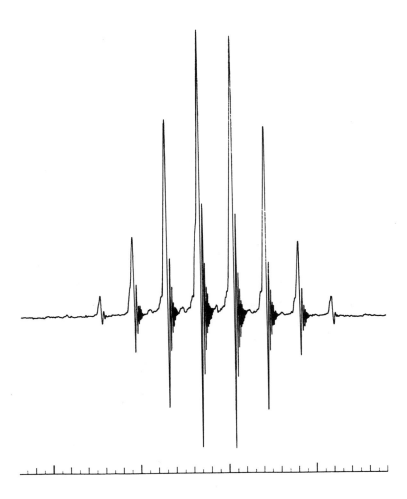

Figure 10.3 ^{31}P NMR spectrum of trimethyl phosphite, $(CH_3O)_3P$ (41.5 MHz)

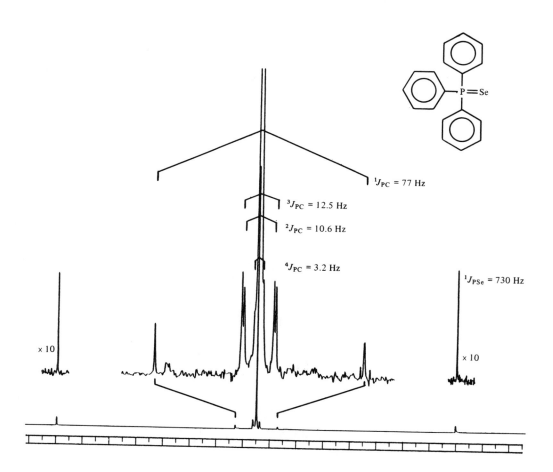

$^1J_{PC} = 77$ Hz

$^3J_{PC} = 12.5$ Hz

$^2J_{PC} = 10.6$ Hz

$^4J_{PC} = 3.2$ Hz

$^1J_{PSe} = 730$ Hz

× 10

× 10

Figure 10.4 ^{31}P NMR spectrum of triphenylphosphine selenide, Ph$_3$PSe (32 MHz in CDCl$_3$)

11

Nitrogen-14 and Nitrogen-15 NMR Spectra

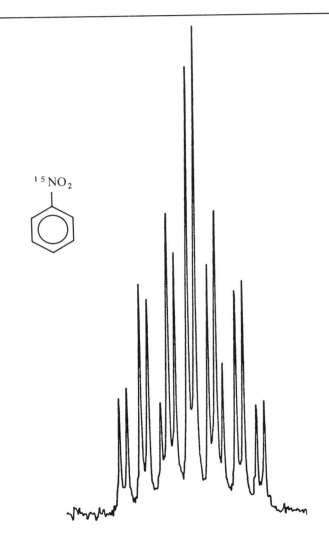

Nitrogen-15 NMR spectrum of nitrobenzene (isotope enriched) (20 MHz in CDCl₃)

The number of compounds containing nitrogen is vast, and there are more distinct nitrogen functional classes in organic chemistry than for any other heteroatom. The ability to observe nitrogen NMR directly is a rich prize for chemists and biochemists alike, but there are obstacles on the way.

11.1 NITROGEN ISOTOPES — ^{14}N AND ^{15}N

Nitrogen-14, with spin = 1, is the major isotope of nitrogen at 99.63% natural abundance, and at various times we have had to take account of its presence because of the effect its quadrupole moment has on the NMR behaviour of other nuclei. Nitrogen-14 NMR spectra are recorded at 7 MHz in a 2.35 T field, but because of its own quadrupole moment, which tends to make the nucleus follow the electric field gradients within the tumbling molecule rather than follow the simpler orientations dictated by $\mathbf{B_0}$, the signals are broadened, often hopelessly, by rapid relaxation. Line widths of hundreds of hertz are common, and it is often difficult to identify the signal above the base line except in simple cases.

The nitrogen-15 isotope has spin $= \frac{1}{2}$, and is in that respect an 'easier' NMR isotope than nitrogen-14.

It suffers from some disadvantages, which can however be overcome. From the Appendix, nitrogen-15 is only 0.37% abundant, and its magnetogyric ratio is negative and small, resulting in a sensitivity which is a million times less than that of the proton. The frequency of observation for ^{15}N NMR is 10 MHz at 2.35 T.

11.1.1 Isotope Abundance

One early solution to recording ^{15}N NMR spectra was to enrich the samples synthetically. The first paper reporting ^{15}N chemical shifts appeared in 1964 and since that date the application of ^{15}N NMR spectroscopy has increased unabated and exponentially. Biochemical incorporation is an attractive parallel study, and this is a rapidly expanding sphere of interest because of the importance of nitrogen in plant and animal metabolism.

The ability to record natural abundance ^{15}N NMR spectra is feasible by making use of the sensitivity enhancement techniques discussed in chapter 7, and a typical natural abundance nitrogen-15 NMR spectrum is shown in figure 11.1. There are two non-equivalent nitrogen sites in the molecule of biotin and two separate nitrogen resonances appear in the spectrum. This spectrum is broad band proton decoupled: the assignment of chemical shift positions in nitrogen NMR is discussed in section 11.2.

Figure 11.1 ^{15}N NMR spectrum of biotin, whose structure is shown at the head of chapter 7 (20 MHz)

11.1.2 Sensitivity Enhancement — INEPT and DEPT

The use of multipulse techniques was discussed throughout the bulk of chapter 7, culminating in the INEPT and DEPT procedures outlined in section 7.6. These methods (including the NOE, and large sample sizes) can be utilised to gain sensitivity in the ^{15}N NMR signal by polarisation transfer from proton. Other pulse methods selectively irradiate the protons directly attached to ^{15}N, giving *selective population transfer*. Additionally in these methods, the limiting pulse repetition rate is dependent on the proton relaxation times (short) and not on the ^{15}N relaxation times (long).

We saw in section 6.9.4 that in proton decoupled ^{15}N NMR spectra, we may observe (at maximum) an NOE of -4.9 which, added to a line intensity of $+1$ (the intensity without NOE) produces a net line intensity of -3.9. The maximum NOE will only arise if dipole-dipole relaxation is the principal mode of relaxation, otherwise it will be less than -4.9 and may (accidentally) be −1 in which case the NOE will cancel out the normal +1 signal intensity and give rise to a zero signal. Where the NOE is likely to lead to this difficulty being undetected, for example with unknown compounds, it is often the practice to eliminate NOE by the inverse gated decoupling discussed in section 7.1: also as discussed there, paramagnetic relaxation agents such as $Cr(ACAC)_3$ are frequently used in these experiments. Lastly, where the NOE leads to negative signals the spectrum can easily be inverted by instrumental methods and presented in conventional form. These practical matters aside, the interpretation of ^{15}N NMR spectra is no different in principle from that of other rare nuclei such as carbon-13: δ-values, multiplicity and J values and the measurement of relaxation times can all make contributions.

11.2 NITROGEN CHEMICAL SHIFTS

Although perhaps surprising, it is important to note that the chemical shifts of nitrogen-14 environments are the same as those for nitrogen-15, since the electronic shielding mechanism is the same for all nitrogen nuclei in a chemical shift sense, whether the nucleus is ^{14}N or ^{15}N.

An introduction to nitrogen chemical shifts was included in chapter 1 (and in figure 1.8): a more extensive view is given in figure 11.2.

Although the range is wide over all, more than 900 ppm, the shifts within each functional type are commonly limited to less than 100 ppm.

Some data in figure 11.2 relate back to studies on ^{14}N chemical shifts: the increase in accessibility of ^{15}N NMR spectra has led to a marked decline in ^{14}N NMR spectroscopy. For chemical and biological interpretive studies, nitrogen-15 is now the method of choice.

11.2.1 Reference Standards for Nitrogen-15 NMR

The chemical shifts in figure 11.2 are quoted with reference to an external sample of liquid ammonia at 25°C. (The shift varies slightly with temperature, which is an inconvenient experimental facet.) Several alternatives have been proposed, but there is difficulty in agreeing on a reference compound which is inert, soluble in organic

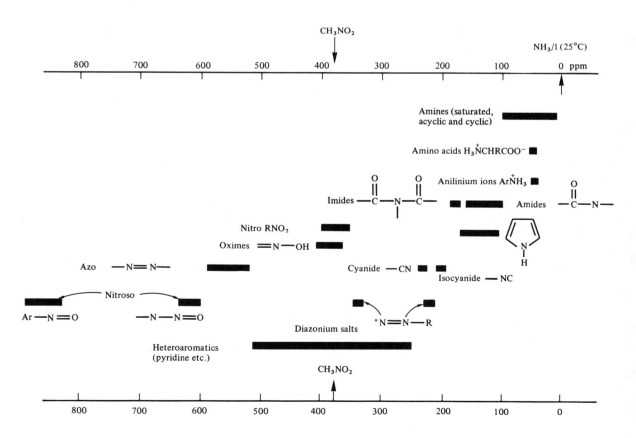

Figure 11.2 Nitrogen-15 chemical shifts

and aqueous media, unaffected by pH and with a chemical shift which would place the reference signal at one end of the ^{15}N spectrum, preferably with most common resonances at higher frequencies (which gives positive δ values).

Nitromethane, CH_3NO_2, is (with CD_3NO_2) extensively used, but fails on the last count, and can itself cause shifts in certain other classes. Its great convenience in use makes it a routine primary standard: with a resonance at δ 380 with respect to liquid ammonia (at 25°C) is is a simple matter to interconvert δ values accurately from one reference to another. Because of the sharp resonances in ^{15}N NMR spectra, most of the following discussion is weighted towards this isotope.

11.2.2 Factors Influencing Nitrogen-15 Chemical Shifts

There are many similarities in the way the ^{15}N and ^{13}C chemical shifts change with molecular environment: thus there are empirical rules giving the increments in chemical shift brought about by additional substitution in amines. The accuracy is however less consistent than in the ^{13}C case. Thus in most cases alkylation of the primary amine to secondary to tertiary moves the resonance to higher frequency, but occasionally to lower frequency. As usual, it is not possible theoretically to reinforce the certainty of the predictions. It is much better in practice to compare the shifts in close models rather than rely on calculated values: this is particularly true where steric factors become as important as electronic factors (for example in cyclic amines). Most interpretive work on nitrogen-15 NMR spectra will involve comparisons among known members of a series, and chemical shift effects can usually be rationalised more successfully within such a limited range of environments.

A few general trends can be seen to correlate with increased or decreased electronic shielding. Thus aliphatic amines are at lowest frequency (shielded by alkyl substitution) and aryl amines are less shielded because the non-bonding electrons on the nitrogen atom are partly accommodated in the aromatic ring. Additional electronegative substitution in the ring leads in general to further deshielding of the nitrogen atom and to higher frequency shifts. Amide nitrogens ($-CONH-$) are well known to be non-acidic because of resonance with the carbonyl group, and the nitrogen-15 NMR resonance bears this out as can be seen from figure 11.2. The heteroaromatic nitrogen-15 shifts, such as in pyridine, reflect the same electronic effects that aromaticity induces in proton and carbon-13 chemical shifts. Other strongly electronegative features arise in functional groups where nitrogen is bonded to oxygen, such as nitro (NO_2) or nitroso (NO).

The δ values seen in figure 11.2 help to bring these qualitative strands into focus.

Worked Example 11.1
Figure 11.3 shows the nitrogen-15 NMR spectrum of $CH_3CONHNMe_2$ recorded at natural abundance with broad band proton decoupling. (It was recorded at 8 MHz with a field strength of 1.9 T.) Assign the resonances according to functional class.

Answer 11.1
The compound is the acetamide of dimethylhydrazine, and from figure 11.2 the amide nitrogen is expected at higher frequency than the tertiary amino nitrogen. Although there are only two nitrogens in the molecule, because of its amide character, it exists as an equilibrium mixture of E and Z forms around the CO–N bond. From the line intensities, one of these isomers gives rise to lines 1 and 3, and the other to lines 2 and 4 (this latter being the more stable).

11.2.3 Influence of Protonation and Solvent on Nitrogen-15 Chemical Shifts

The nitrogen atoms of amines are basic and owe this property to their pairs of non-bonding electrons; the reactivity of these electrons causes shifts to be produced

$$NH_3 \qquad CH_3NH_2 \qquad C_2H_5NH_2 \qquad CH_3CH_2CH_2NH_2 \qquad \begin{array}{c} CH_3 \\ \diagdown \\ CHNH_2 \\ \diagup \\ CH_3 \end{array} \qquad \begin{array}{c} CH_3 \\ | \\ CH_3-C-NH_2 \\ | \\ CH_3 \end{array} \qquad (11.1)$$

$$0 \qquad\qquad 3 \qquad\qquad 25 \qquad\qquad\qquad 21 \qquad\qquad\qquad\qquad 42 \qquad\qquad 56 \text{ ppm}$$

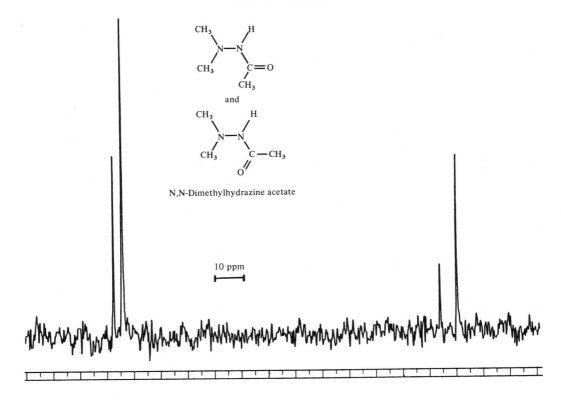

Figure 11.3 ^{15}N NMR spectrum of N,N-dimethylhydrazine acetate Me$_2$NNHCOCH$_3$ (8 MHz)

(11.2)

if the amine is protonated or if the solvent is changed from polar to non-polar. The magnitude of the shift depends on several factors, including pH, the nature of the counterion and on the degree of hydrogen bonding lost or gained.

Unfortunately too, the direction of shift is not uniform. Thus protonation of simple acyclic aliphatic amines usually moves the ^{15}N resonance to higher frequency by up to 25 ppm, while in alicyclic amines the shift in frequency can be from 3 ppm higher to 8 ppm lower. In arylamines such as anilines, the shift on protonation is fairly consistently 3–30 ppm to lower frequency (but very small in aniline itself) while in pyridine it moves the signal 100 ppm to lower frequency. A lower frequency shift (of 160 ppm) also arises in the ^{15}N resonance of azobenzene on protonation.

Although these shifts are contrary, they can be put to use in distinguishing basic from non-basic nitrogen sites within a molecule.

For important biological molecules such as amino acids, pH is an ever present factor in determining nitrogen-15 chemical shifts. Their zwitterionic nature adds to the complications, but there is a generalised trend to lower frequency at lower pH (associated with the anionic form).

Similar complications appear in the (generally smaller) shifts caused by changing solvent, or by changing the concentration in the same solvent. Thus the ^{15}N resonance position for nitric acid moves nearly 30 ppm from a molar solution to the concentrated acid solution. Concentration effects are normally much smaller than this, with 1–2 ppm movements being observed.

Changing solvent (for example from benzene to methanol) certainly shifts nitrogen-15 resonances more than carbon-13 resonances, but this is not really surprising: the magnitude and direction of the shift is unpredictable, but it is typically less than ± 2 ppm and only occasionally as large as 10 ppm.

The very diversity of these shifts has led to definitive studies on the migration of protons within tautomeric systems: thus many details on the equilibria of biological molecules such as amino acids, peptides (or amides), nucleosides and nucleotides have been elucidated. Indeed the details are much too numerous for this brief survey to envelope, and the texts listed in Further Reading should be used in augmentation.

11.3 USE OF PARAMAGNETIC COMPLEXES IN NITROGEN-15 NMR

The chemistry of paramagnetic shift reagents (section 4.10.2) has already been surveyed. In nitrogen-15 NMR, it is mainly the paramagnetic relaxation effect which is sought to circumvent the long relaxation times of the ^{15}N nuclei. Thus $Cr(ACAC)_3$ and $Cr(DPM)_3$ are routinely added in recording ^{15}N NMR spectra on species such as nitrile and nitro compounds where proton enhanced relaxation is not available. The name *paramagnetic relaxation reagent* (PARR) is often applied. In larger molecules, especially if the nitrogen atom bears a proton, the addition of a PARR may not be advantageous.

By selection of different paramagnetic complexes, the influence on relaxation rates may be carried out on specific nitrogen sites. Thus with $Gd(DPM_3)$, it has been shown that the most affected nitrogen spins are (a) the most basic nitrogens and (b) the sterically most accessible nitrogens: the paramagnetic ion in this case effectively eliminates the NOE and the affected signals are reduced. With care, and with detailed interpretation, this *spin labelling* allows distinctions to be made among several nitrogen environments.

11.4 NITROGEN-15 COUPLING CONSTANTS

Enormous collections of ^{15}N coupling constants have been assembled in several texts (listed in Further Reading): many of the values have been derived from enriched samples and the factors influencing the magnitude and sign of J have been carefully documented.

Table 11.1 is useful as an indicator of the most useful couplings for interpretation of structure. The sign of J cannot be derived directly from the spectra, and thus has been omitted from the table (even where known).

The dimensions of J may be of less value, in direct structural work, than the multiplicity of the ^{15}N signal(s) in the spectrum. Where only proton coupling is present, there are sensitivity penalties in recording the coupled spectra because no signal increase is gained from the collapse of the multiplets: various multipulse methods (such as DEPT) give considerable gains even in coupled spectra.

Table 11.1 Representative nitrogen-15 coupling constants. Protonation changes these values slightly

System	Type	Typical J value/Hz
$-N-N-$	$^1J_{NN}$	3–4
$-N=N-$	$^1J_{NN}$	12–15
$R-N-H$	$^1J_{NH}$	60–70
$Ar-N-H$	$^1J_{NH}$	75–95
$\overset{O}{\overset{\|\|}{-C}}-N-H$	$^1J_{NH}$	90
pyrrole (N-H)	$^1J_{NH}$	96
$-\overset{H}{\underset{\|}{C}}-N\!\!<$	$^2J_{NH}$	1
$H-\overset{O}{\overset{\|\|}{C}}-N\!\!<$	$^2J_{NH}$	15
pyrrole (2-H)	$^2J_{NH}$	5
pyridine (2-H)	$^2J_{NH}$	11
$-\overset{H}{\underset{\|}{C}}-\overset{O}{\overset{\|\|}{C}}-N\!\!<$; pyridine (3-H) ; N-methyl aniline	$^3J_{NH}$	1.3–2.0
$-^{13}C-N\!\!<$	$^1J_{NC}$	2–6
$-^{13}\overset{O}{\overset{\|\|}{C}}-N\!\!<$	$^1J_{NC}$	13–15
$Ar-N\!\!<$	$^1J_{NC}$	10–15

Worked Example 11.2
Figure 11.4 (top) shows the $^{15}N-\{^1H\}$ NMR spectrum of formamide ($HCONH_2$), and the coupled spectrum is shown in figure 11.4 (bottom). Explain the number of lines shown in the proton coupled spectrum. (The spectrum was recorded at 20 MHz (4.7 T), at natural abundance.)

Answer 11.2
There is only one chemical shift position for the nitrogen-15 nucleus in $HCONH_2$. (The concept of mutual exchange can be verified from chapter 8.) If the two protons on nitrogen had been magnetically equivalent, the ^{15}N signal would have shown triplet splitting (NH_2) combined with doublet splitting (CH). The two NH protons are therefore magnetically non-equivalent, so the ^{15}N signal shows three different J values, each associated with doublet splittings. The largest coupling (92 Hz) comes from the proton *anti* to oxygen.

Problem Example 11.1
The three coupling constants involved in the above example are ^1J, 92 Hz, ^1J, 88 Hz and ^2J, 14 Hz. Reconstruct figure 11.4 to scale on graph paper.

Problem Example 11.2
Explain the multiplicity of the ^{15}N signal in the nitrobenzene spectrum shown at the chapter head. (Proton coupled ^{15}N NMR spectrum at 20 MHz.) Assume $^3J_{NH} \simeq 2$ Hz, $^4J_{NH} \simeq 1$ Hz and $^5J_{NH} \simeq 0.3$ Hz. Reconstruction to scale will ascribe all but two of the lines.

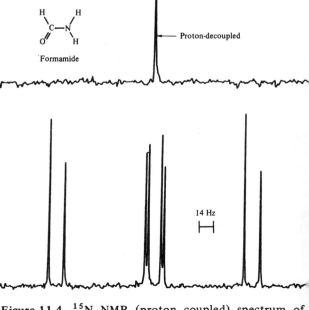

Figure 11.4 ^{15}N NMR (proton coupled) spectrum of formamide, $HCONH_2$, using the DEPT sequence (20 MHz)

Oxygen–17 NMR Spectra

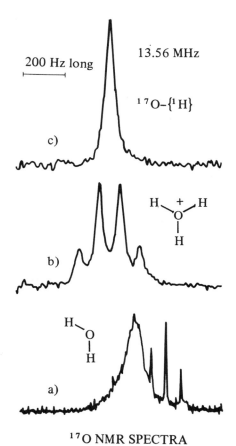

12

200 Hz long

13.56 MHz

$^{17}O-\{^{1}H\}$

c)

H_3O^+

b)

H_2O

a)

^{17}O NMR SPECTRA

(a) H_2O (triplet) in CCl_4

(b) H_3O^+ (quartet) in $SO_2(1)$

(c) $^{17}O-\{^{1}H\}$, also in $SO_2(1)$

Oxygen-17 NMR spectra of H_2O and H_3O^+ (13.5 MHz)

Oxygen has a paradoxical position in analytical chemistry: it is present in many classes of compound, yet few methods can detect its presence directly (rather than by inference or difference). Its position in NMR analysis is also difficult, because the only naturally occurring magnetic isotope is ^{17}O, with an abundance of 0.037% and an over all sensitivity 10^5 times less than that of proton. It also has spin = 5/2, and therefore a quadrupole moment: the number of orientations for its angular momentum vector in a magnetic field is six, as discussed in section 2.13 and illustrated in figure 2.6. Lastly, it has a negative magnetogyric ratio, meaning that its magnetic moment vector is opposite in direction to the angular momentum vector.

The quadrupole moment of ^{17}O means that relaxation rates are fast and therefore the line widths are broad (ranging from 10 to 1000 Hz). The principal relaxation mode is due to the electric quadrupole (which follows the molecule rather than $\mathbf{B_0}$) and this means that dipolar relaxation is a minor contributory. In $^{17}O-\{^1H\}$ NMR spectra, very little NOE is observed, and thus very little signal enhancement comes from this.

All of this notwithstanding, natural abundance oxygen-17 NMR spectra are achievable, and they yield unique information about oxygen functional groups. The potential of the technique in biochemistry is particularly encouraging.

12.1 OXYGEN-17 CHEMICAL SHIFTS

At 2.35 T, oxygen-17 NMR spectra are recorded at 13.5 MHz, and some representative chemical shifts are shown in figure 12.1: a broader subdivision is offered in figure 1.8.

The reference for ^{17}O NMR frequencies is usually 'ordinary' water, with the natural abundance content of 0.037%. Where this is intrusive, as for example in studying water-soluble alcohols or carbohydrates, the water signal can be reduced by using ^{17}O depleted water: another useful chemical shift standard in this case is dioxane, with corrections being made for its own chemical shift (at δ 12 with respect to H_2O).

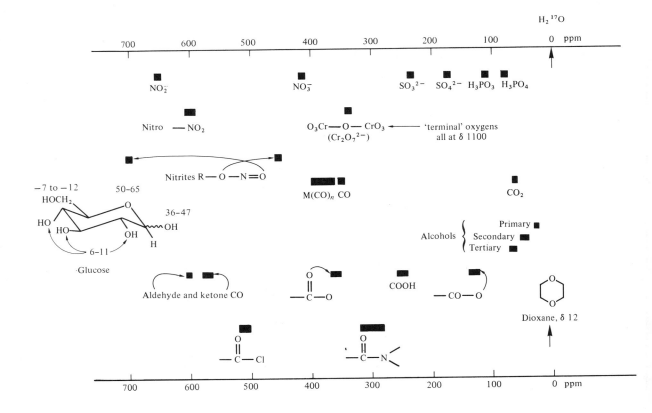

Figure 12.1 Oxygen-17 chemical shifts

This figure shows in part the useful potential of ^{17}O NMR. The oxyacids are very numerous, and many alternative analytical methods exist for studying oxidation states: the large difference in δ values between phosphate and phosphite, sulphate and sulphite and between nitrate and nitrite is revealing. In the dichromate anion the bridge oxygen, singly bonded, is near δ 350 while the remaining terminal oxygens, 'doubly' bonded, are all near δ 1100. The ^{17}O resonances for metal carbonyls are fairly narrowly grouped, and separated from the resonance position of CO itself.

In organic functional classes, there is a useful potential in being able to distinguish primary alcohols from secondary from tertiary: the shifts shown on the formula for glucose (a hexose) are typical of most other carbohydrates, although specific stereochemistry can be a complicating (and informative) feature.

The δ values for singly bonded oxygen ($-O-$) are clearly and consistently at lower frequency than the corresponding doubly bonded oxygen ($=O$) and this is again manifested for C–O and C=O. Thus the two oxygens in ethyl acetate give the simple (natural abundance) oxygen-17 NMR spectrum shown in figure 12.2.

The ^{17}O chemical shift values for various carbonyl compounds is useful additional data to identify these functions (none of which presents problems in more amenable spectroscopic methods). It is perhaps not surprising that the rate of proton exchange in carboxylic acids, and their known dimeric structure, leads to only one time-averaged ^{17}O NMR signal.

The distinction between the singly and double bonded oxygen in organic nitrite esters ($-O-N=O$) contrasts nicely with the observation that in the resonance system of nitro groups ($-NO_2$) both oxygens are, of course, magnetically equivalent.

The involvement of oxygen in hydrogen bonding can be probed by the effects seen in the proton spectra, and these are mirrored in the ^{17}O NMR spectra, but apart from a recognition that the δ values are H-bonding dependent, the amount of shift is variable. The universal occurrence of hydrogen bonding associated with solvation by water in biological systems potentially allows direct study of the processes of water migration.

12.2 OXYGEN-17 COUPLING CONSTANTS

The principles of coupling to ^{17}O are the same as for coupling to other quadrupolar nuclei: a few coupling constants are listed in table 12.1. Thus if ^{17}O couples to a spin $=\frac{1}{2}$ nucleus, that nucleus will split the ^{17}O resonance according to the $(n + 1)$ rule: the oxygen resonance in $-OH$ groups will appear as a doublet for this reason and the signal for H_3O^+ appears as a quartet (as shown at the chapter head): the coupling constant, $^{1}J_{HO}$, in H_3O^+ is 106 Hz. The actual detection of these couplings depends on several important factors discussed at length in other chapters: the residence time of H and O must be sufficiently long for the coupling to be observed (from $\Delta E \cdot \Delta t = h/2\pi$) and this circumstance obtains in a dilute solution of water in carbon tetrachloride but does not in ordinary tap water (see chapter head).

Figure 12.2 ^{17}O NMR spectrum of ethyl acetate (ethyl ethanoate), $CH_3COOCH_2CH_3$ (27 MHz) (chemical shifts referenced to H_2O)

Table 12.1 Representative oxygen-17 coupling constants

System	Type	Typical J value/Hz
$-C-O-H$	$^1J_{HO}$	80
$-C-O-P-$ phosphite esters	$^1J_{PO}$	140–50
$-C-O-\overset{\overset{O}{\|\|}}{P}-$ phosphate esters	$^1J_{PO}$	90–100
$-P=O$	$^1J_{PO}$	150–200
$H-C=O$	$^2J_{HO}$	10
$H-C-O-$	$^2J_{HO}$	35
$H-C-O-C=$	$^2J_{HO}$	7

The quadrupolar relaxation of ^{17}O also interferes with the observation of coupling, both in terms of the quadrupolar decoupling (short life-times in any one spin state) but also because the ^{17}O line widths are broad and only the strongest of couplings will produce a measurable splitting of the lines. For these reasons, few ^2J coupling constants have been measured.

A common observation in formate esters is the large doublet splitting ($J \simeq 35$ Hz) which the formyl proton produces in the alkyl oxygen ^{17}O signal, while in the acyl oxygen signal the splitting is smaller ($J \simeq 10$ Hz). Various explanations have been proposed for this but none stands out as more reasonable than another. In methyl formate ($HCOOCH_3$) for example the three methyl protons couple with the alkyl oxygen ($^2J_{HO} \simeq 8$ Hz) but signal broadening obscures the clarity: double irradiation at the CH_3 protons allows the coupling to the single formyl proton to be more carefully examined.

In general, the observation and measurement of oxygen-17 coupling constants is of greater interest in theoretical chemistry than in aiding the assignment of oxygen-17 NMR signals in natural abundance spectra. In this field, chemical shift parameters are more directly helpful.

NMR Spectra from Other Nuclei

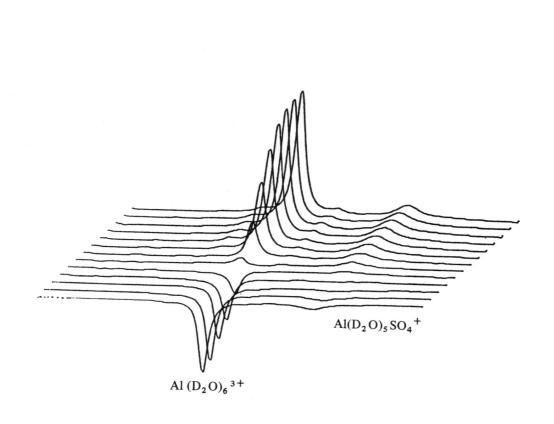

13

$Al(D_2O)_5SO_4^+$

$Al(D_2O)_6^{3+}$

Aluminium-27 NMR spectrum of $Al(D_2O)_6^{3+}$ (20.7 MHz, in D_2O)

The science of NMR is dominated by studies of proton and carbon-13 NMR, followed in interest and importance by the NMR properties of elements with high abundance and sensitivity, such as fluorine-19 and phosphorus-31. Nitrogen NMR and oxygen NMR studies owe part of their extensiveness to the central chemical and biochemical importance of these elements: there are certainly easier NMR elements which have not attracted as much attention.

Having looked at the NMR phenomenon and its applications, through twelve chapters and these six elements, no new concepts need be added to understand the acquisition and value of NMR spectra from the rest of the magnetic nuclei in the periodic table: the Appendix lists some, but not all of these.

13.1 DEUTERIUM NMR SPECTRA

Deuterium features considerably in the NMR studies of other elements; its distinctive triplet splitting (spin = 1) arises in ^{13}C NMR spectra recorded in $CDCl_3$ or C_6D_6,

and its exchange reaction with proton is a valuable means of labelling specifically those sites which possess labile proton, such as OH groups.

Its own magnetic dipole gives it a precessional frequency of 15.3 MHz at 2.35 T and although its natural abundance and sensitivity are low (see Appendix) natural abundance spectra are readily recorded by pulse FT methods.

The natural abundance ^2H NMR spectrum for 1-iodobutane (figure 13.1) illustrates again that in such spectra, each signal arises from chemically equivalent sites in the molecule: there are nine hydrogens in 1-iodobutane but only four non-equivalent sites, so the deuterium NMR spectrum is given by four different isotopomers, each containing one deuteron. The signal intensities (3:2:2:2) reflect the relative probability of each being present in a random distribution of the available deuterium (0.015% chance at each of the nine hydrogen positions).

Because of the ^2H quadrupole moment, the signals are in principle broadened, but there is a bonus in that homonuclear deuterium–deuterium coupling constants are very small, about one fortieth of the corresponding

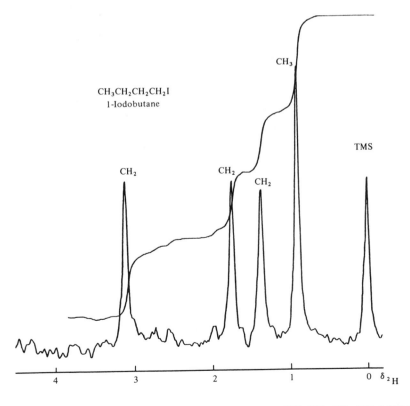

Figure 13.1 ^2H NMR spectrum (at natural abundance) of 1-iodobutane, $CH_3CH_2CH_2CH_2I$ (30.7 MHz, neat liquid. δ 0.9, 1.4, 1.8 and 3.1)

J_{HH} values. This means that for a CD_3CD_2- group, the multiplicity is virtually absent and only two lines are seen: this extends to the general point that ^2H NMR spectra are simplified with respect to the corresponding proton spectra, and synthetic incorporation of ^2H into complex molecules can be followed more easily. In natural abundance spectra, such as figure 13.1, without enrichment, isotopomers with two adjacent deuterons are of course sufficiently rare as to be ignorable.

Much biochemical and kinetic work makes use of the fact that proton exchange reactions such as tautomerism can be studied by measuring the rate of deuterium exchange. A simple example will emphasise the sensitivity of this procedure, particularly in cases of very slow exchange rates. Suppose in a keto–enol tautomerism that the exchange is carried out in the presence of a deuterium donating reagent such as CF_3COOD. Instead of measuring the exchange of protons, we measure the exchange of (say) C–H to C–D. At the start of the experiment, the natural abundance of deuterium in the C–H position is 0.015%: this is recorded and measured from the ^2H NMR spectrum for the compound. After some exchange has taken place, the corresponding signal intensity for the C–H group in the ^2H NMR spectrum will rise (since there will now be *more* than 0.015% of ^2H at that position). To be exact, if the exchange has proceeded only to the extent of exchanging a further 0.015% of the hydrogens at that site, the signal in the ^2H NMR spectrum will have doubled.

The number of proton exchange reactions studied by this technique is large, since even if the molecule is complex, the changes in the ^2H NMR spectrum occur only at sites of proton exchange: even if there are several of these, the relative rates of the exchange can also be measured.

Other uses of deuterium involve specific substitution of ^2H to measure J_{HD} values (see section 4.8) since this leads approximately to the corresponding J_{HH} value by multiplying by 6.5. The phenomenon of isotope shift was also mentioned briefly as being a very small influence (section 5.5) unlike, interestingly, the shift to lower frequency of nearly 0.1 ppm which ^{18}O produces in ^{13}C chemical shifts: this isotope shift can be used as a stereochemical probe since it varies with molecular geometry.

13.2 TRITIUM NMR SPECTRA

Tritium is radioactive (half-life 12.3 years) and thus not naturally abundant, but it is relatively easy to handle without radiation hazard and is an attractive and unique NMR isotope because its sensitivity is 1.2 times greater than that of proton (and it has spin $= \frac{1}{2}$): its resonance frequency at 2.35 T is 107 MHz.

The use of ^3H in labelling studies is associated with several advantages over that of ^2H (and the isotope shifts are of the same order for the two isotopes). With spin $= \frac{1}{2}$, tritium NMR signals are not quadrupole broadened, and it is observed that the chemical shifts of the isotopes ^1H and ^3H are the same, as is so for ^{14}N and ^{15}N. Tritium NMR offers the advantage of much higher sensitivity, and so lower incorporation rates can be used. As in the case of ^2H NMR, proton decoupling is commonly practised: but since γ for ^3H is large and γ for ^2H is small there is a lesser bonus from the NOE in signal enhancement of ^3H NMR signals.

The disadvantages of tritium lie in its radioactivity (not problematic in licensed laboratories) and in the fact there is a lesser bonus from that of the NOE in signal en- ing the isotope.

13.3 BORON-11 NMR SPECTRA

Boron chemistry is very varied, and the element occupies an important bridge position between classical inorganic and organic divisions. The boron-11 isotope is much preferred in NMR terms to boron-10, for reasons that are apparent from a glance at the Appendix. Boron NMR spectroscopy has been used to help elucidate the structures of the boron hydrides, and to identify the existence of intermediates in the hydroboration of alkenes; the use of chemical shift data is the major emphasis, but in the boron hydrides $^1J_{BH}$ for bridge hydrogens is much less than $^1J_{BH}$ for terminal hydrogens, being about 80 Hz and 100–190 Hz respectively.

13.4 ALUMINIUM-27 NMR SPECTRA

The relaxation time stack plot at the chapter head measures T_1 for ^{27}Al NMR signals in aqueous (D_2O) potassium aluminium sulphate. Note first of all that there are two aluminium environments and that the higher frequency signal is associated with longer T_1 than the other signal which is broadened because of short T_1. The interpretation of this is that the major aluminium constituent is the hexa-aqueous complex, $Al(D_2O)_6^{3+}$. This has higher symmetry than the minor constituent $Al(D_2O)_5SO_4^+$, hence the difference in relaxation rates.

Aluminium-27 NMR has also been used to verify that in the Friedel–Crafts acylation reactions involving CH_3COCl and anhydrous $AlCl_3$, there exists a donor–acceptor relationship between the two, and not the formation of $CH_3CO^+AlCl_4^-$.

13.5 SILICON-29 NMR SPECTRA

TMS is used as reference standard for proton, carbon-13 and also for ^{29}Si. Of these three nuclei, chemical importance puts silicon well behind the other two, but silicon-29 NMR spectra are easily obtained, with a natural abundance of 4.7% and a frequency of 20 MHz in a 2.35 T field. From the Appendix, its sensitivity is quite high, and note also that γ is negative: the problems of negative γ have been discussed for nitrogen-15, and multipulse methods such as DEPT can be used to give profitable signal enhancement. Figure 13.2 shows a proton coupled silicon-29 NMR spectrum for silicone oil (the polymer $(CH_3)_3Si-O-Si-(CH_2)_2-O-$) showing the difference in chemical shift between terminal $(CH_3)_3Si$ groups and mid-chain $(CH_3)_2Si$ groups. The signal at higher frequency was recorded at x16 sensitivity, reflecting the smaller number of end-groups to mid-chain groups.

Much of the complex chemistry of silicates in solution has been unravelled by the application of silicon-29 NMR spectroscopy; differences in chemical shift relate to different bonding environments.

13.6 SELENIUM-77 NMR SPECTRA

The splitting pattern in figure 10.4 showed J_{PSe} in $Ph_3P=Se$, and problem example 10.1 invited a prediction of the appearance of the ^{77}Se NMR spectrum. Figure 13.3 shows this spectrum.

Only one chemical shift position for the ^{77}Se nucleus is seen; this signal appears as a doublet, with $J_{PSe} = 731$ Hz.

13.7 CHLORINE, BROMINE AND IODINE NMR SPECTRA

From the Appendix, there is no problem in studying these elements in NMR spectroscopy as far as natural abundance is concerned, and no serious problem in sensitivity when pulse FT recording is used.

The problems are entirely associated with their quadrupole moments, since all have spin greater than $\frac{1}{2}$. From the mechanisms of quadrupole interactions discussed in chapter 2, the deduction can be made that the halogen nuclei will tend, strongly, to follow any electric field gradients within the tumbling molecule: in practice, all covalently bonded halogen atoms also have associated with them strong electric field gradients (since they are all to some degree electronegative). Thus quadrupolar effects completely dominate the electromagnetic properties of these three halogens — in covalent bonds.

The ions (Cl^-, Br^- and I^-) have *symmetrical electrical* distribution, and the problem of the quadrupole

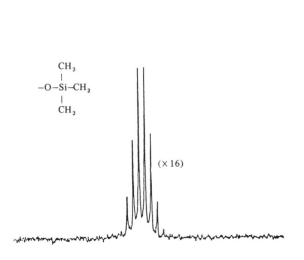

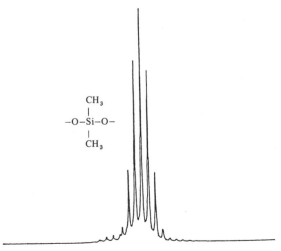

Figure 13.2 ^{29}Si NMR spectrum of silicone oil (39.9 MHz)

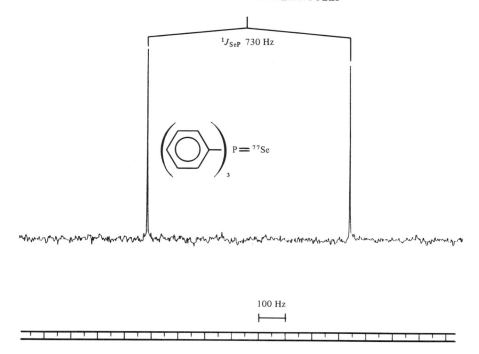

Figure 13.3 ^{77}Se NMR spectrum of triphenylphosphine selenide, Ph_3PSe (15.2 MHz)

moment is reduced, to the extent that the property of the *magnetic* dipole can assert itself, and NMR spectra can be obtained rather more easily.

Halides are important in biological systems and a great deal of detailed information about cell chemistry and ion migration has been deduced from halide NMR spectroscopy. Further Reading lists a reference to more extensive coverage (in *NMR and the Periodic Table*).

13.8 OTHER ELEMENTS AND THEIR NMR SPECTRA

The NMR spectroscopy of the elements in the periodic table is more characterised by similarities than differences, and by way of reaffirming this point we take a look at two interesting spectra of metals. Figure 13.4 is the mercury-199 NMR spectrum of dimethylmercury, CH_3HgCH_3, the biological end-stop of mercury pollution.

As predicted from first order principles, the spectrum consists of one signal, with a multiplicity of seven, in agreement with the $(n + 1)$ rule.

Figure 13.5 shows the tin-119 NMR spectrum for tris(trimethyltin)phosphine, $(Me_3Sn)_3P$. Only one chemi-

cal shift position arises, and the principal effect is the coupling of ^{119}Sn to ^{31}P, giving a doublet for the ^{119}Sn resonance. Although most of the tin present is non-magnetic, and ^{119}Sn is only 8.6% abundant, each isotopomer containing ^{119}Sn has a fair chance of *also* containing a ^{117}Sn nucleus in an adjacent Me_3Sn group, since ^{117}Sn is 7.6% abundant. The chance of both ^{119}Sn and ^{117}Sn being both present in an isotopomer (II) (formulae 13.1), produces satellite splitting of the observed ^{119}Sn resonances by the ^{117}Sn. There is an even smaller chance (nevertheless finite) of an isotopomer (III) containing ^{119}Sn also containing a ^{115}Sn nucleus in an adjacent Me_3Sn group: ^{115}Sn is only 0.35% abundant but, like ^{119}Sn and ^{117}Sn has spin = $\frac{1}{2}$. At low intensity, the ^{115}Sn splits the ^{119}Sn resonance in these doubly endowed isotopomers, so satellite peaks arise around the ^{119}Sn resonance due to $^2J(^{119}Sn, ^{115}Sn)$. Recall again that the isotopomers which give rise to the main ^{119}Sn signal contain neither ^{117}Sn nor ^{115}Sn, and that the isotopomers which give rise to the $^2J(^{119}Sn, ^{117}Sn)$ satellites are different from those that give the ^{115}Sn satellites.

Worked Example 13.1

Predict the multiplicity in the ^{31}P NMR spectrum of $(Me_3Sn)_3P$.

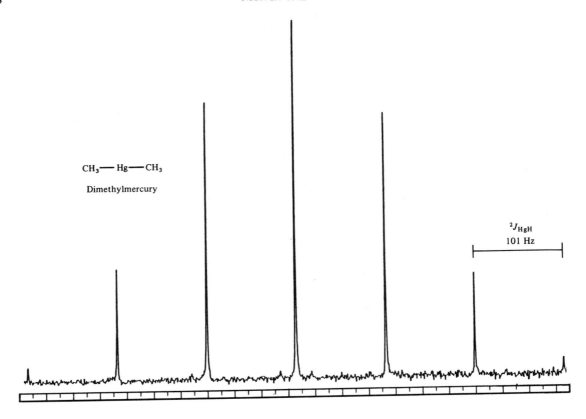

CH₃——Hg——CH₃

Dimethylmercury

$^2J_{HgH}$
101 Hz

Figure 13.4 ^{199}Hg NMR spectrum of dimethylmercury, Me₂Hg (14.2 MHz)

Answer 13.1

Ignoring coupling between phosphorus and protons, then isotopomer (I) will give rise to a doublet (coupling to ^{119}Sn). Isotopomer (II) will give a signal with the same chemical shift value, but split into a double doublet (coupling first to ^{119}Sn and then to ^{117}Sn). The much less abundant isotopomer (III) will again give a signal with the same chemical shift, of lower intensity, and split into a double doublet (coupling to ^{119}Sn and then to ^{115}Sn).

$$(Me_3\ ^{119}Sn)_3P \quad (Me_3\ ^{119}Sn)_2P\ (^{117}SnMe_3) \quad (Me_3\ ^{119}Sn)_2P\ (^{115}SnMe_3)$$
$$(I) \qquad\qquad\qquad (II) \qquad\qquad\qquad\qquad (III)$$

(13.1)

Abundance of tin isotopomers: (I) > (II) ≫ (III)

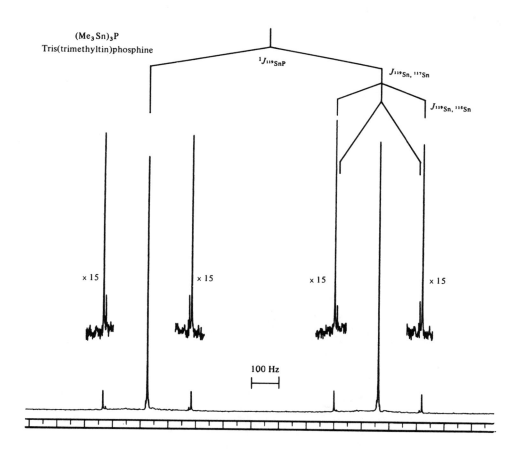

Figure 13.5 ^{119}Sn NMR spectrum of tris(trimethyltin)phosphine, $(Me_3Sn)_3P$ (29.7 MHz)

Background Physics and Biography of NMR

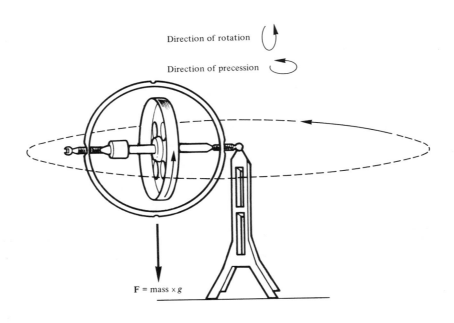

Direction of rotation

Direction of precession

$\mathbf{F} = \text{mass} \times g$

Gyroscope

If we are familiar only with linearly acting forces, then the forces acting on rotating bodies such as gyroscopes provide some unexpected effects: the precise definitions of angular momentum, vector products, and torques cannot be deduced from intuitive thought, and some attempt will be made in this chapter to introduce the most useful rules as they apply to NMR.

Some brief pointers are also included as a reminder of the principles governing electrical and magnetic phenomena, and some biographical notes are added for general interest: the history of NMR can be viewed from the stand-point of the people who made contributions to its development and many of their names have been adopted to identify phenomena in NMR.

14.1 VECTOR QUANTITIES – TORQUE AND ANGULAR MOMENTUM

Elementary physics introduces the distinction between scalars and vectors. Scalar quantities can be represented by a number only, familiar examples being length, temperature and mass. Vector quantities require the specification of their magnitude, direction and sense; thus we can have a force of 5 N acting vertically downwards, and this vector would have the same magnitude and direction as, but the opposite sense from, a force of 5 N acting vertically upwards. The concept of *vector addition* is familiar in the case of two vectors, from the simple parallelogram of forces (see figure 14.1(a)).

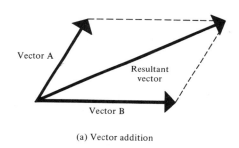

(a) Vector addition

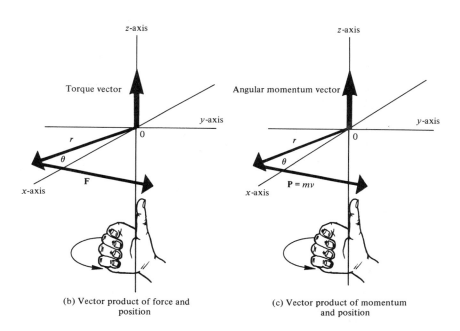

(b) Vector product of force and position

(c) Vector product of momentum and position

Figure 14.1 Combination of vectors. The defined positions of torque and angular momentum vectors are at right angles to the vectors which generate them. With the right hand, imagine turning a screw clockwise: the vector representing the torque or angular momentum lies in the direction indicated by the thumb

The concept of *vector products* is less familiar but two examples are sufficient to illustrate the most important conventional rules that are used in NMR. In figure 14.1(b) the vector **F** is a force, tending to rotate **r** (which is a position vector) around the origin O.

We are concerned in this problem to define the *size of the product* and its *direction* and its *sense*. To specify direction and sense, we can reference the vectors to a set of cartesian coordinate axes, *x*, *y*, and *z*, and if we agree that **F** and **r** lie on the *xy* plane, then the third coordinate can be incorporated by specifying n̂ as a *vector of unit dimension*, lying along the *z*-axis. The *sense* of the vector n̂ is that conventionally defined by the *right-hand screw rule*. Screwing a right-hand screw along the direction and sense of n̂ must be such that by doing so **F** rotates **r** as shown in the figure. The vector product is defined as

$$\mathbf{J} = \mathbf{r}\,\mathbf{F}\,\sin\theta\;\hat{n}$$

J is thus a new vector passing through the origin and acting upwards along the *z*-axis. Its dimension and position tell us all we need to know about the situation specified in the figure. The vector **J** is the *vector moment of a force about a point*, and such a vector is called a *torque*,

precisely defined, and acting at right angles to the *force* which produces it.

If, instead of the vector *force* in figure 14.1(b) we have another vector acting in the same sense, but this time it is the *momentum* of a particle (where momentum **p** is a vector, equal to mass × velocity), then again the vector product of **p** and **r** will be a new vector acting upwards through the origin and at right angles to both **p** and **r**, as in figure 14.1(c). This new product vector is defined as the *moment of momentum* or more usually the *angular momentum vector*.

Note again that, by definition, the angular momentum vector acts through the origin, is at right angles to the direction of rotation, and is in a sense which follows the right hand screw rule in specifying the direction of rotation.

We can now quickly pass to the way in which angular momentum is defined for a massive spinning body: the body will clearly possess momentum of some sort, and we can define its direction of rotation using the rules given above for vector products (including the right hand rule in particular).

Figure 14.2 shows such a body, with two different directions of rotation; the two different angular momen-

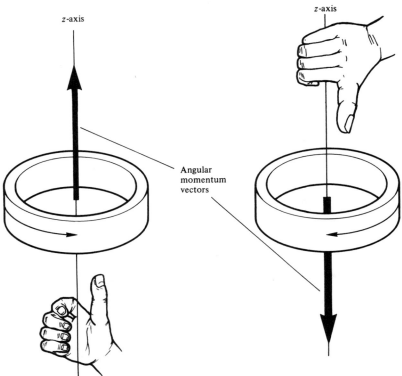

Figure 14.2 The vector representation of angular momentum permits a convenient mathematical treatment of the mechanics of rotating bodies

tum vectors, as defined above, allow us to represent each system fully in terms of dimension, direction and sense.

If the body is not subject to frictional losses, it is reasonable to accept that its own inertia will keep it spinning indefinitely, quite analogously to the effects of inertia on linearly moving bodies.

In order to change the angular motion however, it is not simply a question of applying a *force*, unless this force also generates a *torque*. A force acting at zero distance from the origin will exert *zero torque* on the angular momentum.

> The angular momentum can only be altered if an applied force also produces an applied torque: the direction of such an applied torque is at right angles to the force producing it.

14.2 GYROSCOPIC BEHAVIOUR

Familiar massive spinning bodies are flywheels, bicycle or motorcycle wheels, and toy gyroscopes; it will be instructive to look at these familiar examples and to derive loosely some generalities. The physics of gyroscopes can only be imperfectly demonstrated with the ordinary toy gyroscope, since one end of its spinning axis must always be fixed, and it is impossible to 'see'

momentum or force (including the omnipresent effects of gravity).

We can envisage a gyroscope mounted on a tower as in figure 14.3 with its axis of rotation horizontal, and we can specify that the heavy flywheel is spinning in a clockwise sense, with respect to an observer on top of the tower. If now we can imagine the possibility of observing the system *in the absence of gravity*, then in fact the gyroscope will maintain its position; indeed if the bearings were frictionless, the gyroscope would spin forever.

If gravity is now restored, it supplies a force (equal to $M \times g$) acting downwards through the flywheel.

> The gyroscope does not rotate in the vertical plane, but rotates around the tower in the horizontal plane. This motion is named *precession*.

Viewed from above the tower, this rotation is seen to be *anticlockwise*; spinning the gyroscope in the opposite sense will cause precession in a *clockwise* direction.

Note that the force on the gyroscope acts downwards through the flywheel, but the turning effect which causes the gyroscope to precess around the tower is horizontal. The turning effect is the *torque*.

> The torque vector is at 90° to the force vector.

Another familiar, if less rigorous example is provided by a motorcycle and the gyroscopic properties of its

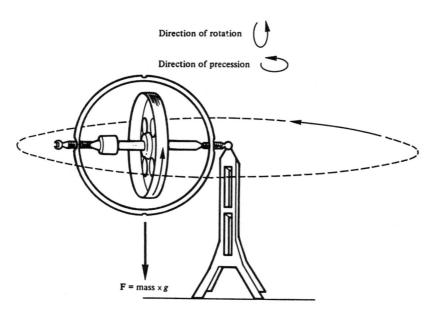

Direction of rotation

Direction of precession

F = mass × g

Figure 14.3 A gyroscope has massive angular momentum in the flywheel. The gravitational force produces an associated torque which causes the gyroscope to precess at constant velocity. The angle through which the gyroscope precesses is a function of the time during which the torque acts

front wheel during cornering at high speed. If the rider leans to the left, his weight exerts a *downwards force* on the gyroscopic wheel, but this produces a *horizontal torque*, turning the wheel's axis to the left and allowing easier cornering.

14.3 MAGNETIC AND ELECTRICAL PHENOMENA

As one of the major subdivisions of physics, electricity and magnetism is worthy of intensive and extensive learning; the minimum knowledge needed to understand NMR is presented here.

14.3.1 Bar Magnets and Magnetic Moments

The strength of a simple bar magnet is measured by the magnetic dipole moment, μ, defined as the torque experienced by the magnetic dipole in a field of unit magnetic flux. It is a vector quantity, and as usual can be represented conveniently in a diagram by an arrow. In an applied field of flux density B_0, the energy of interaction between B_0 and a magnetic dipole μ is given by the negative product of the two ($-\mu \times B_0$).

14.3.2 Wire Loops and Spinning Charges

A magnetic field is set up by an electric current flowing in a circular wire loop. The direction of this electro-magnetic moment vector, in relation to the current flow, is shown in figure 14.4. 'Conventional' direct current flows from + to −, which is in the opposite direction to electron flow (from − to +). The magnetic lines of force

generated by such a simple wire loop are also shown in the figure. (Magnetic moments produced by more elaborate loops can also be calculated, from equations derived by James Clerk Maxwell, but these calculations are of high complexity.)

A spinning negatively-charged body, such as an electron, generates a magnetic field similarly to a wire loop (see figure 2.1(a)). We make the approximation that the electron is a point charge, but note the relative positions of the two arrows representing the magnetic moment vector and the angular momentum vector respectively. The magnetic dipole from a point charge q of mass m, spinning with angular momentum I, is given by

$$\mu = \frac{\text{charge} \times \text{angular momentum}}{2 \times \text{mass}} = \frac{q \times I}{2m}$$

14.3.3 Alternating Current

An alternating current flowing along a linear conductor sets up fluctuating magnetic fields at right angles to the electric potential. This is illustrated in figure 14.5(a). All parts of the electromagnetic spectrum exhibit the same characteristics, the principal difference among them being the wavelength (frequency) of the radiation involved. (James Clerk Maxwell also established these relationships, and explained the involvement of the speed of light in the equations.)

In the electromagnetic spectrum, including the domestic supply of alternating current with frequency of 50 or 60 Hz, the power associated with any part of the sinusoidal wave is proportional to the square of the

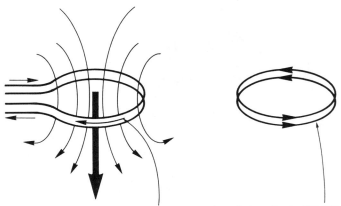

'Conventional' current flowing this way corresponds to electrons flowing this way

Figure 14.4 A loop of wire carrying a direct current generates a magnetic field whose vector representation lies in the direction shown

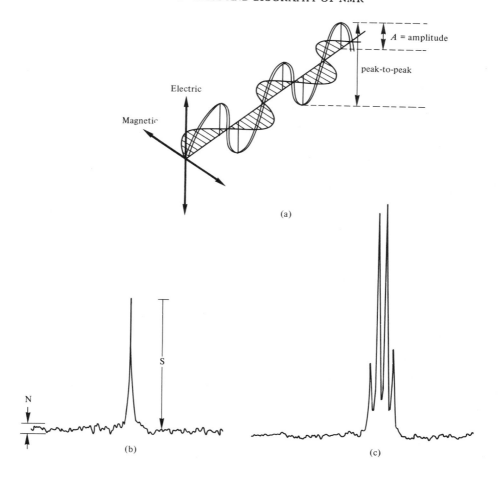

Figure 14.5 (a) Propagation of alternating current and the related magnetic fields. All parts of the electromagnetic spectrum possess these same characteristics. Note that peak-to-peak signal = 2A. (b) Signal-to-noise specification measures (approximately) RMS noise, by dividing peak-to-peak noise by 2.5. (c) The ethylbenzene quartet used to test proton sensitivity in NMR spectrometers

amplitude at that point, and not just to the amplitude. The amplitude (A) varies in time, from high and positive through zero to high and negative, and the effective power is usually quoted as the square root of the averaged-out sum of A^2, the so-called root-mean-square or RMS power. Domestic supplies with working ratings of 110 V or 240 V have RMS voltages of 110 and 240 V respectively; the maximum voltages, corresponding to the peak of the sinusoid, are higher, since

$$\text{RMS voltage} = \frac{\text{maximum voltage}}{\sqrt{2}} = \frac{\text{maximum voltage}}{1.414}$$

14.3.4 Signal-to-noise Ratios

Figure 14.5(b) shows a sharp signal against a fluctuating noise background. To measure the signal strength with respect to noise, it is conventional to specify the noise amplitude in (more or less) RMS form, using

$$\text{noise} = \frac{\text{peak-to-peak signal variation}}{2.5} = \frac{N}{2.5}$$

Since, for a pure sinusoid, peak-to-peak signal variation is equal to twice the amplitude, the divisor would then be $2\sqrt{2}$ or 2.828: it is conventionally accepted that dividing by 2.5 is a sufficiently accurate approximation for noise measurement.

The signal-to-noise ratio (S/N ratio) is then given by

$$\frac{\text{signal amplitude}}{\text{peak-to-peak noise}/2.5} \quad \text{or} \quad \frac{S \times 2.5}{N}$$

Manufacturers of NMR spectrometers generally are

agreed on quoting signal-to-noise specifications for proton with respect to the largest signal in the ethyl quartet of a 1% ethylbenzene solution, with certain other instrument parameters defined. Alternatively, a 0.1% ethylbenzene solution is used, offering the challenging possibility of measuring very sensitive instruments with high signal-to-noise specifications: such a measurement is shown in figure 14.5(c), and gives a S/N ratio of 200:1 corresponding to 2000:1 if the test sample had been at 1% concentration.

Sensitivity in carbon-13 NMR, in a spectrometer working in the pulsed FT mode, can be specified, for example, with respect to the largest aromatic signal in 10% ethylbenzene solution, using the spectrum obtained from a single pulse. The ASTM test, specified by a committee of the American Society for Testing and Materials, uses for this purpose a 60:40 mixture of deuteriobenzene and dioxane: see additional problem 2 on page 103.

14.4 QUADRUPOLE MOMENTS

The term quadrupole moment is borrowed from the science of electrostatics and from the study of dielectric material. The electric potential around an electric charge is a complex function, and in particular the manner in which potential falls off with increasing distance involves (1) the number of charges, (2) their distribution in space and (3) the distance, r, from the charges. A generalised mathematical analysis resolves this variation of potential with respect to r into a convenient expansion series involving different powers of r.

$$\text{potential} = \frac{K_0}{r} + \frac{K_1}{r^2} + \frac{K_2}{r^3} + \dots$$

The constants K_0, K_1, and K_2 depend on the net charge and on its spatial distribution. The K_0 term is simply a measure of the total charge, and its dimension is named the *monopole moment* of the system. The K_1 term is a measure of charge separation, and K_1 is important in systems such as those in figure 14.6(a), (b) and (c). Chemists are familiar with similar situations (in dipolar molecules) and the term *dipole moment* is borrowed from the name given to the constant K_1 in electrostatics. For systems with a substantial K_1 term (strong dipole moment) the higher terms in the expansion involving reciprocal r^3, r^4 and so on, are of markedly less important in specifying the fall-off in electric potential.

The charge distribution in figure 14.6(d) would not give rise to a dipole moment and so the K_1 term in the expansion would be zero; for such a system of charges, the potential falls off in a manner more dependent on higher powers of r, which mathematically makes the term K_2 important; K_2 is called the *quadrupole moment*.

The nomenclature developed in electrostatics to describe more complex charge distributions (involving higher terms such as *octupole moments*) is fortunately of no consequence in NMR.

14.5 HISTORICAL RETROSPECTS IN NMR

The two groups of physicists who pioneered the NMR method published their preliminary findings almost simultaneously. Thus the critical paper by Purcell, Torrey and Pound (working in the Laboratory of Physics Research at Harvard University) was submitted in December 1945 and that of Bloch, Hansen and Packard (of Stanford University, California) in January 1946. The papers are listed in Further Reading.

Purcell recorded the proton NMR signal from 850 mL of paraffin wax, using a radiofrequency bridge circuit operating around 30 MHz, with a field of 0.7 T: his instrument can be seen in the Frontispiece portrait.

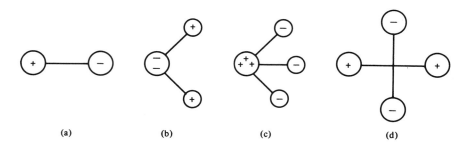

(a)	(b)	(c)	(d)

Figure 14.6 Electrostatics. In all of the above systems, the total net charge is zero. (a), (b) and (c) all have dipoles. (d) Has no net dipole, but possesses a quadrupole moment

Bloch's apparatus used the crossed coil arrangement (as mainly discussed throughout the book) so that he really devised the practice of nuclear induction; his first reported experiment used water as the sample, and his operating frequency was a mere 7.8 MHz.

He concluded his preliminary announcement: 'We have thought of various investigations in which this effect can be used fruitfully. A detailed account will be published in the near future'.

The physicists in 1946 were mainly interested in applying the method to the measurement of nuclear parameters such as the magnetogyric ratios of various elements. It was 1951 before Packard, Arnold and Dharmatti (of Stanford University) were able to resolve three proton signals in a sample of ethanol 1 cm long and 2 mm in diameter. They reported also the results from a series of aliphatic alcohols, and named the phenomenon of chemical shift. (In fact they measured these chemical shifts with respect to the positions of the OH signals!)

They in turn finished their paper prophetically: 'It seems to us that there may be certain chemical problems besides analysis, such as the study of chemical reactions and equilibria, which can be investigated by this method. We are continuing our measurements upon related series of organic liquids and upon the question of the different transverse relaxation times'.

Before long, chemists and physicists together developed NMR into the pivotal technique it now is. The first commercially produced NMR instrument (the Model HR40) was developed and built in the late 1950s by Varian Associates of Palo Alto, within a short distance of Felix Bloch's Stanford laboratories in California.

Felix Bloch and E. M. Purcell shared the Nobel Prize for Physics in 1952.

Bloch predicted the feasibility of pulsed experiments, but it was 1950 before Erwin Hahn observed it in practice. The recognition that Fourier transformation of the free induction decay gave the same information as the continuous wave spectrum was another decade in dawning.

This same decade saw the growth of the essential adjunct to fast FT — the digital computer and the microprocessor. The rate of development of NMR methodology and application accelerated from this time and enabled NMR to be applied to problems of quite astonishing diversity, not only in physics but in chemistry, biochemistry, medicine, geology and in all of their technological offspring. Without the computer ability to control the execution and timing of experiments to an accuracy of a few nanoseconds, these developments would not have occurred.

14.5.1 Biographical Notes

Many surnames in science have become associated with phenomena, constants, equations or units, and in NMR we have seen how these names take upon themselves the nature of definitions. It is easy to overlook the place of the persona in the history of discovery: the following short (alphabetical) listing goes some way to indicating the chronology of the principal players and their scientific import. It is inevitably invidious to include some and to exclude very many others — particularly contemporary scientists of international standing. Selection has been based mainly on one criterion, that the surname is now the accepted label in NMR publications. Bloch, Purcell and Packard are listed for their seminal contributions to NMR.

ARRHENIUS, Svante August, 1859–1927. Swedish chemist whose main work was in electrochemistry. He found experimentally that reaction rates and temperature were related by a straight line relationship ($y = mx + c$) if ln k was plotted against $-E_A/TR + A$, where A is (more or less) constant and E_A is the energy of activation. An alternative form is $k = A \exp(-E_A/RT)$, the Arrhenius Equation. His other researches include the (now topical) greenhouse effect of CO_2 in influencing the temperature of the earth's atmosphere. He was awarded the Nobel Prize in Chemistry for 1903. (He was a collaborator of Van't Hoff.)

AVOGADRO, Amedeo, 1776–1856. Italian physicist. His famous 1811 'hypothesis' stated that equal volumes of all gases (at the same pressure and temperature) contain the same number of molecules: the number in one mole is 6.02×10^{23} — the Avogadro constant, N_A. Although Avogadro's theoretical interests were diverse, his contemporary reputation was slight, to some extent because of his lack of experimentation.

BLOCH, Felix, 1905–1982. American physicist. Born in Zürich, Switzerland, Felix Bloch took up his first post at Stanford University, California, in 1934, and remained there to carry out the research which led to the Nobel Prize. See also Edward M. Purcell. His portrait photograph is in the Frontispiece.

BOHR, Niels, 1885–1962. Danish physicist and Nobel Laureate. Primarily concerned with atomic structure, Bohr showed that an electron moving from one energy state to another absorbs or emits energy following the relationship $\Delta E = h\nu$. (See also Max Planck.)

BOLTZMANN, Ludwig, 1844–1906. Austrian physicist. He treated the problem of the statistical distribution of molecules among available energy states; his now well-known solution (see section 2.16) includes the constant which bears his name.

COPERNICUS, Nicolaus, 1473-1543. Polish monk and astronomer. Arguing against the view of the second century astronomer Ptolemy, Copernicus held that the earth (and other planets) rotated around the sun. His thirty year campaign culminated in the posthumous (1544) publication of his book *On the Revolution of Celestial Spheres*. The book was not banned until 1616, but it remained so until 1835.

DALTON, John (1766-1844). English chemist. Apart from his work on gases, Dalton's greatest contribution to chemistry was in the generalisations he brought to atomic theory, establishing that the principal and characteristic difference between one element and another is the weight of their respective atoms. Multinuclear NMR allows us to make ever-subtler distinctions.

DESCARTES, René, 1596-1650. French mathematician. René Descartes (Des Cartes) was the inventor of 'cartesian' coordinates (more than two hundred years ago).

ERNST, Richard R. Contemporary Swiss scientist, working at the Laboratory of Physical Chemistry, ETH, Zürich. Continuously involved in pioneering work on the pulse FT NMR method and its applications to chemistry.

EYRING, Henry, born 1901 (Mexico). American physicist and educator. Has made many contributions to absolute rate theory.

FARADAY, Michael, 1791-1867, British scientist. As well as discovering the laws of electrolysis, the liquefaction of gases by pressure and the existence of benzene, Faraday discovered electromagnetic induction. Current in one wire wound around an iron core induces a current in another companion wire — but only when the current is switched on and off. He went on to find that if a conductor is rotated in a *magnetic* field, an *electric* current is sustained in the conductor; this was the invention of the dynamo, but it led to Maxwell's theory of electromagnetic radiation.

FOURIER, Jean-Baptiste, 1768-1830. French mathematician. He developed the mathematics of series of the form $a_0 + a_1 \cos \omega t + b_1 \sin \omega t + a_2 \cos 2\omega t + b_2 \sin 2\omega t \ldots$ which permits any periodic function to be expressed as the sum of its individual harmonic parts. In a Fourier Transform, a complex waveform can be described in the time or frequency domains, each being the reciprocal of the other. Note the involvement of ω (angular frequency) and t (time) and recall the connection between angular frequency in radians per second and frequency, f, in hertz ($\omega = 2\pi f$).

FREEMAN, Raymond. Contemporary British physical chemist. Fellow of Jesus College, Cambridge, formerly (1963-73) manager of NMR products at Varian Associates, Palo Alto. Continuously involved in pioneering work on the chemical applications of the pulse FT NMR method, including 2D NMR and AB satellite analysis.

GUTOWSKY, Herbert, Sander, born 1919. Contemporary American chemist who has made major contributions to many areas of physical chemistry, in particular to the use of NMR in kinetic studies.

HAHN, Erwin Louis, born 1921. Contemporary American physicist, now at University of California at Berkeley. Experimentally demonstrated the ability of nuclei to emit signals after the cessation of pulsed excitation.

HARTMANN, Sven, born 1932. Contemporary American physicist now at Columbia Radiation Laboratory, New York. Collaborated with Hahn.

HEISENBERG, Werner Karl, 1901-1976. German physicist. The Heisenberg Uncertainty Principle is fundamental to the behaviour of subatomic particles. Unlike macro bodies, we cannot know the position and momentum of such particles with unlimited precision. This is partly associated with the fact that any attempt to measure (say) the momentum of these particles perturbs the very system which we are trying to observe. The Uncertainty Principle also applies to energy/time measurements.

KARPLUS, Robert, born 1927 in Vienna. Physicist. Has held several American appointments, most recently at University of California in Los Angeles.

LARMOR, Sir Joseph, 1857-1942. British physicist. Larmor studied the action of a magnetic field on the motion of a charged particle, in particular the electron. He considered the orbit of the electron to be circular, and in a magnetic field the normal to the orbit precesses around the field's axis with a frequency given by $eH/4\pi mc$. Larmor precession is exhibited in similar conditions by protons and other magnetic nuclei.

LORENTZ, Hendrik Antoon, 1851-1928. Dutch theoretical physicist. A charged body, moving through electromagnetic fields, is subject to forces which are related by the Lorentz Force Law. Lorentz made many contributions to theories of electromagnetism, and his studies ultimately led to his specifying reference frames for moving bodies, and this almost took him to relativity theory: Albert Einstein (1879-1955) made the vital link in 1905.

In his theories of relativity, Lorentz detailed an equation describing one of the possible distributions of frequencies about a central frequency. This is described by an equation of the form $y = a/(b + cx^2)$, and such a distribution is named Lorentzian; the distribution of energies in NMR is of the same form, and thus the NMR line shape is described as Lorentzian.

MAXWELL, James Clerk, 1831–1879, Scottish physicist. Maxwell was truly a polymath, but his principal scientific achievement was in deriving equations (the Maxwell Equations) to describe the relationship between electric and magnetic fields. This led to the conclusion that light is an electromagnetic wave, and subsequently established that all regions of the electromagnetic spectrum are similar in nature, apart from their frequencies.

OVERHAUSER, Albert W. Contemporary American physicist. Overhauser's research has been wide ranging, involving solid diffusion, ion mobilities and nuclear spin relaxation. It is this last which is named after him as the Overhauser effect: he published this work in 1953 while at University of Illinois, but he has held posts at the University of California and Indiana, and at MIT and Purdue University.

PACKARD, Martin. Contemporary American physicist who worked with Felix Bloch at Stanford University and then joined Varian Associates to work on the development of all aspects of NMR instrumentation.

PASCAL, Blaise, 1623–1662. French mathematician. He built an adding machine, which he named La Pascaline, based on gears, in 1642. Although it did not catch on, the germ of an idea was sown: the computer language of PASCAL acknowledges his imaginative, if humble, innovation, and his name is also associated with the unit of pressure (Pa = N m^{-2} = 10^{-2} millibar).

PLANCK, Max, 1858–1947. German physicist. He was the father of quantum theory: in 1900 he postulated that the energy of an oscillator did not increase continuously, but rather did so in discrete jumps, which he named *quanta*. His theory explained hitherto puzzling experiments, and it has subsequently been applied to many spectroscopic phenomena. In this book we are most concerned with the relationship between the energy gap between two states and the frequency of radiation to which this corresponds. ΔE is proportional to ν, and the constant of proportionality is h, Planck's constant (6.63×10^{-34} J s) (see also Niels Bohr).

POPLE, John A. Contemporary British scientist. Formerly worked in basic physics at the National Physical Laboratory at Teddington; now at the Carnegie–Mellon University in Pittsburgh, USA. Pople was the first person to define and work out the mathematics of the key types of nuclear spin systems.

PURCELL, Edward Mills, born 1912 (Illinois). American physicist. Worked both at Harvard University, and as Group Leader in the Radiation Laboratory at Massachussets Institute of Technology. Joint winner of the Nobel Prize in Physics in 1952. See also Felix Bloch. (His portrait photograph is in the Frontispiece.)

SHOOLERY, James N. Contemporary American chemist. Has made indefatigable advances in the application of NMR to the solution of chemical problems: his research work at Varian Associates earned him the award of Industrial Research and Development Scientist of the Year in 1983.

TESLA, Nikola, 1856–1943. American electrical engineer, born in what is now Yugoslavia. The SI unit named after him is used to measure magnetic flux density, and is equal to 10^4 gauss.

Van't HOFF, Jacobus Hendricus, 1852–1911. Dutch chemist. Made major contributions to chemical kinetics (partly in collaboration with Arrhenius) and first proposed the relationships between structure and space which led to the concept of tetrahedral methane. He received the first ever Nobel Prize for Chemistry in 1901.

Van der WAALS, Jan D., 1837–1923. Dutch physicist. The main interest of van der Waals was in improving the accuracy of the gas laws by taking account both of the size of molecules and of their mutual attraction and repulsion. Winner of the Nobel Prize for Physics (1910).

14.6 NOCTURNAL PROCESSES

A novice refrigerator salesman was asked by a prospective buyer how the automatic defrost worked, and he spent a fruitless half hour discussing sensors, thermostats, relays and time switches, without making a sale. Afterwards, his manager abused him for wasting time.

'But what should I have done?' he asked.

The manager instructed him. 'You should have told him it happens during the night. That's all he needs to know to run the 'fridge'.

Many NMR and computer phenomena can be used successfully in interpretation (even though imperfectly understood in the absolute) if they are accepted as happening during the night. We bring similar acceptance daily to our use of car engines and gearboxes, electric motors, and radio-television receivers.

Tables of Reference Data

ELEMENTS

Symbol	Element	W.t	Symbol	Element	W.t
	Hydrogen	1		Strontian	46
	Azote	5		Barytes	68
	Carbon	54		Iron	50
	Oxygen	7		Zinc	56
	Phosphorus	9		Copper	56
	Sulphur	13		Lead	90
	Magnesia	20		Silver	190
	Lime	24		Gold	190
	Soda	28		Platina	190
	Potash	42		Mercury	167

The elements — as John Dalton saw them in 1808

Proton Data

Table 15.1 Proton chemical shifts (δ) for CH_3, CH_2 and CH groups attached to functional group X, where R = alkyl and Ar = aryl

X	CH_3X	$R'CH_2X$	$R'R''CHX$
$-R$	0.9	1.3	1.5
$-CH^b \overset{\overset{a}{CH_2}}{\underset{O}{\diagdown}}$	1.3	a 3.5	b 3.0
$\diagdown{=}$	1.7	1.9	2.6
$\diagdown{=}-={=}-={=}-$ (i.e. end-of-chain)	1.8		
$={-}\diagdown{=}{-}{=}$, etc. (i.e. in-chain)	2.0	2.2	2.3
$\diagdown{=} N -$	2.0	–	–
$-\equiv$	2.0	2.2	–
$-COOR, -COOAr$	2.0	2.1	2.2
$-CN$	2.0	2.5	2.7
$-CONH_2, -CONR_2$	2.0	2.0	2.1
$-COOH$	2.1	2.3	2.6
$-COR$	2.1	2.4	2.5
$-COAr$	2.5	2.8	2.9
$-SH, -SR$	2.1	2.4	2.5
$-NH_2, -NHR, -NR_2$	2.1	2.5	2.9
$-I$	2.2	3.1	4.2
$-CHO$	2.2	2.2	2.4
$-Ph, Ar$	2.3	2.6	2.9
$-NHAr$	2.5	2.9	–
$-Br$	2.6	3.3	4.1
$-NHCOR, -NRCOR$	2.9	3.3	3.5
$-Cl$	3.0	3.4	4.0
$-OR$	3.3	3.3	3.8
$-\overset{+}{N}R_3$	3.3	3.4	3.5
$-OH$	3.4	3.6	3.8
$-OCOR$	3.6	4.1	5.0
$-OAr$	3.7	3.9	4.0
$-OCOAr$	3.9	4.2	5.1
$-NO_2$	4.3	4.4	4.6
$-F$	4.3	–	–

Table 15.2 Influence of functional group X on the chemical shift position (δ) of CH_3, CH_2 and CH protons β to X

X	For β-shifts, add the following to the δ values given in table 15.1		
	CH_3-C-X	CH_2-C-X	$CH-C-X$
$-C=C$	0.1	0.1	0.1
$-COOH, -COOR$	0.2	0.2	0.2
$-CN$	0.5	0.4	0.4
$-CONH_2$	0.25	0.2	0.2
$-CO-, -CHO$	0.3	0.2	0.2
$-SH, -SR$	0.45	0.3	0.2
$-NH_2, -NHR, -NR_2$	0.1	0.1	0.1
$-I$	1.0	0.5	0.4
$-Ph$	0.35	0.3	0.3
$-Br$	0.8	0.6	0.25
$-NHCOR$	0.1	0.1	0.1
$-Cl$	0.6	0.4	0
$-OH, -OR$	0.3	0.2	0.2
$-OCOR$	0.4	0.3	0.3
$-OPh$	0.4	0.35	0.3
$-F$	0.2	0.4	0.1
$-NO_2$	0.6	0.8	0.8

Table 15.3 Proton chemical shifts (δ) for CH_2 and CH groups bearing more than one functional substituent. Modified Shoolery rules

Note:

for $H_2C\begin{smallmatrix}X^1\\\\X^2\end{smallmatrix}$ $\delta CH_2 = 1.2 + \Sigma a$

Less accurate for $HC\begin{smallmatrix}X^1\\-X^2\\X^3\end{smallmatrix}$ but use $\delta CH = 1.5 + \Sigma a$

X	a	X	a
$-=$	0.75	$-Ph$	1.3
$-\equiv$	0.9	$-Br$	1.9
$-COOH, -COOR$	0.7	$-Cl$	2.0
$-CN, -COR$	1.2	$-OR, -OH$	1.7
$-SR$	1.0	$-OCOR$	2.7
$-NH_2, -NR_2$	1.0	$-OPh$	2.3
$-I$	1.4		

Table 15.4 Proton chemical shifts (δ) for protons attached to unsaturated and aromatic groups

Structure	δ	Structure	δ
H—≡—R	1.8*	$CH_2=CH$—CO— (H on terminal)	5.8
H—≡—OH	2.4*	(methyl-substituted vinyl ketone)	6.0
H—≡—=—, etc.	2.7*	(methyl-substituted vinyl ketone)	6.2
H—≡—Ph	2.9*	Ph—=⟨H / CO— (cis or trans)	6.6
H—≡—CO—	3.2*	H / Ph =—CO— (cis or trans)	7.8
$H_2C=C\big\langle {}^R_{R'}$	4.6	H_b, H_c =⟨ H_a OCO—	a, 4.9 b, 4.6 c, 7.3
$H_2C=\!=\!=$—, etc.	4.9	N—C⟨ H / =O	7.8
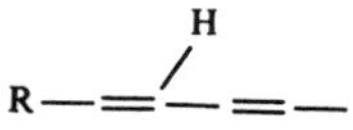 R—=⟨H =— (in-chain)	6.2	RO—C⟨ H / =O	8.0
$\big\langle^H_R C=C\big\langle$	5.3	RC⟨ H / =O	9.6
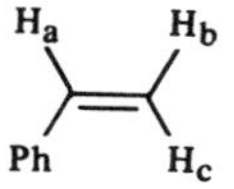 H_a, H_b / Ph, H_c	a, 7.0 b, 5.0 c, 5.3	PhC⟨ H / =O	9.9
(cyclohexene ring) =CH	5.6		
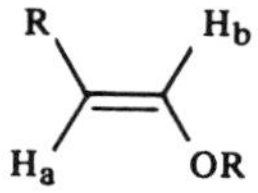 R, H_b / H_a, OR	b, 6.5–7.5 a, 4.5–5.0		
Ph–H	7.27 (see table 15.5)		

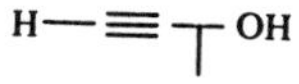

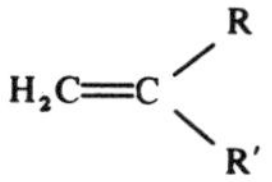

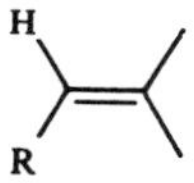

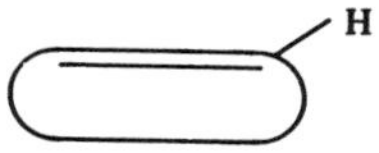

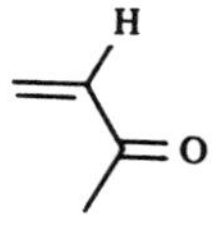

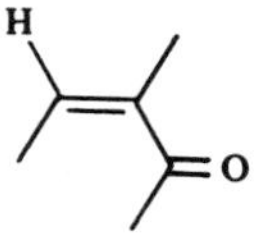

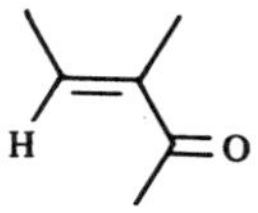

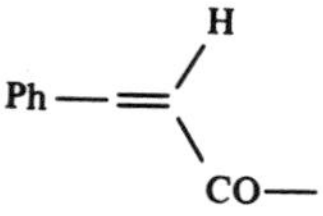

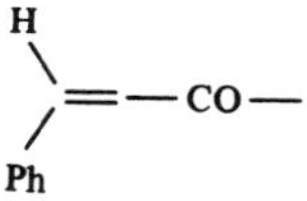

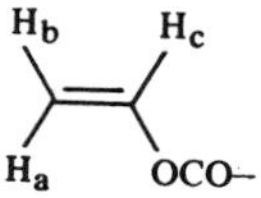

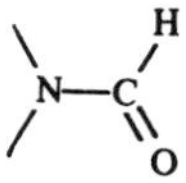

naphthalene: α 7.7, β 7.5

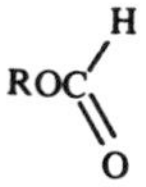

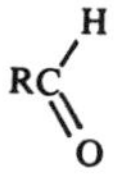

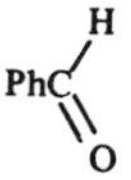

pyridine: γ 7.4, β 7.0, α 8.5

(dihydropyran): 4.5, 6.2

pyrrole (N–H): β 6.1, α 6.5

thiophene (S): β 7.1, α 7.2

furan (O): β 6.3, α 7.4

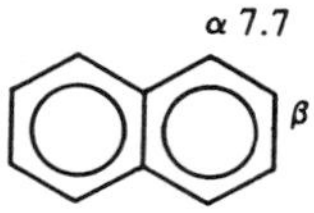

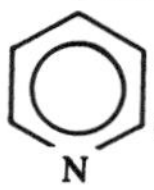

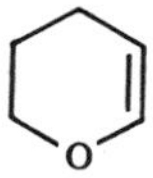

*Alkyne proton signals removed on deuteriation, and δ values increased by a trace of pyridine.

Table 15.5 Influence of functional group X on the chemical shift of protons on benzene rings (benzene δ 7.27)

X	ortho	meta	para
$-CH_3$, R	−0.15	−0.1	−0.1
—=	+0.2	+0.2	+0.2
−COOH, −COOR	+0.8	+0.15	+0.2
−CN	+0.3	+0.3	+0.3
$-CONH_2$	+0.5	+0.2	+0.2
−COR	+0.6	+0.3	+0.3
−SR	+0.1	−0.1	−0.2
$-NH_2$, −NHR	−0.8	−0.15	−0.4
$-N(CH_3)_2$	−0.5	−0.2	−0.5
−I	+0.3	−0.2	−0.1
−CHO	+0.7	+0.2	+0.4
−Br	0	0	0
−NHCOR	+0.4	−0.2	−0.3
−Cl	0	0	0
$-NH_3^+$	+0.4	+0.2	+0.2
−OR	−0.2	−0.2	−0.2
−OH	−0.4	−0.4	−0.4
−OCOR	+0.2	−0.1	−0.2
$-NO_2$	+1.0	+0.3	+0.4
$-SO_3H$, $-SO_2Cl$, $-SO_2NH_2$, etc.	+0.4	+0.1	+0.1

Table 15.6 Proton chemical shifts (δ) for OH, NH and SH groups

Protons of NH, OH and SH groups show special characteristics. All are removed by deuteriation (see page 53) and all are affected by solvent, temperature and concentration (see pages 57–59). Signals for ROH protons will appear as a singlet or as a multiplet, depending on whether coupling to neighbour protons is observed (see page 70). Primary amines with concentrated sulphuric acid are completely protonated (to RNH_3^+): proton exchange is suppressed, and the signal 'disappears' because of coupling to ^{14}N, with $J_{NH} \approx 50$ Hz (see page 75). Secondary and tertiary amines with concentrated sulphuric acid give a sharpened line at low field, because ^{14}N relaxation is so rapid that no N–H coupling is observable.

ROH	0.5–5.0	Higher for enols (11.0–16.0) Lines often broadened
ArOH	4.5	Raised by hydrogen bonding to ≈ 9.0 Chelated OH, ≈11.0
RCOOH, ArCOOH	10.0–13.0	
RNH_2, RNHR'	5.0–8.0	Lines usually broadened
$ArNH_2$, ArNHR'	3.5–6.0	Occasionally raised. Lines usually broadened
$RCONH_2$, RCONHR'	5.0–8.5	Lines frequently very broad, and even unobservable
RCONHCOR'	9.0–12.0	Lines broadened
RSH	1.0–2.0	
ArSH	3.0–4.0	
=NOH	10.0–12.0	Often broadened

Table 15.7 Proton–proton coupling constants

System	J/Hz	System	J/Hz
(*gem*)	6–18 depending on the electronegativities of the attached groups (note: $O=C\langle^H_H$, 42)		$^2J_{ae}$ 10
$CH_a{-}CH_b$ (*vic*)	depends on dihedral angle: see section 4.6.2		$^3J_{aa}$ 10–13
			$^3J_{ae}$ 2–5
	0–7		$^4J_{ee}$ 1–2
(*cis*)	5–14		$^4J_{ac}$ 8
			$^4J_{bc}$ 0.2
(*trans*)	11–19		$^4J_{ab}$ 18
	4–10		$^nJ_{ab}$ <1 usually $^4J > {}^6J > {}^5J$
(*cis or trans*)	allylic 0–2		$^4J_{ab}$ 0.6
	10–13		
	ortho, 7–10 *meta*, 2–3 *para*, 0–1		

Carbon-13 Data

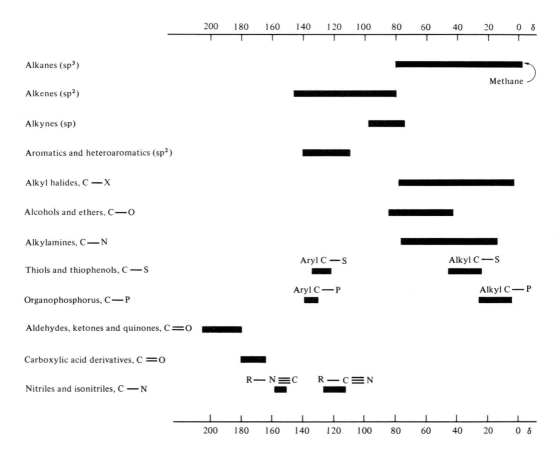

Figure 15.1 ^{13}C chemical shift summary chart (δ values)

Table 15.8 ^{13}C Chemical shifts (δ) in alkane groups

Representative Alkanes and Cycloalkanes

Methane CH.	δ −2.3	ethane CH$_3$CH$_3$ $\quad$ δ 5.7

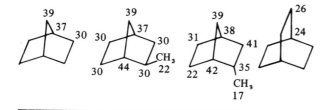

16 15 $\quad$ 15 propane	25 $\quad$ 13 13 $\quad$ 25 butane	24 25 24 $\quad$ 24 isobutane	23 $\quad$ 29.5 14 $\quad$ 33 $\quad$ ( )n long alkyl chain

Cycloalkanes

Ring size	3	4	5	6	7	8	9	10
Shift (δ)	−2.9	23.3	26.5	27.3	29	28	27	26

Bicycloalkanes

Empirical predictions for other alkane carbons

Chemical Shift (δ) = Constant + $\Sigma\alpha$ + $\Sigma\gamma$ + $\Sigma\delta$

α-carbons − the increment varies for CH$_2$, CH and C carbons

α-CH$_3$ groups ⎫
β-carbons $\quad$ ⎬ do not count these (the constant includes them)
$\quad$ ⎭

	Constant	Increment for each carbon substituent				
		α-carbons			γ-carbons	δ-carbons
		−CH$_2$−	−CH−	−C−		
−CH$_3$ carbons	6.80	9.56	17.83	25.48	−2.99	0.49
−CH$_2$−carbons	15.34	9.75	16.70	21.43	−2.69	0.25
−CH−carbons	23.46	6.60	11.14	14.70	−2.07	0
−C−carbons	27.77	2.26	3.96	7.35	0.68	0

Table 15.9 ^{13}C Chemical Shifts (δ) in alkenes

Representative alkenes and cycloalkenes

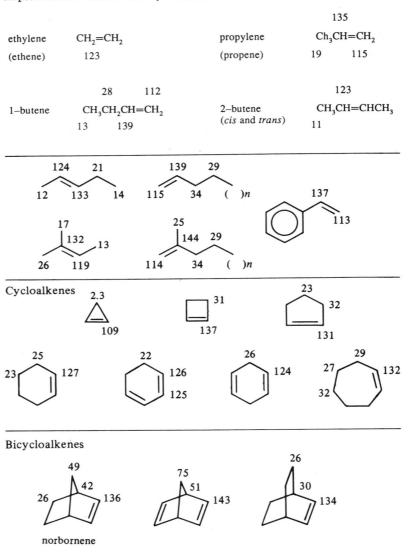

Cycloalkenes

Bicycloalkenes

Table 15.9 (continued)

Empirical predictions for other alkene carbons

Chemical shift (δ) = 123 = Σ (increments for carbon atoms)

$$C - C - C - C = C - C - C - C$$

	γ	β	α		α'	β'	γ'
increments	-2	$+7$	$+10$		-8	-2	$+2$

base value   123

Table 15.10 ^{13}C Chemical shifts (δ) in alkynes

Representative alkynes

acetylene (ethyne)	CH≡CH δ 72	
R–C≡CH	R–C≡C–R^1	C$_6$C$_5$–C≡CH
83 66	82	83 78
C$_6$H$_5$–C≡C–R		C$_6$H$_5$–C≡C–C$_6$H$_5$
86		90

Empirical predictions for other alkyne carbons

Chemical shift (δ) = 72 + Σ (increments for carbon atoms)

$$C - C - C - C - C \equiv C - C - C - C - C$$

	δ	γ	β	α		α'	β'	γ'	δ'
increments	$+0.5$	0	$+5$	$+7$		-6	$+2$	-1	$+0.5$

base value 72

Table 15.11 ^{13}C Chemical shifts (δ) in aromatic and heterocyclic molecules

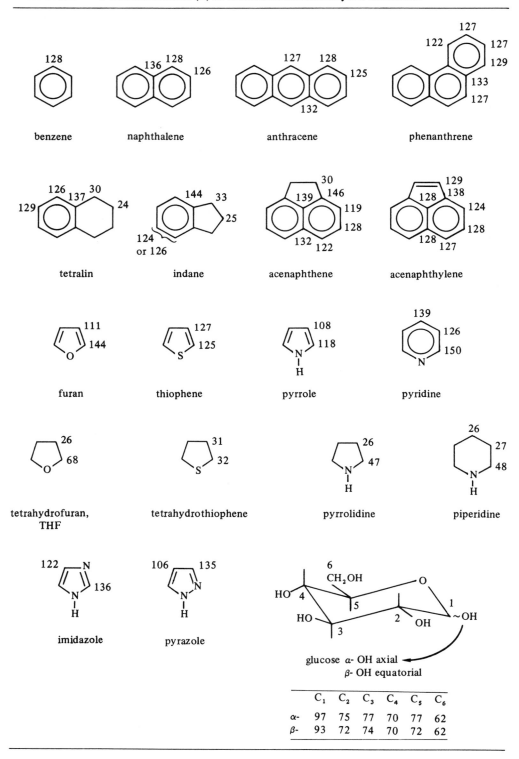

	C_1	C_2	C_3	C_4	C_5	C_6
α-	97	75	77	70	77	62
β-	93	72	74	70	72	62

Table 15.12 Influence of functional group X on the chemical shift of nearby carbons in alkane chains $\left(\begin{array}{c} X-C-C-C-C- \\ \alpha \quad \beta \quad \gamma \end{array}\right)$

X	α-shift			β-shift	γ-shift
	X–CH$_2$–	X–CH– | R	X–C– R|...R		
	1° or	2° or	3°		
–CH$_3$	9	6	3	9	–3
–R see table 15.8					
axial –CH$_3$	1	–	–	5	–6
equatorial –CH$_3$	6	–	–	9	0
(in cyclohexanes)					
–CH=CH$_2$	22	16	12	7	–2
–C≡CH	4	–	–	3	–3
–C$_6$H$_5$, –Ar	23	17	11	10	–3
–F	70	–	–	8	–7
–Cl	31	35	42	10	–5
–Br	19	28	37	11	–4
–I	–7 to –20	–	–	11	–2
–NH$_2$, –NHR, –NR$_2$	29	24	18	11	–4
–NO$_2$	62	–	–	3	–5
–NHCOR, –NRCOR	10	–	–	0	0
–NH$_3$+	25	–	–	7	–3
–CN	3	4	–	2	–3
–SH	2	–	–	2	–2
–OH	50	45	40	9	–3
–OR	50	24	17	10	–6
–OCOR	52	50	45	7	–6
–COOH, –COOR, –CON$\langle$	20	16	13	2	–3
–COR, –CHO	30	24	17	2	–3
–SO$_3$H, –SO$_2$N$\langle$	50	–	–	3	0

Table 15.13   Influence of functional group X on the chemical shift of nearby carbons in alkene groups and benzene rings

Base values: for alkenes, δ 123 (ethylene)
for benzenes, δ 128 (benzene)

X	Alkenes		Benzenes			
	C-1	C-2	C-1 (ipso)	ortho	meta	para
$-CH_3$	10	-8	9	0	0	-2
R, ⌇⌇⌇	16	-8	15	0	0	-2
R, ⌇⌇⌇	23	-8	21	0	0	-2
$-CH=CH_2$	15	-6	9	0	0	-2
$-CH\equiv CH$	$-$	$-$	-6	4	0	0
$-C_6H_5$, $-Ar$	13	-11	13	-1	1	-1
$-F$	25	-34	35	-14	1	-5
$-Cl$	3	-6	6	0	1	-2
$-Br$	-8	-1	-5	3	2	-2
$-I$	-38	7	-32	10	3	-1
$-NH_2$	$-$	$-$	18	-13	1	-10
$-NHR$	$-$	$-$	20	-14	1	-10
$-NR_2$	$-$	$-$	22	-16	1	-10
$-NO_2$	22	-1	20	-5	1	6
$-NHCOR$, $-NRCOR$	$-$	$-$	10	-7	1	-4
$-CN$	-15	15	-16	4	1	6
$-SH$	$-$	$-$	4	1	1	-3
$-OH$	$-$	$-$	27	-13	1	-7
$-OR$	29	-39	30	-15	1	-8
$-OCOR$	18	-27	23	-6	1	-2
$-COOH$, $-COOR$, $-CON\diagdown$	4	9	2	2	0	5
$-COR$, $-CHO$	14	13	9	1	1	6
$-SO_3H$, $-SO_2N\diagdown$	$-$	$-$	16	0	0	4
$-PMe_2$	$-$	$-$	14	1.6	0	-1
$-PAr_2$	$-$	$-$	9	5	0	0

Table 15.14 ^{13}C Chemical shifts (δ) in carbonyl groups
Solvent shifts, $\pm 2\delta$, are commonly observed

R—CHO	aliphatic aldehydes*	200–205
Ar—CHO ⎫ ⫽—CHO ⎬	aryl and conjugated aldehydes*	190–194
R—CO—R′	dialkyl ketones	205–218
Ar—CO—R ⎫ Ar—CO—Ar ⎬ ⫽—CO— ⎭	aryl and conjugated ketones	196–199

cyclohexanone derivatives — 209–213

cyclopentanone derivatives — 214–220

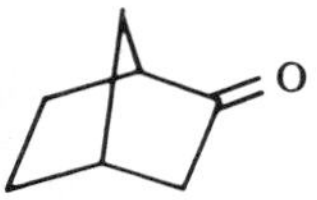

bicyclic ketones — 215–219

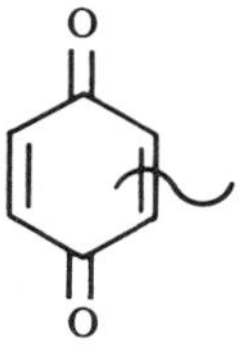

simple quinones — 180–187

R—COOH ⎫ R—COO⊖ ⎬	carboxylic acids and salts	166–181
R—COO—R′	aliphatic esters	169–176
Ar—COOAr ⎫ ⫽—COO—⫽ ⎬	esters with conjugation in the acid *or* alcohol moiety	164–169
lactones	lactones	170–178
—CO—O—CO—	anhydrides, all classes	163–175
—CON⟨	amides, all classes including lactams	162–184
—CO—NH—CO—	imides	168–179
—COCl	acyl chlorides, all classes	167–172
—NH—CO—NH—	ureas	153–163
—O—CO—O—	carbonates	152–156

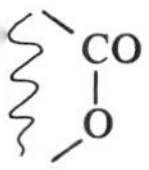

*Aldehyde CO shows a doublet in off-resonance decoupled spectra.
Note: furan-2-aldehyde, δ CO, 177.

Table 15.15 ^{13}C Chemical shifts (δ) for carbons in various multiple-bonded environments

R—C≡N	nitriles	114–124
R—N≡C	isonitriles	156–158
R—N=C=O	isocyanates	120–130
⟩C=NOH	oximes	148–158
⟩C=NNHCONH₂	semicarbazones	158–160
⟩C=NNH—	hydrazones	145–149
CH₂ 2.7 ‖ C 195 ‖ O	ketene	
CH₂ 75 ‖ C 214 ‖ CH₂ 75	allene	C_1 and C_3 show α-substituent effects similar to alkenes — Ranges: C_1 and C_3, 80–125; C_2 200–220
—N=C=N—	carbodiimides	140
M(CO)$_n$	metal carbonyls	190–230
C_3O_2	carbon suboxide	−14.6

Table 15.16 ^{13}C Chemical shifts (δ) for methyl groups in common environments

$CH_3 - Ar$	side-chain	20–21
$CH_3 - OAr$	aryl ethers	56
$CH_3 - OR$	alkyl ethers	59

$$CH_3 - \overset{\overset{\displaystyle O}{\|}}{C} - R \qquad \text{Me ketones} \qquad 26\text{–}31$$

$$CH_3 - \overset{\overset{\displaystyle O}{\|}}{C} - O - R \qquad \text{acetates} \qquad 20\text{–}22$$

$$CH_3 - O - \overset{\overset{\displaystyle O}{\|}}{C} - R \qquad \text{Me esters} \qquad 51\text{–}52$$

$$CH_3 - N{\Big\langle} \qquad \text{2° and 3° amines} \qquad 30\text{–}45$$

$$CH_3 - \overset{\overset{\displaystyle O}{\|}}{C} - N{\Big\langle} \qquad \text{acetamides} \qquad 24$$

$$CH_3 - {\Big\rangle} N - \overset{\overset{\displaystyle O}{\|}}{C} - R \qquad \text{2° and 3° amides} \qquad 31\text{–}39$$

(Note: $CH_3 - NH - COOEt$ 15)

$$\underset{X}{\overset{CH_3}{\diagup}}{=}\diagdown \qquad \text{where X is halogen, CN, CO} \qquad 13\text{–}19$$

Note:

$$\underset{17\ CH_3 \quad\ CH_3\ 13}{\overset{26\ CH_3 \qquad H}{\diagup\ \diagdown}}{=}$$

steric effects difficult to predict

Table 15.17 ^{13}C–^1H Coupling constants. The values given are near average. Electronegative substituents, and increasing bond angle strain both cause increases in the coupling constants

System		J/Hz
$-\overset{\mid}{\underset{\mid}{C}}-H$	$^1J_{CH}$	125
Cl_3C-H		208
$\overset{\diagdown}{\diagup}C=\underset{\diagdown}{C}-H$		150–80
⬡—H		160
$-C\equiv C-H$		250
$-O-\overset{\mid}{\underset{\mid}{C}}-H$		140
$\overset{\diagdown}{\diagup}N-\overset{\mid}{\underset{\mid}{C}}-H$		133
$O=\underset{\mid}{C}-H$		170–220
$N\equiv C-H$		270
$-\overset{\mid}{\underset{\mid}{C}}-\overset{\mid}{\underset{\mid}{C}}-H$	$^2J_{CH}$	10
$O=\overset{\mid}{\underset{\mid}{C}}-\overset{\mid}{\underset{\mid}{C}}-H$		0–30
$-\overset{\mid}{\underset{\mid}{C}}-\overset{\mid}{\underset{\mid}{C}}-$	$^1J_{CC}$	35
$\overset{\diagdown}{\diagup}C=C\overset{\diagup}{\diagdown}$		80
$-C\equiv C-$		55 (170 in HC≡CH)
$O=C-\overset{\mid}{\underset{\mid}{C}}-$		50–60
$\underset{⬡}{C-C}$		55–60

Table 15.18 ^{13}C Relaxation times – T_1 (in seconds). The values given are approximate, since many literature values differ. T_1 is temperature dependent: most measurements were made around 30°C

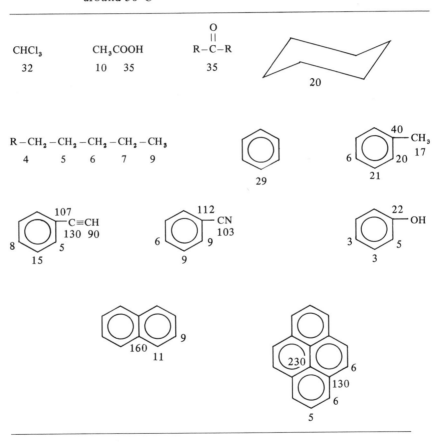

CHCl$_3$ CH$_3$COOH   O
                                          ‖
32   10   35   R–C–R

                                          35   20

R–CH$_2$–CH$_2$–CH$_2$–CH$_2$–CH$_3$

   4   5   6   7   9

                                                                           40
                                                                              CH$_3$
                                                                           20   17
                                                                     6
                                                29   21

        107   112   22
          C≡CH   CN   OH
        130 90   103
   8   5   6   9   3   5
        15   9   3

          160   9
                 11   230
                                                        6
                                                     130
                                                        6

                                                     5

Other Data

Table 15.19   Solvents used in NMR work

Solvent	Approximate δ for ^{1}H equivalent (as contaminant)	^{13}C δ value(s)	b.p./°C	f.p./°C
acetic acid-d_4	13 and 2	21, 177	118	16.6
acetone-d_6	2	30, 205	56	−95
acetonitrile-d_3	2	0.3, 117	82	−44
benzene-d_6	7.3	128	80	5.5
carbon disulphide	−	193	46	−108.5
carbon tetrachloride	−	97	77	−23
chloroform-d	7.3	77	61	−63
deuterium oxide	4.7–5	−	101.5	3.8
dimethylsulphoxide-d_6	2	43	189	18
methanol-d_4 (CD$_3$OD)	3.4	49	65	−98
hexachloroacetone	−	124, 126	203	−2
pyridine-d_5	7.5	124 to 150	115	−42
toluene-d_8	7.3 and 2.4	21, 125 to 138	110	−95
trifluoroacetic acid-d	13	115, 163 (quartets)	72	−15
dioxane	3.7	67	101	11.8

Table 15.20   Greek alphabet

Capital	Small (or lower case)	Name	Capital	Small (or lower case)	Name
A	α	alpha	N	ν	nu
B	β	beta	Ξ	ξ	xi
Γ	γ	gamma	O	o	omicron
Δ	δ	delta	Π	π	pi
E	ϵ	epsilon	P	ρ	rho
Z	ζ	zeta	Σ	σ	sigma
H	η	eta	T	τ	tau
Θ	θ	theta	Υ	υ	upsilon
I	ι	iota	Φ	ϕ	phi
K	κ	kappa	X	χ	chi
Λ	λ	lambda	Ψ	ψ	psi
M	μ	mu	Ω	ω	omega

Further Reading

1. OF HISTORICAL INTEREST

Purcell, E. M., Torrey, H. C. and Pound, R. V., *Phys. Rev.*, **69**, 37 (1946)

Bloch, F., Hansen, W. W. and Packard, M., *Phys. Rev.*, **69**, 127 (1946)

Bloch, F., *Phys. Rev.*, **70**, 460 (1946)

Arnold, J. T., Dharmatti, S. S. and Packard, M., *J. Chem. Phys.*, **19**, 507 (1951)

The first two of these papers are the original announcements of successful NMR observation, the third is extensive (and includes all of the mathematics of the Bloch equations); the fourth paper is the first report of proton chemical shift within the same molecule. All make fascinating reading, and portray the tentative beginnings of the method with appealing understatement.

2. LESS COMPREHENSIVE NMR DISCUSSIONS

Kemp, W., *Organic Spectroscopy*, 2nd edn, Macmillan, Basingstoke (1987), chapter 3

Williams, D. H. and Fleming, I., *Spectroscopic Methods in Organic Chemistry*, 3rd edn, McGraw-Hill, London (1980), chapter 3

Dyke, S. S., Floyd, A. J., Sainsbury, M. and Theobald, R. S., *Organic Spectroscopy: An Introduction*, Longman, London (1978), chapter 4

All of these books emphasise the interpretive approach in organic structure determination. Physical chemistry discussion on fundamentals can be found in the following.

Banwell, C. N., *Fundamentals of Molecular Spectroscopy*, 2nd edn, McGraw-Hill, London (1972)

McLaughlan, K. A., *Magnetic Resonance*, Clarendon Press, Oxford (1972)

Atkins, P. W., *Physical Chemistry*, 2nd edn, Oxford University Press, Oxford (1982)

3. MORE PHYSICAL NMR DISCUSSIONS

Harris, R. K., *Nuclear Magnetic Resonance Spectroscopy*, Pitman, London (1983)

Günther, H., *NMR Spectroscopy*, John Wiley, Chichester (1980)

Abraham, R. J. and Loftus, P., *Proton and Carbon-13 NMR Spectroscopy*, Heyden, London (1978)

Becker, E. D., *High Resolution NMR*, Academic Press, New York (1980)

Theory and instrumental details are treated mathematically in these texts, with less emphasis on structural application of the method.

4. MORE COMPREHENSIVE NMR DISCUSSIONS

Emsley, J. W., Feeney, J. and Sutcliffe, L. H., *High Resolution NMR Spectroscopy*, Pergamon Press, Oxford (1965)

Harris, R. K. and Mann, B. E., *NMR and the Periodic Table*, Academic Press, London (1978)

Müllen, K. and Pregosin, P. S., *Fourier Transform NMR Techniques*, Academic Press, London (1976)

Levy, G. C., Lichter, R. L. and Nelson, G. L., *Carbon-13 Nuclear Magnetic Resonance Spectroscopy*, 2nd edn, John Wiley, New York (1980)

Shaw, D., *Fourier Transform NMR Spectroscopy*, 2nd edn, Elsevier, Amsterdam (1987)

Breitmaier, E. and Voelter, W., *Carbon-13 NMR Spectroscopy*, 3rd edn, VCH Publishers (UK), Cambridge (1987)

Morrill, T. C., (Ed.), *Lanthanide Shift Reagents in Stereochemical Analysis*, VCH Publishers (UK), Cambridge (1987)

Levy, G. C. and Lichter, R. L., *Nitrogen-15 Nuclear Magnetic Resonance Spectroscopy*, John Wiley, New York (1979)

Bax, A. D., *Two-dimensional Nuclear Magnetic Resonance in Liquids*, D. Reidel, London (1982)

Gadian, D. G., *NMR and Living Systems*, Clarendon Press, Oxford (1982)

Sandström, J., *Dynamic NMR Spectroscopy*, Academic Press, London (1982)

Evans, E. A. (Ed.), *Tritium NMR Spectroscopy and Applications*, John Wiley, Chichester (1985)

There are also several research journals (both primary and review type) but these are in general intended for a readership of considerable expertise in NMR, and mainly deal with the phenomenon itself, rather than its application. The Royal Society of Chemistry publishes a series of *Specialist Periodical Reports on Nuclear Magnetic Resonance*.

Pergamon Press, Oxford, publish *Progress in Nuclear Magnetic Resonance Spectroscopy*, edited by J. W. Emsley, J. Feeney and L. H. Sutcliffe: this is a very important source of review papers.

Academic Press publish the *Journal of Magnetic Resonance* and also *Annual Reports in NMR Spectroscopy*, edited currently by G. A. Webb. John Wiley publish *Topics in Carbon-13 NMR Spectroscopy* and *Magnetic Resonance in Chemistry*.

Sadtler Guide to Carbon-13 NMR Spectra, Heyden, London. Carbon-13 spectra for 500 compounds are given, with tabular listing of another 500 by chemical shift.

Sadtler Guide to the NMR Spectra of Polymers, Heyden, London. Proton NMR spectra of representative commercial polymers (plastics, fibres, lubricants, surfactants). Useful for fingerprint comparisons.

Sadtler Spectra Handbook of Esters, Heyden, London. Given the vast number of esters (tens of thousands) this selection of 2000 proton NMR spectra is a valuable companion volume to a collection of infrared spectra of the same compounds: used mainly for fingerprint identifications.

Wiberg, K. B. and Nist, B. J., *The Interpretation of NMR Spectra*, Benjamin, New York (1962). Contains many fully analysed non-first order proton spectra.

5. COLLECTIONS OF NMR SPECTRA

It is nearly essential to have access to spectral catalogues, to gain experience and confidence in tackling proton and carbon-13 assignments.

NMR Spectra Catalog, Volumes 1 and 2, Varian Associates, Palo Alto. This consists of 700 assigned proton spectra, all recorded at 60 MHz CW.

Aldrich Library of NMR Spectra, Aldrich Chemical Co., Milwaukee. This also is exclusively proton NMR spectra (8500 in total). 2 volumes, 2nd edition.

Johnson, L. F. and Jankowski, W. C., *Carbon-13 NMR Spectra*, Krieger Publishing, Florida (copyright 1972 by John Wiley). This is a collection of 500 proton decoupled carbon-13 NMR spectra, with assignments.

Sadtler Standard Spectra are collected in a continuously updated publication which includes infrared, ultraviolet, proton NMR and carbon-13 NMR spectra. This is an invaluable reference, from which the following are extracts:

Sadtler Handbook of Proton NMR Spectra, Heyden, London. A collection of 3000 spectra.

Sadtler Guide to NMR Spectra, Heyden, London. This guide contains brief discussions on the features of proton NMR spectra. It has 480 proton NMR spectra, with tabular listing of 130 compounds which give a single resonance signal.

6. COLLECTIONS OF NMR DATA

NMR data in tabular form, while more comprehensively available, are often overwhelming in scope. Several such compilations exist.

Handbook of NMR Spectral Parameters (proton only), Heyden, London (1979)

Atlas of Carbon-13 NMR Data, Heyden, London (1979)

Bremser, W., Ernst, L., Fachinger, W., Gerhards, R., Hardt, A. and Lewis, P. M. E., *Carbon-13 NMR Spectral Data*, 4th edn, VCH Publishers (UK), Cambridge (1987)

Brevard, C. and Granger, P., *Handbook of High Resolution Multinuclear NMR*, John Wiley, London (1981). Mainly aimed at instrument operators, setting out guidelines for machine parameter adjustments.

7. PHYSICS AND MATHEMATICS

Excellent supplementary texts, going far beyond the minimum needed for a basic understanding of NMR, are:

Purcell, E. M., *Electricity and Magnetism*, McGraw-Hill, New York (1965)

Troup, G. J., *Mechanics*, Longmans, Victoria, Australia

Brigham, E. O., *The Fast Fourier Transform*, Prentice Hall, New Jersey (1974)

Answers to Problem Examples

CHAPTER 1

1.1 Proton at 100 MHz, 2 signals. Carbon-13 at 25 MHz, 2 signals. Oxygen-17 at 13.5 MHz, 1 signal. Nitrogen-15 at 10 MHz, 1 signal.

1.2 (a) 1.4 T, (b) 4.7 T, (c) 14 T.

1.3 δ 1.3 and δ 4.0, 540 Hz apart.

1.4 δ 30 and δ 70, 2000 Hz apart.

1.5 For acetophenone, (a) ^1H around δ 7 and 1–4, (b) ^{13}C around δ 0–60, δ 120 (aromatic) and δ 180–200 (CO).

For acetamide (a) ^1H around δ 1–4, (b) ^{13}C around δ 0–60 and δ 180–200 (CO). ^{15}N around 100–150 ppm to higher frequency than liquid ammonia at 25°C.

1.6 Five times those for 1.4 T, that is 0.1 J mol^{-1} for proton and 0.025 J mol^{-1} for carbon-13.

CHAPTER 2

2.1 Taking the precessional frequency of carbon-13 approximately one quarter that of proton, the same is true for γ, which for carbon-13 is therefore approximately 0.67×10^8 rad T^{-1} s^{-1}. A more exact figure is given in the Appendix. γ does not change with field.

2.2 1.4 (approximately).

2.3 μ for the electron is 1837 times that for the proton, that is 9.27×10^{-24} J T^{-1}. This is named the Bohr magneton, μ_B.

2.4 32°, 59.5°, 80.2°.

2.5 Methylamine has a stronger dipole than ammonia, and we might expect a stronger electric field gradient. Because of the high symmetry of the tetrahedral ammonium ion the ^{14}N nucleus will not be significantly oriented by field gradients.

2.6 (a) 57 ppm, (b) 85 ppm.

2.7 (a) 28 ppm, (b) 13 ppm.

CHAPTER 3

3.2 1 ppm at 100 MHz is 100 Hz; 10 ppm = 1 kHz. 1 ppm at 25 MHz is 25 Hz; 200 ppm = 5 kHz.

3.3 2 kHz for proton, 10 kHz for carbon-13.

3.4 (a) 0.24 and (b) 0.12 Hz per data point.

3.5 1024.

CHAPTER 4

4.1 Only at low temperatures do the axial and equatorial environments have sufficiently long life times to enable distinctions to be made in NMR.

4.2 In enols, 2; in keto, 2. (In practice the $CH_3 CO$ signals overlap, so five signals only are seen.)

4.3 The δ values are (a) 3.3, (b) 3.7, (c) 0.9.

4.4 The δ values are (a) 2.1, (b) 3.3, (c) 2.6.

4.5 The δ values are (a) 3.8, (b) 2.9, (c) 2.6.

4.6 The δ values are (a) 2.0, 4.1 and (0.9 + 0.4). (b) (1.5 + 1.7 + 1.3), (0.9 + 0.3 + 0.35). (c) 2.6, (1.3 + 0.3), 0.9. (d) (1.2 + 1.3 + 1.7), 3.3 (not 3.7).

4.7 (a) 7.8, 6.6, (b) 9.9, (c) 9.6.

4.8 (a) 7.47, 7.47, 7.47, (b) 7.97, 7.47, 7.67, (c) 7.12, 7.17, 7.17.

4.10 Methyl isobutanoate (methyl isobutyrate) $CH_3 OCOCH(CH_3)_2$.

4.11 7 Hz.

4.12 (a) Phosphorus-31, ten lines; proton, doublet. (b) Carbon-13: the CF_3 carbon will be a wide quartet of doublets, and the COOH carbon a narrow quartet of doublets. (Note that without the $^{13}C–^{13}C$ doublet splitting, the spectrum would be as in figure 5.10. The fluorine-19 signal will be split widely into a quartet, and each line of this then splits into narrow quartets.)

4.13 (a) AA'BB'C, (b) ABCD, (c) AA'BB'B''B''''

4.15 (a) triplet, 1:2:1 (b) triplet of doublets, 1:1:2:2:1:1.

4.16 (a) Nothing, except perhaps a shift in the OH signal, (b) the OH signal will 'disappear', and the HOD signal appears near δ 4.7, (c) same as in (b).

4.17 CH_3 (triplet), $CH_2 NO_2$ (triplet), middle CH_2 (sextet).

4.18 Table 15.4 gives A, δ 7.0 (observed δ 6.75); M, δ 5.3 (observed δ 5.7) and X, δ 5.3 (observed δ 5.3).

Table 15.5 gives all ring protons at δ 7.47 (observed δ 7.3). J_{AM} = 22 Hz; J_{AX} = 12 Hz; J_{MX} = 2 Hz.

4.19 Five lines, 1:2:3:2:1.

4.20 Br has a strong quadrupole, and ethyl bromide has a large field gradient: Br follows the electric field and is decoupled from proton.

4.21 Estimated δ values, 6.55 and 8.10. $\Delta\nu$ = 93. Estimated J, 10 Hz. $\Delta\nu:J \approx 9.3$.

4.22 $\Delta\nu$ is 3.6 MHz. J = 9 Hz. $\Delta\nu:J = 4 \times 10^5$

4.23 At the CH_3 resonance frequency.

4.24 The spectrum has some non-first order features, but it can be analysed as if for first order as follows. The alkene protons couple, giving doublets; when the CH_3 and CHO protons are decoupled (triple resonance) this is all that remains (top left). Double resonance has removed the CH_3 quartet splittings; the CHO splits *only* the nearer alkene proton (into a double doublet). In the fully coupled spectrum, the CH_3 splits the nearer alkene proton strongly (quartets) while the double doublet of the alkene proton near aldehyde is split into narrow quartets.

4.25 J (measured) = 18 Hz, which indicates *trans*.

Additional Problems

1. $ClCH_2 CH_2 CH_2 Cl$.
2. $CH_3 CH_2 CH(Cl)NO_2$.
3. Salicylic acid sulphonates *para* to the OH group.
4. $C_6 H_4$ group: *ortho* to NO_2 at δ 8.2, *meta* to NO_2 at δ 7.6. Cyclopentadienyl group: nearest phenyl, at δ 5.5; other two at δ 5.8. (Without empirical data these could not be predicted.)
5. $C_6 H_5 CH(NH_2)CH_3$.
6. (a) Restricted rotation, (b) diastereotopicity.
7. *p*-bromophenetole, p-$BrC_6 H_4 OEt$.

CHAPTER 5

5.1 The calculated δ values (with observed values in brackets) are (a) C-1 and C-6 22.13 (23); note the line intensity is nearly double that of other signals since two carbons are present. (b) C-2 27.99 (28). (c) C-3 41.79 (42). (d) C-4 19.71 (21). (e) C-5 14.35 (14).

5.2 The calculated δ values (with observed values in brackets) are 131 (132) and 117 (119).

5.3 The calculated δ values, based on the *calculated* values from problem example 5.1 (with observed values in brackets) are (a) C-1 14 + 9 = 23 (24), (b) C-2 20 + 45 = 65 (66), (c) C-3 42 + 9 = 51 (49), (d) C-4 28 − 3 = 25 (25) remaining two methyl groups unaffected by the substitution of OH; prediction would therefore leave them at δ 22, but additional means of distinction identifies them as being at different positions as shown in figure 5.6.

5.4 The hydrocarbon skeleton needed for both is 2-methylbutane, whose chemical shifts were calculated in worked example 5.1 to be δ 10, 22 (× 2), 30 and 32. The OH substitutes differently in each case, but the primary alcohol figure is used in both (that is + 50). The δ values for 2-methyl-1-butanol are predicted as 10, 19, 29, 39 and 72. For 3-methyl-1-butanol they are predicted as 22, 22, 27, 41 and 60. The latter is the major constituent, with observed δ values of 23, 23, 25, 42 and 61.

5.5 (a) 25 (15 + 10), 33 (16 + 17) and 25 (15 + 10). (b) 22 (15 + 7), 66 (16 + 50), 22 (15 + 7).

5.6 C-1, 141 (123 + 18), C-2, 96 (123 − 27).

5.7 Vanillin: calculated δ values from C-1 to C-6 are 135, 115, 145, 146, 117 and 122. C-1, C-3 and C-4 are low intensity peaks. This leaves ambiguity between C-2 and C-5, and between C-3 and C-4. Methyl salicylate: calculated δ values from C-1 to C-6 are 117, 157, 115, 134, 121, and 131. C-1 and C-2 are low intensity peaks. This leaves ambiguity between C-3 and C-5.

5.8 (a) In vanillin, δ 190–194, (b) in vinyl acetate, the alcohol part has a double bond 'in conjugation', so δ 164–169, (c) although the acid part is unsaturated, it is not in conjugation, so δ 169–176.

5.9 δ values are (a) vinyl acetate, 20–22, (b) vanillin, 56, (c) methyl salicylate, 51–52.

5.10 C-1 δ 131.8 (77 Hz); C-2 and C-5 δ 132.6 (10.6 Hz); C-3 and C-5 δ 128.5 (12.5 Hz); C-4 δ 131.5 (3.2 Hz).

Additional Problems

2. Benzene shows a 1:1:1 triplet for ^{13}C coupled to one deuteron. Dioxane shows a 1:2:1 triplet for ^{13}C coupled to two protons. Taking the carbon-13 frequency as 75 MHz gives 10 ppm = 750 Hz: as nearly as can be estimated on this scale, $^1J_{CD}$ is 27 Hz and $^1J_{CH}$ is 150 Hz.

3. Since carbon-13 is recorded at 20 MHz, proton is decoupled at 80 MHz and fluorine at 75 MHz. The two carbon resonances are 73.6 ppm apart and at 20 MHz this is 1472 Hz. Thus $^1J_{CF}$ is 320 Hz; $^2J_{CF}$ is 40 Hz; $^1J_{CH}$ is 210 Hz and $^2J_{CH}$ is 5 Hz. (All values taken from the spectrum by estimation.) The CF_3 carbon is a quartet of small triplets, the CH_2 carbon gives a triplet of quartets.

CHAPTER 6

6.1 The A_1 line is associated with transition 1 (figure 6.4) therefore the A_2 line is associated with transition 2. This is regressive with transition 4 (X_2 line split sharply) and progressive with transition 3 (X_1 line split broadly). (Note that the relative signs of J cannot therefore be determined by spin tickling in a simple AX case: three spins are necessary, as in AMX systems.)

6.2 Irradiation at X_1 gives a positive INDOR signal; irradiation at X_2 gives a negative signal.

6.3 14 μs.

6.4 y' magnetisation after a 2 μs pulse is approximately 40% of the 90° pulse (7 μs) the z-magnetisation remains nearly 90% of the M_0 value.

6.5 γ H = 26.75; γ P = 10.8; γ Si = −5.3. Maximum changes in the line intensities from unity are (a) for ^{31}P–$\{^1H\}$ (1 + 1.24) = 2.24 (b) for ^{29}Si–$\{^1H\}$ (1 − 2.52) = −1.52.

CHAPTER 8

8.1 Δt = 1/390 s (0.0026 s). Maximum rate for resolution is 390 times per second: this means that at 100 MHz shorter life-times can be distinguished.

8.2 Same as in worked example 8.2: field makes no difference.

8.3 Estimated $\Delta\nu$ about 7 Hz. t_c = 0.06 s.

CHAPTER 9

9.1 The positions of the quartets are indicated by the numbers on the spectrum of figure 9.4: thus, (a) CF_3 shows four lines at positions 1, 6, 9 and 10, (b) C-1 shows four lines at positions 2, 4, 5 and 7, (c) C-2/C-6 show four lines in the quartet at position 8 and (d) C-3/C-5 show the smallest quartet at position 3.

Appendix of Magnetic Isotopes

Isotope	Spin	Natural abundance (%)	γ (10^7 rad T^{-1} s^{-1})	Sensitivity* Relative to proton	Sensitivity* Absolute (at natural abundance)	Frequency at 2.35 T (MHz)
^{1}H	$\frac{1}{2}$	99.98	26.75	1.00	1.00	100.000
^{2}H	1	1.5×10^{-2}	4.1	9.65×10^{-3}	1.45×10^{-6}	15.351
^{3}H	$\frac{1}{2}$	0	28.5	1.21	0	106.663
^{7}Li	3/2	92.58	10.4	0.29	0.27	38.863
^{9}Be	3/2	100	-3.8	1.39×10^{-2}	1.39×10^{-2}	14.053
^{11}B	3/2	80.42	8.6	0.17	0.13	32.084
^{13}C	$\frac{1}{2}$	1.108	6.73	1.59×10^{-2}	1.76×10^{-4}	25.144
^{14}N	1	99.63	1.9	1.01×10^{-3}	1.01×10^{-3}	7.224
^{15}N	$\frac{1}{2}$	0.37	-2.7	1.04×10^{-3}	3.85×10^{-6}	10.133
^{17}O	5/2	3.7×10^{-2}	-3.6	2.91×10^{-2}	1.08×10^{-5}	13.557
^{19}F	$\frac{1}{2}$	100	25.2	0.83	0.83	94.077
^{23}Na	3/2	100	7.1	9.25×10^{-2}	9.25×10^{-2}	26.451
^{27}Al	5/2	100	7.0	0.21	0.21	26.057
^{29}Si	$\frac{1}{2}$	4.7	-5.3	7.84×10^{-3}	3.69×10^{-4}	19.865
^{31}P	$\frac{1}{2}$	100	10.8	6.63×10^{-2}	6.63×10^{-2}	40.481
^{33}S	3/2	0.76	2.1	2.26×10^{-3}	1.72×10^{-5}	7.670
^{35}Cl	3/2	75.53	2.6	4.70×10^{-3}	3.55×10^{-3}	9.798
^{37}Cl	3/2	24.47	2.2	2.71×10^{-3}	6.63×10^{-4}	8.156
^{39}K	3/2	93.1	1.2	5.08×10^{-4}	4.73×10^{-4}	4.667
^{51}V	7/2	99.76	7.0	0.38	0.38	26.289
^{55}Mn	5/2	100	6.6	0.18	0.18	24.664
^{57}Fe	$\frac{1}{2}$	2.19	0.86	3.37×10^{-5}	7.38×10^{-7}	3.231
^{59}Co	7/2	100	6.3	0.28	0.28	23.614
^{63}Cu	3/2	69.09	7.1	9.31×10^{-2}	6.43×10^{-2}	26.505
^{65}Cu	3/2	30.91	7.6	0.11	3.52×10^{-2}	28.394
^{75}As	3/2	100	4.6	2.51×10^{-2}	2.51×10^{-2}	17.126
^{77}Se	$\frac{1}{2}$	7.58	5.1	6.93×10^{-3}	5.25×10^{-4}	19.067
^{79}Br	3/2	50.54	6.7	7.86×10^{-2}	3.97×10^{-2}	25.053
^{81}Br	3/2	49.46	7.2	9.85×10^{-2}	4.87×10^{-2}	27.006
^{89}Y	$\frac{1}{2}$	100	-1.3	1.18×10^{-4}	1.18×10^{-4}	4.899

Table continued from page 233

Isotope	Spin	Natural abundance (%)	γ (10^7 rad T^{-1} s^{-1})	Sensitivity* Relative to proton	Absolute (at natural abundance)	Frequency at 2.35 T (MHz)
^{95}Mo	5/2	15.72	1.7	3.23×10^{-3}	5.07×10^{-4}	6.514
^{97}Mo	5/2	9.46	−1.8	3.43×10^{-3}	3.24×10^{-4}	6.652
^{103}Rh	$\frac{1}{2}$	100	−0.84	3.11×10^{-5}	3.11×10^{-5}	3.147
^{109}Ag	$\frac{1}{2}$	48.18	−1.3	1.01×10^{-4}	4.86×10^{-5}	4.652
^{113}Cd	$\frac{1}{2}$	12.26	−5.9	1.09×10^{-2}	1.33×10^{-3}	22.182
^{115}Sn	$\frac{1}{2}$	0.35	−10	3.5×10^{-2}	1.22×10^{-4}	32.699
^{117}Sn	$\frac{1}{2}$	7.61	−10	4.52×10^{-2}	3.44×10^{-3}	35.625
^{119}Sn	$\frac{1}{2}$	8.58	−10	5.18×10^{-2}	4.44×10^{-3}	37.272
^{125}Te	$\frac{1}{2}$	6.99	−8.4	3.15×10^{-2}	2.20×10^{-3}	31.596
^{127}I	5/2	100	5.4	9.34×10^{-2}	9.34×10^{-2}	20.007
^{129}Xe	$\frac{1}{2}$	26.44	−7.4	2.12×10^{-2}	5.60×10^{-3}	27.660
^{135}Ba	3/2	6.59	2.7	4.90×10^{-3}	3.22×10^{-4}	9.934
^{137}Ba	3/2	11.32	3.0	6.86×10^{-3}	7.76×10^{-4}	11.113
^{169}Tm	$\frac{1}{2}$	100	−2.2	5.66×10^{-4}	5.66×10^{-4}	8.271
^{171}Yb	$\frac{1}{2}$	14.31	4.7	5.46×10^{-3}	7.81×10^{-4}	17.613
^{183}W	$\frac{1}{2}$	14.4	1.1	7.20×10^{-4}	1.03×10^{-5}	4.161
^{187}Os	$\frac{1}{2}$	1.64	0.6	1.22×10^{-5}	2.00×10^{-7}	2.303
^{195}Pt	$\frac{1}{2}$	33.8	5.8	9.94×10^{-3}	3.36×10^{-3}	21.499
^{199}Hg	$\frac{1}{2}$	16.84	4.8	5.67×10^{-3}	9.54×10^{-4}	17.827
^{205}Tl	$\frac{1}{2}$	70.5	15.4	0.19	0.13	57.708
^{207}Pb	$\frac{1}{2}$	22.6	5.6	9.16×10^{-3}	2.07×10^{-3}	20.921

*Sensitivity *relative to proton* varies with the cube of the ratio of magnetogyric ratios. *Absolute sensitivity* is found by multiplying relative sensitivity by the natural abundance. See section 3.6.2.

Compendium of Acronyms in NMR

We live in an acronymous age, but these shorthand collections of letters (*Greek – akros*, tip, and *onyma*, name) are often as much designed to amuse as to inform. They have a correct usefulness, provided they are defined in context. The following short listing includes only those acronyms used in (or having relevance to) the book: a recent listing of computer simulation programmes in NMR gives several hundreds, and a typical chemical catalogue will contain many thousand others. For uniformity, all abbreviations and acronyms in this book have been given in upper case letters, without full points (except ppm!).

ACAC	acetylacetone (or —ato)
ADC	analogue-to-digital converter
ADEPT	automatic analysis of distortionless enhancement by polarisation transfer spectrum (see DEPT)
ASTM	American Society for Testing and Materials
ATP	adenosine triphosphate
BB	broad band
CABSA	connectivity by AB satellite analysis; see CCCP
CAN	compendium of acronyms in NMR
CAT	computer for averaging of transients
CCCP	carbon–carbon connectivity plot (for Russian readers, Union of Soviet Socialist Republics); see CABSA
CIDNP	chemically induced dynamic nuclear polarisation
COSMIC	computer originated structure models from INADEQUATE-derived coupling data
COSY	correlation spectroscopy
Cp	cyclopentadene (or —yl)
CP	cross polarisation
CPMAS	CP with MAS
CPMG	Carr–Purcell–Meiboom–Gill pulse train
CPU	central processing unit

CSA	chemical shift anisotropy
CW	continuous wave
DEPT	distortionless enhancement by polarisation transfer
DMF	N,N-dimethylformamide
DMSO	dimethylsulphoxide
DNA	deoxyribonucleic acid
DNMR	dynamic NMR
DPM	Dipivaloylmethane, $(Me_3 CCO)_2 CH_2$ (same as THD)
DSS	dimethylsilapentanesulphonic acid, Na salt, $Me_3 Si(CH_2)_3 SO_3 Na$
EPR	electron paramagnetic resonance (same as ESR)
ESR	electron spin resonance (same as EPR)
FID	free induction decay (for gas chromatographers, flame ionisation detector)
FIRFT	fast inversion recovery Fourier transform
FOCSY	fold-over correlation spectroscopy (modified version of SECSY)
FOD	dimethylheptafluorooctanedione (or —ato), $Me_3 CCOCH_2 COC_3 F_7$
FT	Fourier transform
HUP	Heisenberg uncertainty principle (for some reason, this is never used as an acronym)
INADEQUATE	incredible natural abundance double quantum experiment
INDOR	internuclear double resonance
INEPT	insensitive nuclei enhanced by polarisation transfer
IRFT	inversion recovery Fourier transform
IUPAC	International Union of Pure and Applied Chemistry
MAR	magic angle rotation (same as MAS)
MAS	magic angle spinning (same as MAR)
MQ	multiple quantum
NOE	nuclear Overhauser effect
NOESY	NOE spectroscopy

NQR	nuclear quadrupole resonance	SPI	selective population inversion
OR	off resonance	SRFT	saturation recovery Fourier transform
PANIC	parameter adjustment in NMR by iterative calculation	SSB	spinning side bands
PARR	paramagnetic relaxation agent	THD	tetramethylheptanedione (or —ato) (same as DPM)
PE	proton enhancement		
PSFT	progressive saturation Fourier transform	THF	tetrahydrofuran
		TMR	topical magnetic resonance
QD	quadrature detection	TMS	tetramethylsilane, Me_4Si
RF	radio frequency	TSP or TSPA	trimethylsilylpropionic acid, Na salt
RMS	root-mean-square		$Me_3SiCH_2CH_2COO^-Na^+$
RNA	ribonucleic acid	TSP-d_4	the deuterated analogue of TSP,
SEBBORD	spin echo broad band off resonance decoupling		with $-CD_2CD_2COO^-Na^+$
		VT	variable temperature
SECSY	spin echo correlation spectroscopy	WAHUHA	Waugh, Huber and Haeberlen pulse
SEPT	spin echo polarisation transfer		train
S/N	signal-to-noise		

Index

Full versions of all indexed acronyms are given in the Compendium of Acronyms in NMR (p. 235); some common ones are also given in full here.